Foundations of Quality Risk Management

Risk management titles from Quality Press

Risk Management Using Failure Mode and Effect Analysis (FMEA)
D. H. Stamatis

Managing Organizational Risk Using the Supplier Audit Program
Lance B. Coleman Sr.

Quality Risk Management in the FDA-Regulated Industry, Second Edition
José Rodriguez-Pérez

The Art of Integrating Strategic Planning, Process Metrics, Risk Mitigation, and Auditing
Janet Bautista Smith

Problem-solving titles from Quality Press

Root Cause Analysis: The Core of Problem Solving and Corrective Action, Second Edition
Duke Okes

Introduction to 8D Problem Solving
Donald W. Benbow and Ali Zarghami

Innovative Business Management Using TRIZ
Sunil Kumar V. Kaushik

The Logical Thinking Process: A Systems Approach to Complex Problem Solving
H. William Dettmer

New from Quality Press

Connected, Intelligent, Automated: The Definitive Guide to Digital Transformation and Quality 4.0
N. M. Radziwill

Culture Is Everything: How to Become a True Culture Warrior and Lead Your Organization to Victory
Jeff Veyera

Beyond Compliance Design of a Quality System: Tools and Templates for Integrating Auditing Perspectives
Janet Bautista Smith with Robert Alvarez

The ASQ Certified Quality Improvement Associate Handbook, Fourth Edition
Eds. Grace L. Duffy and Sandra L. Furterer

For more information on Quality Press titles, please visit our website at: http://www.asq.org/quality-press

Foundations of Quality Risk Management

A Practical Approach to Effective Risk-Based Thinking

Jayet Moon

Quality Press
Milwaukee, Wisconsin

American Society for Quality, Quality Press, Milwaukee 53203

Printed in the United States of America
25 24 23 22 21 SWY 6 5 4 3 2

Library of Congress Cataloging-in-Publication Data

Names: Moon, Jayet, author.
Title: Foundations of quality risk management : a practical approach to effective risk-based thinking / Jayet Moon.
Description: First Edition. | Milwaukee : Quality Press, 2020. | Includes bibliographical references and index. | Summary: "A comprehensive reference and thorough introduction to risk management and risk-based thinking from a quality perspective and using quality tools"—Provided by publisher.
Identifiers: LCCN 2020029337 (print) | LCCN 2020029338 (ebook) | ISBN 9781951058326 (paperback) | ISBN 9781951058340 (adobe pdf) | ISBN 9781951058333 (epub)
Subjects: LCSH: Risk management. | Quality control.
Classification: LCC HD61 .M5866 2020 (print) | LCC HD61 (ebook) | DDC 658.15/5—dc23
LC record available at https://lccn.loc.gov/2020029337
LC eBook record available at https://lccn.loc.gov/2020029338

♾ Printed on acid-free paper

Quality Press
600 N. Plankinton Ave.
Milwaukee, WI 53203-2914
E-mail: authors@asq.org
The Global Voice of Quality®

This book is dedicated to A. R. Moon

If you don't run the risk of change, you don't have the benefit of advancement.

—Andrew Cuomo, governor of New York

If you only take small risks, you are only entitled to a small life.

—Robin Sharma, author of *The Monk Who Sold His Ferrari* book series

If you don't invest in risk management, it doesn't matter what business you're in, it's a risky business.

—Gary Cohn, former director of the United States National Economic Council

Table of Contents

Tables and Figures

Foreword

Over the few decades we have spent in the industry, we have seen risk management evolve, mature, and incrementally broaden in scope. Decades after the introduction of risk management concepts into the mainstream, we saw these often implemented without application of the right mindset and rigor that can provide real results that affect the bottom line. In this world of ever-changing implications of risk, it is more important that we focus on the right process, one that is agile enough to make a desired impact in an uncertain business climate; this book suitably addresses how a risk-based approach can be used toward accomplishing this. Generally, risk is considered a negative term in most industries, but considering its positive aspects can really help us leverage organizational strengths to capitalize on opportunities in a climate of uncertainty. It was high time that quality management embraced the true definition of risk, beyond its negative side. After ISO 9001:2015's refocus on risk, there was a need for a guidebook that could help harmonize QMS and risk management. We see great value in this book, not only for beginners, who can take advantage of the simplicity with which complex concepts have been explained, but also for experts, who can use this text, as the author has suggested in the Preface, as a self-calibration tool and a reference manual.

Jayet has dedicated much of his career to mastering risk management. In this book, Jayet uses his passion for the topic to make risk management an exciting and intriguing concept for the reader. It is not uncommon for ambiguous "risk management" documentation to be created and applied at a surface level in hopes of achieving compliance to standards; however, this book makes it clear why this should not be the intended process or only outcome. Jayet has ensured the reader will understand exactly what risk management is and understand how to apply practical, value-added risk management methods and tools to identify, prevent, and solve the most important real-world problems. This is the real value of risk management. Jayet's ability to use modern examples from various industries and practical life situations helps articulate a clear case for the importance of risk management. This book highlights why and how the field of risk management is evolving and rapidly growing. It is becoming ever more critical within quality, engineering, business, services, and beyond. With this book, Jayet has created a single-source reference for the most influential risk management processes, standards, concepts, and tools. We highly recommend it to anyone looking to gain knowledge on the topic.

Arun Mathew
Associate Director, Quality Risk Management
Abbvie, Inc.
Chicago, IL

Michael Michetti
Design Quality Engineering Manager
Medtronic
Boulder, CO

Preface

Risk management is compulsory.
Risk management is indispensable.
Risk management is necessary for compliance.

We have heard this many times. Almost every industry has its own niche version of risk management and has some resources dedicated to its organizational processes for management of risk. But here is the truth:

Risk management often fails.
Risk management often becomes a paper exercise.
Risk management becomes reactive and passive.

These points apply to many industries, from national security and banking to healthcare, from the food industry to medical devices and beyond. Banks, which historically have had large armies staffed in risk management departments, could not foresee the U.S. housing market crash of 2008. The automotive industry has a very detailed, hierarchical, and industry-standard risk-based failure modes analysis process, yet is hit by losses of millions of dollars each year due to safety-related recalls. Each year, the food and medical device industries, where risk management is legally mandated by the U.S. Food and Drug Administration, recall hundreds of products released from their production sites that can severely harm people. The spread of COVID-19 to pandemic levels could be attributed to flaws in healthcare security intelligence, which in turn resulted from incorrect risk identification, risk assessments, and risk communication.

Is risk management even worth it? The answer is: more than ever before. Let us discuss why.

Before diving into this book, I would like to tell you a few *actual truths* about risk management, which are:

1. **Risk management is wired into us.**

   Evolution has bestowed upon us humans, by way of certain neuronal connections, a brain that continually processes risk. Everything in this book, or any standard or any other book on risk management, at its fundamental base really draws from what we often do subconsciously. When you walk in a crowded street, you are continually identifying risks, assessing them, evaluating them, and monitoring them. Your sense of risk is high when it's a new street or a new town. The sense of risk is low when it's a familiar street. The same applies in business and organizational environments. It's the same brain that thinks for you in a boardroom or in a strange alley. The trick here is to understand another truth, which is that risk management is "exhausting" for the brain. The brain has a mind of its own. So, in seemingly normal situations, the brain will underplay risks and, at times, try to normalize scenarios that really aren't normal. While there may have been some survival advantages gained in doing so for the early *Homo sapiens,* this becomes a great weakness for the modern human who is called on to make risk-based decisions at the workplace on a routine basis. At the base of all the failures of risk management in all industries, you will find that incorrect perceptions, due in part to incorrect assumptions and biases, led to incorrect risk responses, which in turn led to organizational disasters.

This book, with its foundations in solid, proven theory, will refresh your brain, engender self-awareness, and reset your mind's risk calibration, whether it be for complex organizational decisions or day-to-day departmental decision making. The book itself is calibrated to major ISO, ANSI, and IEC standards, whose references you will find in almost every chapter. So the next time you have that gut feeling for an important business decision, pass it through the lens of risk-based thinking and risk-based decision making, as described in Chapters 4 and 5, and overcome your internal biases by reading up on the theory of cognitive aspects of risk-based decision making in Chapter 37.

2. **Risk management is proactive.**

   Reactive risk management is a misnomer. It really means disaster management. This book is not for that. Risk management involves a lot of "futures thinking," which is quite hard. This book provides a platform and structure, along with methods and tools, to accomplish this difficult task. Again, many failures of risk management activities in the past have resulted from poor understanding of organizational context. This is critical to ensure proactiveness. Chapters 14 and 16, coupled with Chapters 10 and 15, delve into this and guide the reader in comprehending the organizational context such that the risk processes may be customized and consequently be most effective and efficient. The fundamental base of this book is built on the risk management framework per ISO 31000:2018. Proactive thought is embedded in this framework. Chapter 6 explains how this transfers over and forms the base of preventive risk-based thought championed by ISO 9001 since its 2015 edition. Multiple chapters in the middle of the book deal with major steps in the risk management framework by first introducing the fundamentals and then, in complementary chapters, going into detailed theory (e.g., see Chapters 7 and 12 for risk identification; Chapters 7, 25, and 27 for risk analysis; Chapters 13, 26, and 27 for risk evaluation; and Chapters 9 and 28 for risk modification). These activities within the risk management framework are preconditions for a proactive system that is flexible and adaptable enough to mount effective and efficient risk responses to anticipated and unanticipated risks.

3. **Risk management is holistic.**

   One problem with traditional quality risk management is that it is often very siloed. This book takes a slightly different approach to presenting risk management concepts. While it presents many old and proven techniques, it also dares to bring to the reader's attention some bold new methods and theories. The first of these are presented in Chapter 1, which describes the scope of risk management right from the enterprise level to the product, process, or service level. Traditionally, product-, process-, or service-level risk management has been the mainstay of quality teams in manufacturing organizations. What about the other levels? They may or may not exist on paper, but people are certainly making decisions at those levels and considering risks, consciously or subconsciously, while making those decisions, which will no doubt impact product-, process-, or service-level risk. Chapter 1 aims to make the reader aware of this hierarchy. When you set this hierarchy in your organizational context, you will be able to locate yourself and be aware of the rungs of decision making above and below you, which not only affect the risks at your level but also affect the success or failure of risk management efforts at your level. All theory in this book is based on the ISO 31000:2018 framework that applies to risk management for all levels in an organizational hierarchy.

4. **Risk management is an essential part of continual improvement and change management.**

   ISO 31000:2018 talks about continual improvement of risk management through learning and experience. This book talks about engendering continual improvement through risk management. Risk mitigation by design, discussed in Chapter 38, introduces new concepts to help guide improvements not only through initial design but also via specific redesigns as needs for change emerge. Risk vigilance through risk monitoring and review (described in Chapters 30, 31, and 32) will reveal many opportunities for improvement. Risk management acts as the first line of defense when indications of a risk emerge for preemptive action and can guide efforts to permanently improve the system to make it risk resilient. Chapter 34 provides an approach for risk-based monitoring of internal organizational processes, while Chapter 39 provides approaches for risk-based supplier and vendor oversight. Modern organizations are much more dynamic than those of 50 years ago. There is greater volatility, uncertainty, complexity, and ambiguity (see Chapter 12), which makes it incumbent upon the organization to install robust change management systems that form the base of adaptability and flexibility in the face of changing internal and external conditions. Here, too, risk management plays a central role. By correct and timely identification, analysis, and evaluation of upcoming risks, proper and commensurate risk responses can be planned, which protect, sustain, and create value for the organization.

5. **Risk response is different than risk reaction.**

   Risk management occurs with or without a structured or documented process in an organization. As mentioned, we are continually making decisions by factoring in a variety of risks in our daily lives. The same is true for organizational decision makers. For example, the COVID-19 pandemic affected all businesses. Even within different companies in the same sector, we see different risk outcomes based on risk planning (Chapters 18 and 19) or a lack thereof. In the face of uncertainty, top executives tried to manage external risk by modulating internal response. Some failed, while some fared better. Adoption of risk management practices and methods, many of them explained in detail in this book, will lead to risk readiness and a better response in the face of a realized risk, as opposed to a knee-jerk reaction, which will often be misguided. This even holds true in cases of unanticipated risks. The existing risk management framework working in synchrony with change management systems will always fare better than an emergency ad hoc response. Monitoring and review of leading indicators of risks (Chapters 30 and 31) can help the organization apply preemptive risk responses to prevent larger impacts from negative risks.

6. **Risk is the effect of uncertainty on objectives.**

   The etymological roots of the word "risk" can be traced back to the Arabic word رزق (pronounced *rizq*), which translates to "God's favor or fate." As humans became more seafaring, this word morphed with and into the Greek word ριζα (pronounced *rhiza*) for "roots," which was a Homeric metaphor for avoiding danger. Latins associated this word with cliffs, and the words *resicum*, *risco*, and *riscus* came to mean cliffs (and the risk associated with them), which were to be avoided and sailed around as they jutted out from the sea like "roots" and damaged ships nearing land. In this word lies the etymological root of the Spanish *riesgo* and the French *risque*. In sixteenth-century Germany, as massive profits were made by sea traders who undertook long, risky voyages to bring back valuable commodities from the East, the word morphed into *rysigo*, which came to mean "a daring or enterprising undertaking." This was the first time a positive connotation was associated with the word. Indeed, the human anthropological journey can be said to be reflected in the etymological journey of this word. The progression from leaving everything in gods' hands to venturing out cautiously, to undertaking dangerous ventures *suo moto* for profit, shows the increasing agency in human actions through the ages.

   In this book we follow the definition of risk from ISO 31000:2018, which looks at both the upside and downside of risk—its positive and negative aspects. To some readers, this may be a new concept. One-tailed definitions of risk (based on reduction and avoidance of negative risk only) will lead to one-dimensional risk management, which at best will result in zero losses. No company becomes successful by aiming for zero loss; they become successful by aiming for large profits and gains. Two-tailed definitions of risk management allow us to leverage the existing risk management framework for organizational benefit and not just prevention of loss. Chapters 2, 3, 6, and 11 discuss this issue in detail, and other chapters further advance this thinking. While the theory and tools in this book apply to both types of risk, a reader who is familiar with only the negative aspects will come to realize the power of this expanded scope as they progress through the book.

7. **Risk management leads to greater efficiency and profits.**

   When risk is identified, assessed, and evaluated in a structured manner, keeping the organizational context front and center, it leads to good decision making in terms of risk modifications and treatments. It also leads to greater risk readiness and well-defined risk responses. An overall increase in organizational risk maturity (Chapter 17) leads to risk-intelligent decision making, which often leads to great benefits for the organization.

8. **Risk management is difficult.**

   It is easy to convert risk management into a paper exercise, conduct token risk assessments, and have signed, sealed, and approved files for minimal compliance purposes. It is much harder to holistically and effectively conduct risk management activities that actually affect the organization's bottom line in a positive manner. The hurdles are manifold. First, it's easy to get the context of risk management wrong. It is not a plug-and-play process; it needs to be nurtured and grown specific to an organizational environment, with due consideration to internal and external environment and the relevant interfaces. Second, even if the context is right, there may not be sufficient inclusivity and pervasiveness of the risk management processes and apparatus. If key stakeholders are missed or if risk management remains a siloed, single-level exercise, it may not affect the organization in a positive and meaningful way. Third, even if the context is right and sufficient inclusivity is realized, there needs to be a strong framework for risk governance that encompasses all levels of decision making, encourages ethical and independent thought, and challenges conventions. Finally, all people involved in the risk management process should have the applicable knowledge, skills, and abilities to participate and contribute to structured risk assessments and consequent processes. Chapters 21, 23, 24, 32, 33, 36, 41, 42, 43, 44, 45, and 46 present a plethora of tools and methods for the reader to choose from. By themselves, these standalone tools will not add any value. It is only when they are used in the right context, by the right stakeholders, at the right time, with the right interpretation, and in conjunction with the right processes, that their usage can result in value creation.

9. **Risk management should be harmonized with data analysis.**

   In Industry 4.0, there is no dearth of data (i.e., information). Industry 4.0 takes the digitization engendered by 3.0 and magnifies it to provide near-universal accessibility and connectivity. Capacity for accurate data gathering

> has increased like never before, entering our personal devices, homes, cars, and sometimes even our bodies. These increased data points and enhanced analytics can together be used to enhance predictive, risk-based decision making. The effect of 4.0, however, is only as good as an organization's infrastructure to leverage the connectedness of systems. Even if an artificial intelligence (AI) with an IQ greater than 200 could be provided, smartness in terms of business decision making involves "futures thinking" and consequence analysis (Chapters 8 and 24). It means processing the final decision by considering multiple parameters, which include cascading effects, material outcomes, financial outcomes, and even emotional outcomes, to assign a probability of success to one decision. In short, the ultimate AI is equipped with risk-based thinking. Data analysis within a risk management framework can help make sense of the continual inflow of information and ensure visualization of the state of business by ranking and filtering. It can also help manage the connectedness of the business footprint by exposing gaps and prioritizing actions (Chapter 40). Organizations should reassess data analysis as it pertains to risk management processes, as many new sources of data mean newer sources of information not only for risk identification but also for risk monitoring. A risk management system from Industry 3.0 based on small data sets and lesser data points will be significantly less effective than a risk management system that embraces and leverages the power of big data and connectedness.

The scope of this book goes slightly beyond the traditional definition of "quality risk." This is in harmony with the adoption of a two-tailed definition of risk (including positive and negative aspects) from ISO 31000 by ISO 9001 in 2015. This expansion of scope in the gold standard framework for quality management systems (QMS) was done to embed preventive thought in systems, but the proactiveness gained by this integration of QMS with risk management can be leveraged to promote, manage, and sustain beneficial change and enrich the value of the organizational work product (Chapters 11, 22, 23, and 38). Our environment is fraught with internal and external uncertainties. Risk management allows us to make sense of these uncertainties in objective terms and challenges us to inculcate adaptability and flexibility to not only sail through volatility but, where possible, to profit from it.

Since 2015, many national and international standards have adopted risk-based approaches (e.g., ISO 19011:2018, as detailed in Chapter 35) and prescribe activities commensurate to and driven by risk. This book was not written to fulfill compliance with any of these standards but instead was compiled in a way that can allow a reader of any level of expertise to immediately use concepts of risk management for organizational benefit. In learning and implementing risk-based practices as described in this book, you will find that many clauses in these standards that are based on risk management foundations are automatically satisfied.

I would like to end this preface with some words from New York governor Andrew Cuomo's April 26, 2020, coronavirus briefing:

> *So, it's hard, it's hard to make change. It's hard to make change in your own life, let alone on a societal collective level. But if you don't change, you don't grow. And if you don't run the risk of change, you don't have the benefit of advancement.*[1]

Whether you are a novice or an expert, this book will help you by providing knowledge, theory, methods, and tools to do just that—to *run the risk of change* for the *benefit of advancement.*

—Jayet Moon

1. "Video, Audio & Rush Transcript: Governor Cuomo Announces Completion of Nation-Leading L Project Tunnel Rehabilitation with No Shutdown," New York State, April 26, 2020, https://www.governor.ny.gov/news/video-audio-rush-transcript-governor-cuomo-announces-completion-nation-leading-l-project-tunnel.

Acknowledgments

The author is deeply thankful to his family for their constant support and motivation. He is greatly indebted to Arun Mathew of Chicago, IL, for his help, guidance, and contributions to this manuscript.

The author also thanks Adam Brooks of Baltimore, MD, and Patricia Fleenor of Denver, CO, for their help.

This book also would not have been possible without Sharon Woodhouse and the patience, understanding, and encouragement of the Quality Press team.

Finally, the author thanks ASQ for being the thought leader in quality and continually providing forums for quality professionals around the globe to learn and excel.

CHAPTER 1

Introduction to Risk Management

PRODUCTS, SERVICES, SYSTEMS, AND ORGANIZATIONS continually face a multitude of risks that may hamper their functioning and lead to a variety of failures. These risks may be operational, commercial, environmental, technological, financial, political, or even social and cultural. In today's world, management of risk is not only an aspiration but a necessity for a successful organization to maintain its profits and reputation.

On a basic level, holistic organizational risk strategy is based on the following three pillars (see Figure 1.1):

1. Enterprise risk management
2. Operational risk management
3. Product-, process-, or service-level risk management

Enterprise risk management is the coordinated approach for centralized management of risks and their cascade from the strategic mission level.
Operational risk management is the coordination and control of all risky activities of the system at the operational business unit or functional level in order to successfully achieve the predefined expected operational outputs and objectives.
Product-, process-, or service-level risk management focuses on managing the day-to-day ground-level risks in terms of the specific end deliverables of the organization to its customers.

The aim of all risk management activities is the following:

- Realistic assessment of the organizational objectives and path to their achievement
- Prevention of undesired outcomes
- Continuous improvement
- Value sustenance and value addition

The organization can use the vehicle of risk management to leverage strengths to act on opportunities and assess weaknesses to mitigate threats. These actions in response to risk should be proportionate to the potential impact of the risk on the organization

FIGURE 1.1 Risk management pillars.

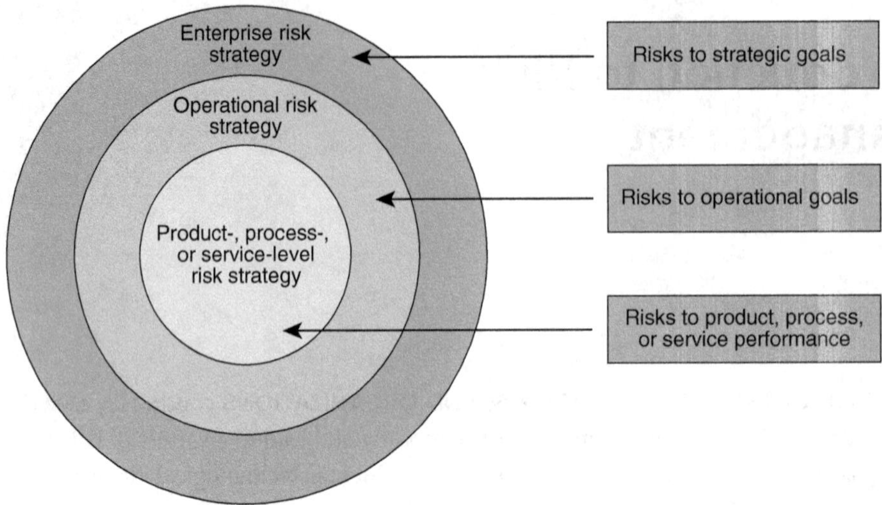

and its products or services. The success of risk management is dependent on a large extent to the organizational risk governance.

> **Risk governance** refers to the structural framework that governs the organizational risk management activities and related decision making. It encompasses policies, procedures, and processes that dictate risk management approaches, methods, and oversight.

Risk governance varies tremendously from sector to sector and company to company. Some companies do not have any enterprise risk management at all, while others have no product-level risk management. Many companies have multiple decentralized risk management processes used by disparate functions and departments. It is important for a quality and risk professional to understand the criticality of the risk management framework of one's organization and the governance of that framework to ensure success. This entails defining levels of accountability and ownership of cascading risks. It also entails identifying current risk policies, procedures, and stakeholder responsibilities in terms of risk and risk escalation pathways.

While it is easy to get lost in the myriad interpretations of and approaches to risk management, this book attempts to distill the basic risk management concepts into a practical risk-based approach. Fundamentally, for a risk professional, the risk-based approach depends on a clear understanding of the system itself, the threats and opportunities that surround it, and, finally, finding ways to modify risks for organizational benefit.

From a top level, the aim of enterprise risk management is to look at aggregate risk. While there is significant value in doing so, assessment of risk at succeeding levels of tactical planning is equally important to ensure effective risk management.

FIGURE 1.2 An example of hierarchical risk management.

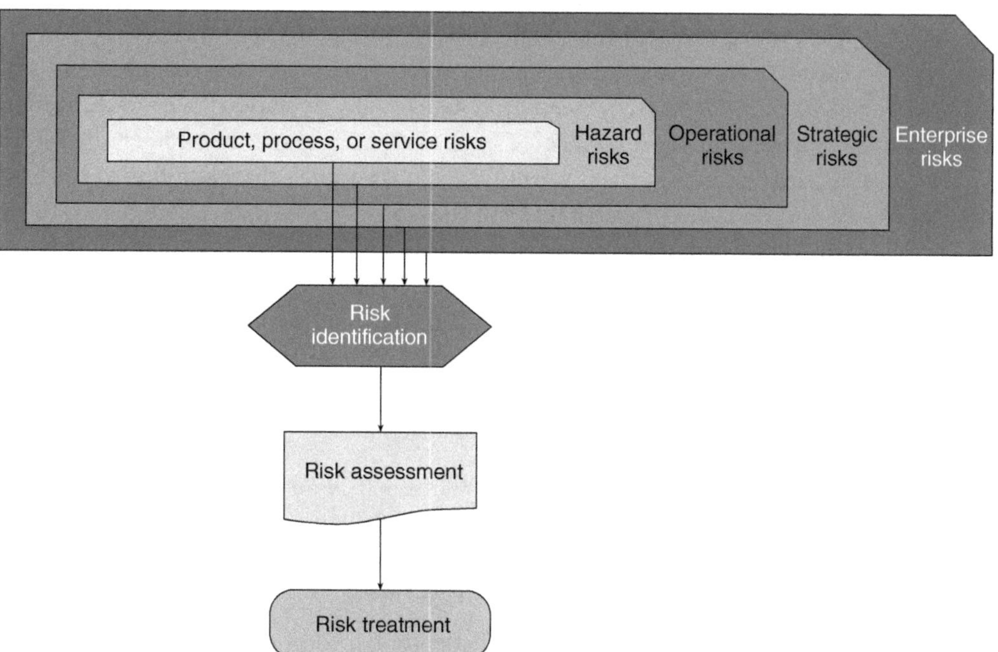

A version of such hierarchical risk management at succeeding levels is shown in Figure 1.2.

After understanding the organizational context, the risk management practitioner must structurally break down the basic drivers of risks at various levels to assess and evaluate the same per organizational needs. This evaluation should be captured in risk assessments that serve not only as documentation of the comprehensive efforts for identification, analysis, and evaluation of potentially risky events but also as a risk register according to which these events are documented and correspondingly monitored and controlled.

The level at which the risk is assessed, analyzed, and treated is important. Hierarchical risk management starts from the enterprise level, flows over to the functional level, and then moves on to the subsequent levels of products, processes, and services.

In Figure 1.2, five levels are shown. Depending on the industry or company, these may change, and further levels may be added or deleted. In the hierarchical context, for this model, the five levels shown here are defined as follows:

1. **Enterprise risk management**—The overarching high-level risk management process that looks at risks as aggregate threats to or opportunities for the enterprise. This process will directly affect strategy setting.
2. **Strategic risk management**—The management of risks to an organization's achievement of strategic goals and objectives that have been set earlier.

3. **Operational risk management**—The management of risks that affect the routine workflows set in place to deliver organizational goals. These risks will affect the operational goals that cascade from the strategic goals.
4. **Hazard risk management**—An iterative process of risk management that focuses on the hazards faced by systems. Daily operations of an organization occur despite the presence of multiple hazards and hazardous situations. Hazard risk management scientifically looks at the exposure afforded by these hazards in terms of probability and consequence. Often, this significantly overlaps with risk management at other levels.
5. **Product, process, or service risk management**—This most detailed rung of risk management focuses on individual and specific failure modes arising from the hazards and attempts to assess each failure separately in order to manage component-specific risk. Often, this falls in the realm of quality departments in manufacturing and some service organizations.

An enterprise-wide risk management framework is just as important as functional expertise in product, process, or service risk management. Generally, in many sectors, the risk management functions are decentralized and uncoordinated. The value of dealing with risk holistically from an enterprise standpoint is the following:

1. Leadership support and high-level attention, thereby ensuring correct resource allocation
2. Strategic objectives at front and center, and synchrony between top-level and bottom-level risks, thereby allowing for effective end-to-end risk management
3. High-level steering control in terms of risk culture, risk appetite, and loss tolerance

It must be clarified that certain publications define hazard risk management through the lens of enterprise risk management as exposures that can cause loss without any possibility of a gain. They define hazards as major adverse events such as fires and earthquakes. This view of hazard risks is noninclusive and looks at hazards from financial or insurance standpoints only. This book does not take that approach. Hazards are continually present in the world around us. Normal operations take place despite them, and, indeed, we aim to mitigate the formation of hazardous situations from hazards continually so that benefits can be obtained despite the presence of the hazard. For example, it was understood that traffic at intersections was hazardous, so traffic lights were installed. A petroleum refinery has a risk of fire, so not only do we insure the refinery but also use fire-retardant materials as much as we can and take many other precautions.

When hazards are seen from an operational standpoint, they can help us define specific product, process, and service risks as well—as we shall do in the coming chapters of this book. Let us now turn our attention to the confluence of quality management and risk management.

CHAPTER 2

Quality and Risk Management

THE AMERICAN SOCIETY FOR QUALITY (ASQ) defines *quality* as:

> *1) the characteristics of a product or service that bear on its ability to satisfy stated or implied needs;*
> *2) a product or service free of deficiencies.*[1]

Quality management is an organizational process that ensures consistent quality to satisfy and, where possible, delight the customer. Quality management includes, as appropriate, quality planning, quality assurance, quality control, and quality improvement. The Plan–Do–Check–Act (PDCA) cycle is inherent in this definition, as shown in Figure 2.1.

Quality planning not only details the expected systemic activities and methods to ensure sustained quality, but also comprises preventive strategies and proposed actions in a structured format composed of system, operational, and functional deliverables.

Quality assurance is the immediate outcome of the plan, which puts the preventive thought into action by focusing on problem or error prevention. This is a creative phase where hazards are anticipated and resulting issues are attempted to be mitigated by robust design thinking during formative stages. This is, in effect, risk mitigation by design. Risk management can assist and enable a structured quality assurance function since foundationally both are based on the same preventive philosophy.

Quality control focuses on problem detection and reaction after an issue has been discovered. This is an important activity since now the risk to quality has been realized and detected. But detection and local solution of the issue do not add any long-term value to the system. The discovered issues must be analyzed in the broader context and a level of response must be decided. Using risk management, this risk can not only be anticipated with ready mitigations but also be qualitatively and quantitatively measured, prioritized, and controlled throughout the life cycle.

Quality improvement starts with an analysis of performance to discover deficiencies, and focuses on a systematic approach to improving performance in order to achieve and

1. American Society for Quality, "Quality Glossary of Terms, Acronyms & Definitions: ASQ," ASQ, accessed June 20, 2020, https://asq.org/quality-resources/quality-glossary/.

FIGURE 2.1 Quality management and PDCA.

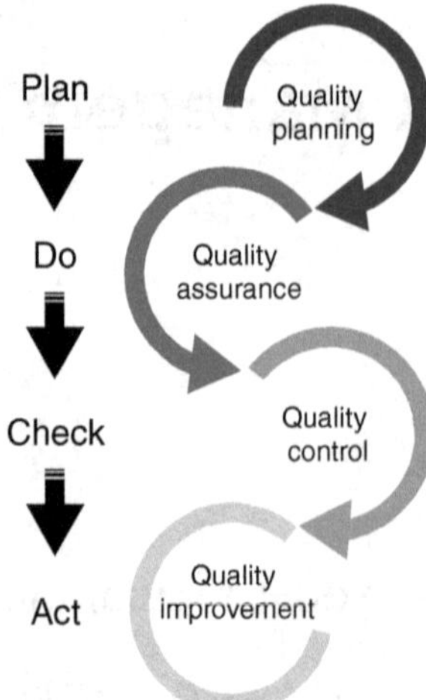

exceed goals and objectives. A quality improvement is realized as a positive effect of a change engendered to prevent issues. Again, phased risk management, which continually anticipates, measures, and tracks risk, becomes a yardstick for the quality improvement process and provides a meaningful baseline to measure changes and their effects.

Quality and risk management work in natural harmony, and together magnify the proactive, prevention-based approach, reducing the reactive defect detection and rejection to practicably low levels.

RISK MANAGEMENT AND THE PROCESS APPROACH

The *process approach* is an organizational strategy of managing and controlling a process and various interacting subprocesses within the organization. Any activity that has an input and output is a process. If a process is converting an input to an output, it means there are certain sets of subactivities within the process that enable this change.

Figure 2.2 shows a simple representation of a process. The realization of outputs of the process is contingent not only on the inputs but also on the actual "processing" step, whereby the activities convert the input to output. The success of this set of activities depends on overcoming resistance, barriers, or hurdles and monitoring their output and modulating parameters to ensure desired output.

A risk-based process approach focuses on anticipation of the resistance, barriers, and hurdles—and their preemptive mitigation to an acceptable level—such that the desired level of output is maintained. Resistance, barriers, and hurdles can be hazards, hazardous situations, faults, or failures that hamper operability and negatively affect the process outputs. To control the process, one must understand its hazards and anticipate the outcome of the realization of hazards on the process outcome.

FIGURE 2.2 The process approach.

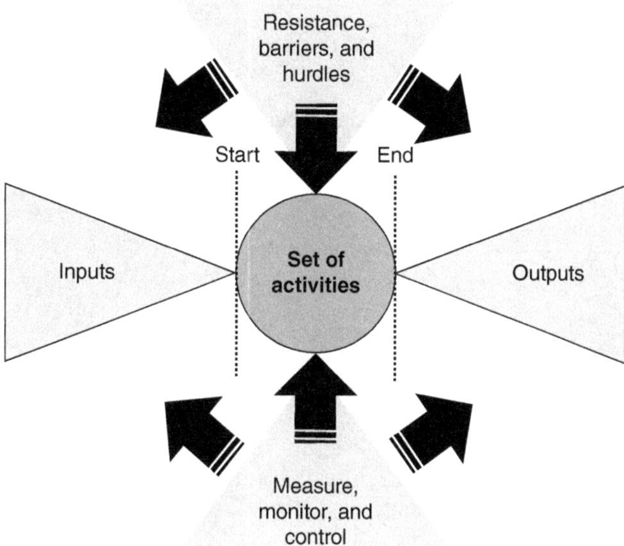

This can be accomplished by incorporating risk management by using the PDCA approach:

- Risk planning to ensure a systematic scheme or framework for realization of risk management activities
- Risk identification by analyzing the set of activities within the process and its critical points
- Risk analysis and prioritization to consider preventive mitigations or level of risk acceptance
- Risk monitoring and control to keep an eye out for pain points and emergent issues

Thus, risk management, PDCA, and the process approach are all part of quality management and feed into and from one another (Figure 2.3).

Risk-based thinking is a *philosophy* and not a set of tools. Risk-based thinking will not automatically follow by simply creating a risk analysis document or a risk manager position within a company. Risk-based thinking must be tied and aligned to the culture of a company, such that its objectives, whether they be individual or organizational, incorporate this approach.

While enterprise risk management propagates a top-down approach to risk management, risk mitigation by design (RmD) aims for a bottom-up approach. ISO 9001:2015 removed the earlier preventive action clause and introduced risk-based thinking, which, by nature, is preventive in spirit. By practicing RmD (more details in Chapter 38) in its true form, the designers of products, processes, and services adopt a risk-based mindset to preemptively mitigate subsystem-specific, foreseeable risks. This results in low-risk products, processes, and services, which in turn allow greater tolerances for operational

FIGURE 2.3 Confluence of risk management, process approach, and PDCA with quality management.

FIGURE 2.4 PDCA and risk management.

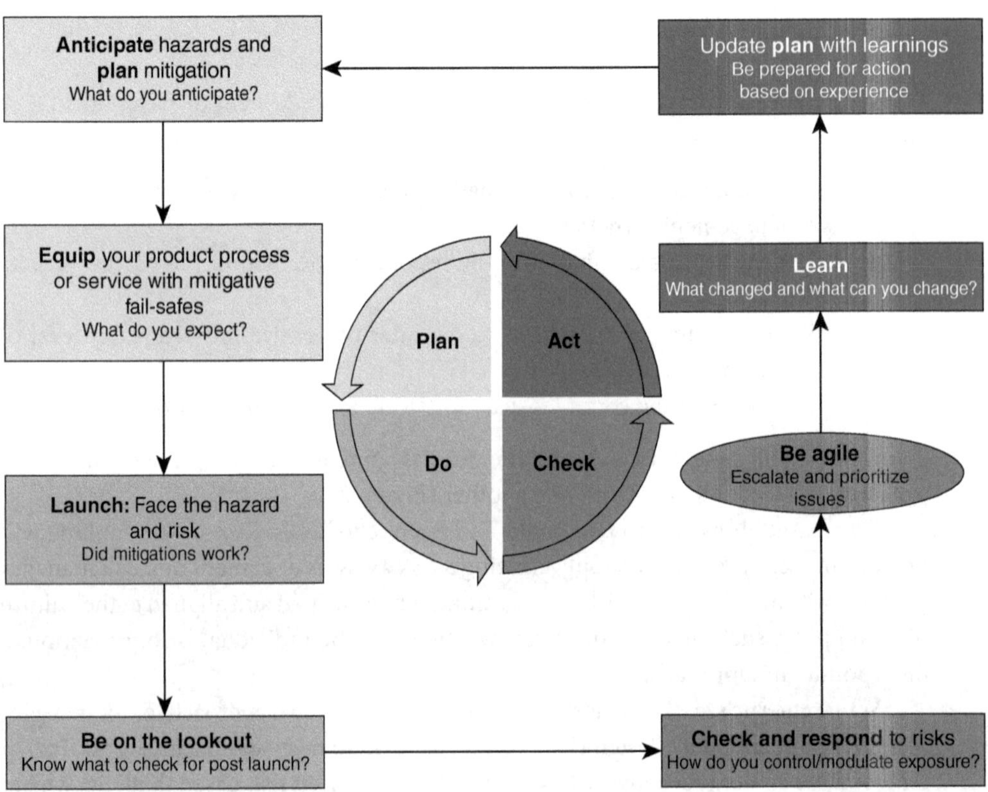

FIGURE 2.5 PDCA to risk management with traditional steps.

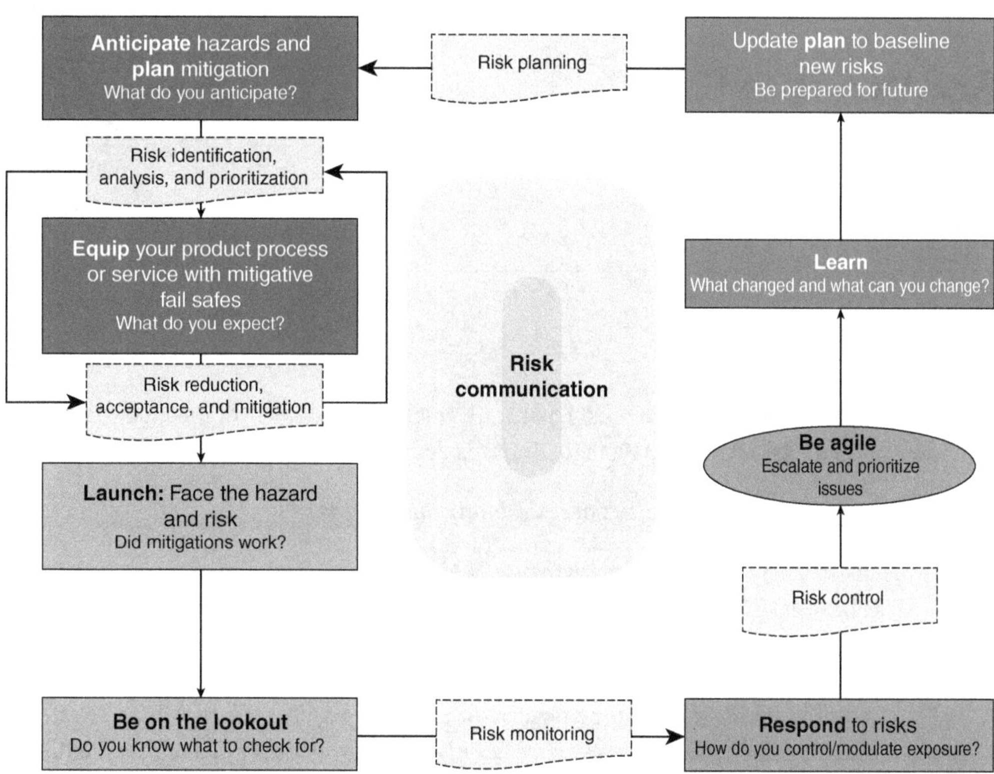

and subsequently strategic risks. Safe products and processes may encourage positive risk taking by engendering confidence in top management, which in turn will lead them to strategically leverage strengths to capitalize on business opportunities.

Thus, risk managed at one level allows for opportunities for value creation at other levels. Mismanaged risks at top level may lead to significant reduction in value because risks may magnify as they shift through levels.

Another way to look at the process in terms of product-, process-, or service-level decision making is through the prism of PDCA as shown in Figure 2.4.

We start by anticipating the risks to plan proactive mitigations and preventive controls for them in the Plan phase. In the Do phase, we launch the product, process, or service. In the Check phase, we determine if the design-based mitigations worked (monitoring) and if the residual risk was indeed as expected, if any alarm signals or risk warnings appeared, and if any unforeseen risks emerged. In the Act phase, we implement the learnings for the risks that occurred in the earlier phases by enabling better preventive controls in the system. We document the new risks and assess their impact on the system, which is then followed by new controls for the same.

The traditional steps of risk management are added to these steps and shown in Figure 2.5. We will continue to discuss these steps in the coming chapters.

CHAPTER 3

So, What Is Risk?

TO BEGIN, let us look at the most basic, universal, and simple—yet most conceptual—definition of risk. Per ISO 31000:2018, *risk* is defined as:

Effect of uncertainty on objectives.[1]

It means that any *effect* due to any *cause*, which leads to deviation from expectation, is risk. In organizational enterprise terms, the effect of not meeting objectives is the consequence of risk. These objectives may be safety related, performance related, or related to failure reduction or sales growth.

Moreover, these effects can be positive or negative. Positive effects will accelerate an organization's achievement of goals, while negative effects will hinder this achievement. The achievement of *objectives* is the purpose of the organization and thus is the purpose of risk management. These objectives can be systemic; can be strategic; can be product, process, or service related; and can pertain to any or all functional levels of the organization. The objective can also be nonfailure of the product or successful intended use of the product.

To further understand the definition of risk, let us consider an example. The organization in Figure 3.1 adopted a staggered approach to its end goal by defining three time-based interim objectives in its action plan.

An impactful adverse event, "1," just before achievement of Objective 2, derailed the schedule, and the deviation from plan objectives (delta 1 and delta 2) led to the failure to achieve the end goal. This is an example of negative risk, the uncertainty due to events related to nonachievement of objectives.

Similarly, in the scenario above, a positive event could have led the organization to get back on track and achieve the end goal before the end of the mandated time frame. If this were to happen, it would be an example of positive risk, the uncertainty due to events related to accelerated achievement of objectives. A positive risk is known as upside risk or can simply be called an opportunity (an opportunity with uncertain

---

1.

FIGURE 3.1 Time-based objectives realization.

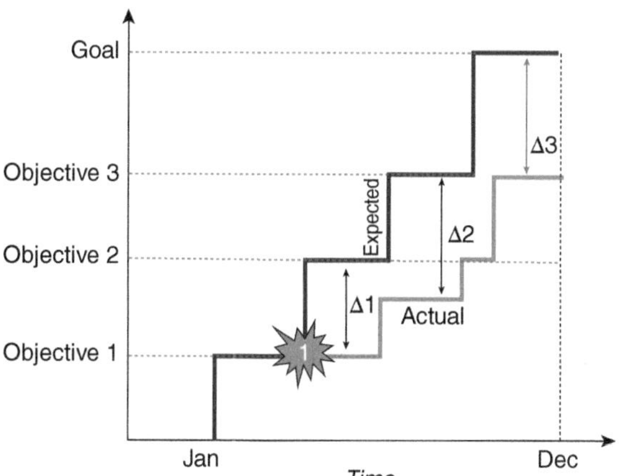

possibility of a gain). In some industries, such as the financial sector, where two-tailed risks are obvious (e.g., a stock market investment that can lead to profit or loss), this definition is well subscribed to. In other industries, such as the medical device sector, risk has been historically associated with a negative connotation. Here, the relevant ISO standards for medical devices (ISO 13485:2016 and ISO 14971:2019) slightly differ from ISO 31000:2018. Some risks, indeed, may not have a positive outcome or an opportunity associated with them. Still, medical device risk management aims to address the positive aspects of a treatment by using risk-benefit analyses, which are detailed in a separate chapter in this book. ISO 9001:2015, on the other hand, is well aligned with the definition in ISO 31000:2018 and uses the word "opportunity" for upside risk. The theory presented in this book applies to both aspects of risk, and a practitioner in any industry will be able to use the theory and tools presented in the coming chapters for holistic organizational risk management. A risk need not always be avoided, regardless of positive or negative aspects, but should always be managed to reduce disruptions related to uncertainty.

Any event with the potential to impact objectives, either alone or in combination, may give rise to risk. Risk management is simply the management of potential negative and positive events, by timely assessment and evaluation, to assess threats and opportunities in order to modify them to achieve sustained or accelerated achievement of goals.

ISO/Guide 73:2009 defines *uncertainty* as:

> *State of deficiency of information related to, understanding or knowledge of an event, its consequence or likelihood.*[2]

---

2. ©ISO. This material is reproduced from ISO Guide 73:2009, with permission of the American National Standards Institute (ANSI) on behalf of the International Organization for Standardization. All rights reserved.

The whole concept of risk-based thinking depends on the reaction to uncertainty. The cornerstone of risk management is science-based uncertainty management. If the organization in the example above had managed uncertainty, it could have maintained control of the schedule by leveraging possible positive events and minimizing negative events. As the book progresses, we will discuss, in a lot of detail, the final product-, service-, or process-level risk management and present various tools and methods for the same. Here, we take some time to present the very top view of risk management. As risk management progresses from enterprise level to lower levels, the negative aspects of risk tend to become more pronounced than the positive aspects, as focus shifts to prevention of failures.

In the next chapter, we will look at the foundational concepts of risk-based thinking and how it treats event uncertainty.

CHAPTER 4

Risk-Based Thinking

THE GOOD NEWS IS THAT, as humans, we are natural risk takers. We are pioneers who constantly seek to conquer uncharted territory. The bad news is that risk-taking traits in humans are a gift of natural selection, which takes a brute-force approach to evolution, thereby exposing most of us to major mistakes.

For example, one caveman could choose to trust his gut and enter an unknown dark cave while another caveman could choose to wait in the bush for a few hours to check if the cave already housed a saber-toothed tiger. We may find the confident and gutsy caveman who traipses into the cave very daring, but if there did happen to be a tiger in the cave, we would have to admire the other caveman's level-headed approach.

The factor that differentiates gut-based thinking and risk-based thinking is the human attitude toward uncertainty. The *Cambridge English Dictionary* defines *uncertainty* as:

A situation where something is not known.[1]

The next important realization in the development of risk-based thinking is that, by default, the probability of an uncertain event is *unknown*. Thus, the risk of an uncertain event is unknown as well. However, if we can use objective information to assign a probability to a previously uncertain event, then we can ascribe a risk to an event. *Probability* is defined as:

The level of possibility of something happening or being true, or, in mathematics, a number that represents how likely it is that a particular thing will happen.[2]

The modern theory of probability was inspired by games of chance. The seventeenth-century Frenchman and mathematician Pierre de Fermat proved to a gambler that certain combinations of dice in the long term had a higher probability of winning than other

1. Cambridge English Dictionary, s.v., "uncertainty," accessed June 22, 2020, https://dictionary.cambridge.org/us/dictionary/english/uncertainty.
2. "The Possibility That Something Will Happen - Synonyms and Related Words," Macmillan Dictionary, accessed July 7, 2020, https://www.macmillandictionary.com/us/thesaurus-category/american/the-possibility-that-something-will-happen.

combinations. In Fermat's eyes, this was not a game of chance but a game of probabilities, and a person who understood the die's probabilistic distribution could *probably* profit from it. The profit would be commensurate to the risk a gambler was willing to take.

To clarify, consider a game where people bet money on the outcome of a double dice toss. For example, John and Steve both participate in this game and each bets $100. John is a gut thinker and Steve is a scientific thinker.

John chooses the number 5 because his father's birthday is on the fifth of the month. Steve uses concepts of probability to choose a number. Knowing that there are 36 outcomes in a double dice throw, per Figure 4.1, Steve calculates that the highest probability of occurrence is for the number 7.

It does not mean that Steve is guaranteed a win, but by using a science-based method, Steve progressively increases his chances of winning as the dice are rolled successively, as can be seen in Table 4.1.

Thus, Steve has used a risk-based approach to this game by quantifying probability, or the occurrence of success. John, on the other hand, has a much lower probability of winning if he bets on 5 every time; and if he randomly chooses new numbers for every bet, no prediction can be made regarding his chances, which have now become uncertain.

Probability theory led to a great transformative change in the business of insurance and gave birth to the field of actuarial science. James Dodson developed mortality tables, which predicted the probability of death or survivorship of certain populations;

FIGURE 4.1 Probability distribution of two simultaneously cast fair dice.

Cumulative roll count	Probability
2	$\frac{1}{36}$
3	$\frac{2}{36}$
4	$\frac{3}{36}$
5	$\frac{4}{36}$
6	$\frac{5}{36}$
7	$\frac{6}{36}$
8	$\frac{5}{36}$
9	$\frac{4}{36}$
10	$\frac{3}{36}$
11	$\frac{2}{36}$
12	$\frac{1}{36}$

TABLE 4.1 Increasing the probability of winning via successive bets on number 7.

Throw number	Probability of Steve's win
1	16.60%
2	30.50%
3	42.10%
4	51.70%
5	59.80%
6	66.50%
7	72.10%
8	76.70%
9	80.60%
10	83.80%
11	86.50%
12	88.70%
13	90.65%

these tables were used to decide long-term insurance premiums. This was the first notable application of probability and consequence in large-scale commerce. These tables were immediately successful, and insurance companies that did not use these tables often found themselves failing.

Now that we have discussed the importance of probability in risk, let us discuss *the consequence*. *Consequence* is defined as:

A result or effect of an action or condition.[3]

To adopt a risk-based approach means to place the impact or consequence of risk front and center. While the probabilities of different impacts or consequences may differ, one must consider all possible consequential scenarios to not only measure various risk impacts but, where possible, determine aggregate risk.

Risk-based thinking is preventive thinking. It focuses on prevention of problems before they occur. Consequence analysis is a critical step in achieving this. To prevent a problem, one has to foresee it. Most importantly, one must foresee the consequence along with the probability of the consequence.

Thus, the essence of risk-based thinking is to inculcate a mindset that leads us to foresee threats and opportunities and estimate them with an objective level of certainty such that targeted modifications and controls can be built into the design and surveillance of systems.

3. Lexico, s.v., "consequence," accessed July 7, 2020, https://www.lexico.com/definition/consequence.

CHAPTER 5

Risk-Based Decision Making

RISK-BASED THINKING is not only preventive but also preemptive. A dynamic risk management system will engender preemptive thinking that will lead the system owners to deploy mitigations or modifications in anticipation of developing or emerging changes in the risk landscape. The foundation of preventive and preemptive thought lies in the decision-making process. At its core, risk-based thinking is simply a science-based decision-making process founded on risk.

The University of Massachusetts Dartmouth published the graphic shown in Figure 5.1 to explain an effective decision-making process.

This model has been shown here since almost all decision-making models follow this simple framework in one form or another with only slight modifications. Leveraging the Dartmouth model, for the purposes of this book, *risk-based decision making* can be defined as:

> *A structured process for identifying necessary and appropriate courses of action based on analysis of relevant information and evaluation of known or anticipated risks associated with each alternative action.*

Joseph J. Myers from the U.S. Coast Guard has presented a process for risk-based decision making, which is based on the following sequential order:[1]

- Establish the decision structure
- Perform the risk assessment
- Apply the results to risk management decision making
- Monitor effectiveness through impact assessment
- Facilitate risk communication

In this chapter we will focus on aspects of the decision structure. The coming chapters of this book will address risk and impact assessment in great detail.

It is necessary to define the decision structure such that the decision-making flow incorporates the views of and, where necessary, the approval of relevant stakeholders.

1. J. J. Myers, "Risk-Based Decision Making," *Journal of Safety and Security at Sea* 64, no. 1 (2007): 6–10.

FIGURE 5.1 Decision-making steps.

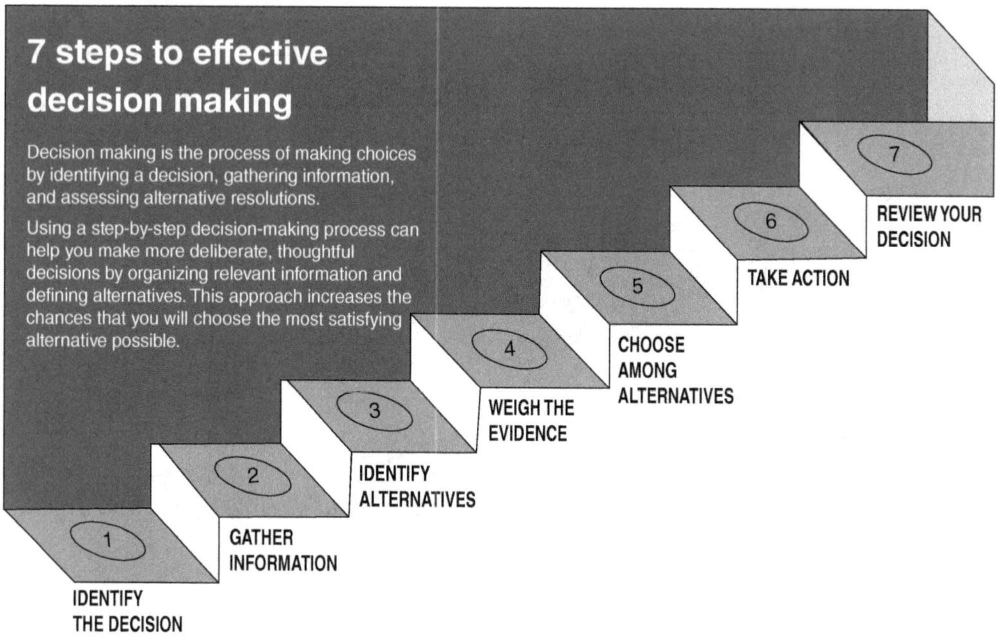

Source: University of Massachusetts Dartmouth, "Decision-Making Process," First Year Course Modules, UMass Dartmouth, accessed June 22, 2020, https://www.umassd.edu/fycm/decision-making/process/.

These stakeholders must be supplied with, where appropriate, risk assessments that allow all parties to be on the same page and to discuss targeted implications and/or consequences (along with constraints) for further top-level review and judgment. Such a method relies on the formulation of making a decision first and then assessing its impact and acceptability. Aven and Kørte have given a model that fits these principles.[2] In their model, the issue and decision alternatives undergo a risk and decision analysis, which is then viewed through the lens of stakeholder values, goals, criteria, and preferences coupled with management review and judgment to finally arrive at a decision. At times, the final decision may be to evaluate other decision options, and the cycle is continued.

In this book, we will propound a new model of risk-based decision making based on the Dartmouth model, which leverages risk-based thinking to pinpoint success and failure factors of a decision and builds on Aven and Kørte's model as shown in Figure 5.2.

This model embeds the preventive approach during the formulation phase of the decision by forcing the anticipation of failures and, where possible, evaluating their impacts. Thus, instead of making a decision and assessing its risk, we are using principles of risk management to formulate and modify the decision as the risk-based process progresses.

---

2. T. Aven and J. Kørte, "On the Use of Risk and Decision Analysis to Support Decision-Making," *Reliability Engineering & System Safety* 79, no. 3 (2003): 289–299.

FIGURE 5.2 Risk-based decision-making model.

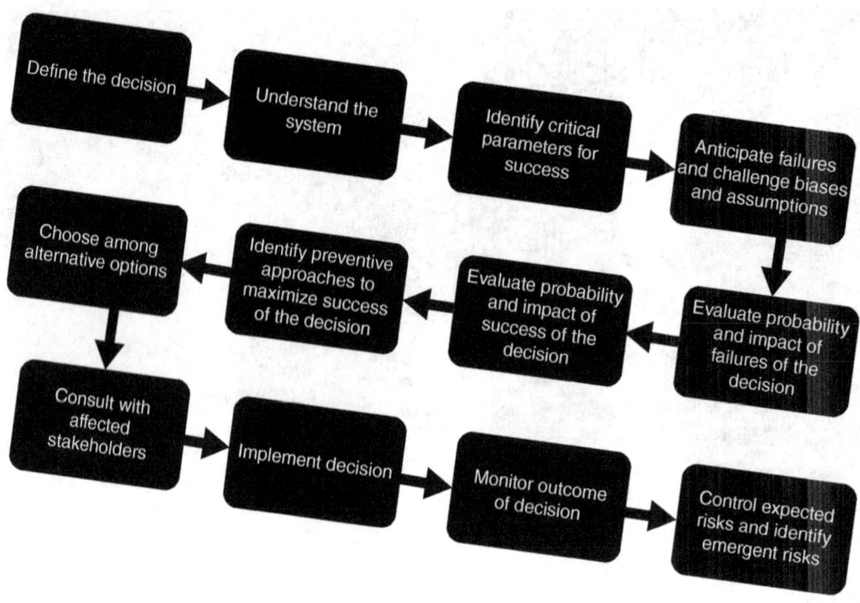

FIGURE 5.3 Risk-driven decision making leading to exploitation of opportunities and mitigation of threats.

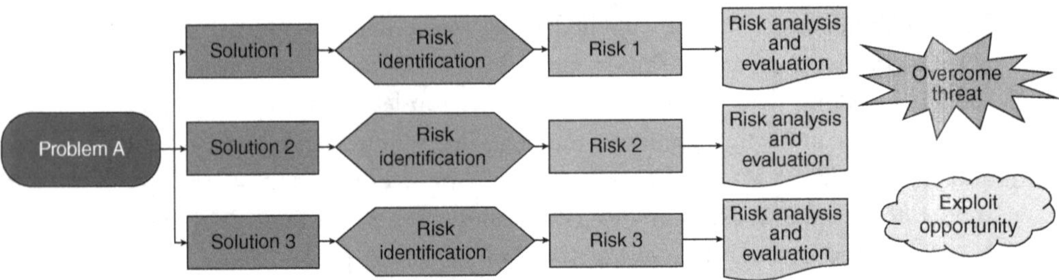

Risk-based thinking and risk-based decision making should lead to risk-based solution determination. As quality and risk professionals, we continually find ourselves facing choices among multiple paths in the face of problems. The theory of risk management provides a structured method to deal with such situations and arrive at solutions.

The application of concepts of risk management does not mean that we take the path of least resistance or the path of least risk. It means that we assess and evaluate threats and opportunities and take the path that will leverage our strengths for maximum value. Risk management may not, at all times, aim to lower risks as much as possible, but instead helps to anticipate problems and their solutions so that commensurate preparations can be made in case of risk realization.

In Figure 5.3, Risk 1, which is associated with Solution 1, need not be "less" than Risks 2 or 3. Per risk-based solution determination, the deciding factor should be whether the organization has relevant strengths to convert the risk into an opportunity. If not, the risk should be deemed a threat to steer clear of. If there are no upsides to risks and all the risks are negative, then the solution associated with the risk with the lowest threat level should be chosen. The coming chapters will go into great detail about risk identification, analysis, and evaluation.

CHAPTER 6

ISO 9001 and Risk Management

ISO 9001 IS THE INTERNATIONAL standard that specifies requirements for a quality management system (QMS). Organizations across the globe pursue certification to this standard, which is used to demonstrate commitment to quality along with consistent customer-focused value creation and sustenance in the products and services created or marketed by the organization.

In Clause 0.1, ISO 9001:2015 mentions that the standard employs the PDCA cycle and risk-based thinking. It goes on to say:

> *Risk-based thinking enables an organization to determine the factors that could cause its processes and its quality management system to deviate from the planned results, to put in place preventive controls to minimize negative effects and to make maximum use of opportunities as they arise.*[1]

ISO 9001, in its 2015 version, also removed the section on preventive actions. The idea is that life-cycle risk identification, analysis, evaluation modification, and monitoring, which are outcomes of the risk management process, are, by nature, preventive.

The standard draws attention to the risks associated with organizational contexts and objectives. It specifically mentions the risks again in the clauses outlined on p. 21.[2]

The focus of these clauses is summarized in Table 6.1.

The standard expects the risk management to stem from the organizational leadership, which echoes the foundational message of enterprise risk management. On the other end of the spectrum, the standard also expects in Clause 5 that a risk that affects conformity of products must be identified and addressed, thus covering the whole gamut of the hierarchical risk spectrum discussed earlier. Implicitly, one may interpret

---

Clause 4.4.1

The organization shall determine the processes needed for the quality management system and their application throughout the organization, and shall address the risks and opportunities as determined with requirements of Clause 6.1.

Clause 5.1.1

The top management shall demonstrate leadership and commitment with respect to quality management system by promoting the use of process approach and risk-based thinking.

Clause 5.1.2

Top management shall demonstrate leadership and commitment with respect to customer focus by ensuring that the risks and opportunities that can affect conformity of products and services and the ability to enhance customer satisfaction are determined and addressed.

Clause 6.1

When planning for the quality management system, the organization shall consider the issues referred to in 4.1 and the requirements referred to in 4.2 and determine the risks and opportunities that need to be addressed to:

a) give assurance that the quality management system can achieve its intended result(s);
b) enhance desirable effects;
c) prevent, or reduce, undesired effects;
d) achieve improvement.

Clause 6.1.2

The organization shall plan:

a) actions to address these risks and opportunities;
b) how to:
    1) integrate and implement the actions into its quality management system processes (see 4.4);
    2) evaluate the effectiveness of these actions.

Actions taken to address risks and opportunities shall be proportionate to the potential impact on the conformity of products and services.

NOTE 1: Options to address risks can include avoiding risk, taking risk in order to pursue an opportunity, eliminating the risk source, changing the likelihood or consequences, sharing the risk, or retaining risk by informed decision.

NOTE 2: Opportunities can lead to the adoption of new practices, launching new products, opening new markets, addressing new clients, building partnerships, using new technology and other desirable and viable possibilities to address the organization's or its customers' needs.

Clause 9.1.3

The organization shall analyze and evaluate appropriate data and information arising from monitoring and measurement. The results of analysis shall be used to evaluate the effectiveness of actions taken to address risks and opportunities.

Clause 9.3.2

The management review shall be planned and carried out taking into consideration the effectiveness of actions taken to address risks and opportunities.

Clause 10.2.1

When a nonconformity occurs, including any arising from complaints, the organization shall update risks and opportunities determined during planning, if necessary.

TABLE 6.1 Risk focus of ISO 9001:2015 clauses.

Clause	Focus
4.4.1	QMS processes should address the upside and downside of risks
5.1.1	Enterprise support for risk-based thinking
5.1.2	Product- and service-level risk management
6.1	Ensuring outcomes of risk management through QMS planning
6.1.2	Integration of QMS and risk management; focus on the upside of risk as opportunity
9.1.3	Monitoring of risk outcomes
9.3.2	Risk oversight by leadership
10.2.1	Post-market / life-cycle risk management

that the standard is asking the organization to implement risk management at various levels corresponding to the quality activities at those levels, which may include strategic, operational, and program, product, and service level via scope/context setting, risk assessments, risk evaluations, and risk treatment as shown in Figure 6.1.

It should be clarified that the standard is not explicitly asking for a formal risk management process, and that certification to this standard may not be contingent on such a requirement. It simply directs attention toward risk management—a set of practices and techniques that can significantly accelerate the accomplishment of the same goals as ISO 9001 in a structured fashion that:

1. Improves organizational governance
2. Establishes and sustains a continual improvement culture and framework
3. Enables evidence-based decision making
4. Improves customer satisfaction
5. Ensures consistent quality by accomplishing all of the above

FIGURE 6.1 Risk management process overview.

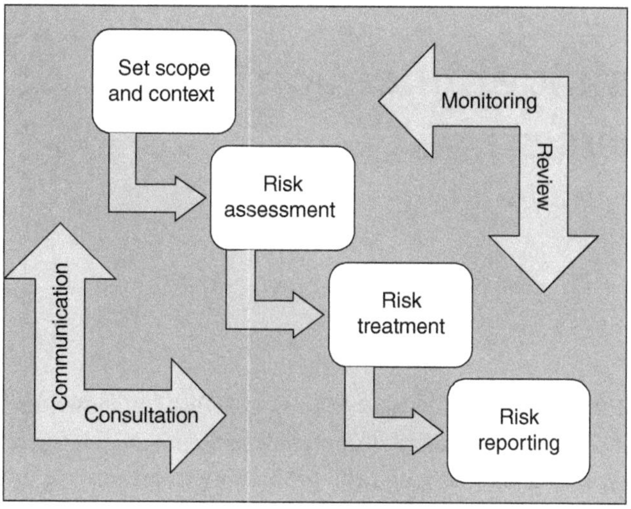

RISK, OPPORTUNITY, AND ISO 9001

In section 0.3.3, the standard mentions:

> Opportunities can arise as a result of a situation favourable to achieving an intended result, for example, a set of circumstances that allow the organization to attract customers, develop new products and services, reduce waste or improve productivity. Actions to address opportunities can also include consideration of associated risks. Risk is the effect of uncertainty and any such uncertainty can have positive or negative effects. A positive deviation arising from a risk can provide an opportunity, but not all positive effects of risk result in opportunities.[3]

The standard addresses the fact that positive deviations arise from risk and must be considered. Risks may not always have a negative outcome and is not always to be avoided.

Now that we have a high-level overview of risk and its nature, let us get into the details and talk about risk identification and analysis.

3. ©ISO. This material is reproduced from ISO 9001:2015, with permission of the American National Standards Institute (ANSI) on behalf of the International Organization for Standardization.

CHAPTER 7

Basic Risk Identification and Analysis

IN POPULAR MODERN DICTIONARIES, risk is defined as shown in Table 7.1.

The first common theme here (among these definitions) is the reference to chance or possibility. It follows that when the probability of an adverse event increases, the risk increases proportionally.

It is much riskier to walk on ice than concrete because the probability of slipping is higher on ice. Note that we have not yet even considered the level of consequence of slipping, which may result in a bruise, bleeding, broken bones, and so on.

Probability, like risk, is everywhere around us. For example, the probability of you driving to work in a snowstorm depends on the following:

1. If you can walk through the snow to get to your car
2. If you can start your car in the freezing conditions
3. If the road is icy and slippery
4. If you can drive on icy roads
5. If a minor accident blocks the road
6. If a major pileup halts traffic
7. If the snowstorm turns into a whiteout blizzard

Obviously, the probability of each event happening is different, and, even if the event occurs, it may still be likely that you will be able to reach work. On a qualitative scale, the probabilities range from very certain to extremely unlikely. One might argue that a person could also die from the cold while driving and never reach work. The chance of "dying due to cold" is so low that it sounds preposterous. At the same time, if that does happen, it will be the event with the most severe outcome. Such events are called *black swan* events. These are events of such low probability that they cannot be predicted with any amount of computational accuracy. These events are extremely impactful and usually are far beyond the normal realm of practical expectations. I have included this here only to introduce the concept of a black swan. One could never hope to complete risk assessments practically if all imaginable black swan events were included.

Now, let's say I am your friend and my objective is to ensure that you get to work safely. I will do everything in my power to maximize your probability of getting to

TABLE 7.1 Dictionary definitions of risk.

Source	Definition of risk
Macmillan	"The *possibility* that something *unpleasant* or *dangerous might happen*"
Merriam-Webster	"*Possibility* of *loss* or *injury*"
Dictionary.com	"Exposure to the *chance* of *injury* or *loss*; a *hazard* or *dangerous chance*"
Cambridge	"The *possibility* of *danger, defeat*, or *loss*"
Oxford	"*Chance* or *possibility* of *danger, loss, injury* or other *adverse consequences*"

Sources: Macmillan Dictionary, s.v., "risk," accessed June 15, 2020, https://www.macmillandictionary.com/us/dictionary/american/risk_1; Merriam-Webster Dictionary, s.v., "risk," accessed June 15, 2020, https://www.merriam-webster.com/dictionary/risk; Dictionary.com, s.v., "risk," accessed June 22, 2020, https://www.dictionary.com/browse/risk?s=t; Cambridge Dictionary, s.v., "risk," accessed June 15, 2020, https://dictionary.cambridge.org/us/dictionary/english/risk; Oxford Learner's Dictionaries, s.v., "risk," accessed June 15, 2020, https://www.oxfordlearnersdictionaries.com/us/definition/english/risk_1?q=risk.

TABLE 7.2 Frequency or occurrence table.

Term	Description
High	Occurrence is likely (often or frequent)
Medium	May occur but not often or frequently
Low	Rare occurrence (unlikely)

work. But I have limited resources and I need to prioritize the probabilities to ensure I use my resources in the best way possible. So, using the key shown in Table 7.2, I assign a "probability" to each event listed earlier (see Table 7.3).

Now, I could go ahead and reduce all high-probability events, or pick the easiest ones to reduce, but there is another way. If another dimension is introduced, I can focus my resources and expend them in a still more efficient manner. This dimension is *consequence*, also known as *impact* or *severity*.

Per the dictionary definitions of risk we reviewed earlier, the second common theme we see is in the mention of loss, injury, and adverse events. Negative risk proportionally increases based on the severity of an adverse event.

The severity is the consequence of the risky event. In this case, severity is the level of disruption caused, as seen in Table 7.4.

Table 7.5 includes a column for "severity" of each outcome as described earlier in Table 7.3 and reproduced here in the second column.

A simple definition of risk that lends itself to mathematical conversion is:

Risk is the combination of the probability of the occurrence of a consequence and the severity or impact of the consequence.

Similarly, by focusing on the negative outcome of *harm* as the injury or damage to people, property, or environment, ISO Guide 63:2019 defines *risk* as:

TABLE 7.3 Tabulation of events, outcomes, and their probabilities.

Ways in which you do not get to work	Outcome	Probability of event happening	Rationale for the probability
Slipping and falling while walking through snow to get to the car	You get a bruise, get first aid, and get to work late	Medium	You do not have snowboots
Slipping and falling while walking through snow to get to the car	You break a bone and cannot go to work	Low	You have strong bones and will likely break the fall
Car does not start due to dead battery	You take a cab and arrive slightly late	High	You have not replaced the battery in a long time
Car skids on icy roads but you control the car	You arrive at work slightly late	Medium	Roads are very icy and you have worn tires
Car skids on icy roads and you are unable to control the car	You lose control and go off the road; you need to be towed and do not get to work	High	Your path has lots of iced-over bridges and you have worn tires
A minor accident on the road has slowed traffic	You arrive at work late	Medium	Icy roads can often cause minor accidents leading to slow but moving traffic
A major pileup on the road halts traffic	You arrive at work late	High	The road has many bridges that ice over, traffic is usually fast, and this often causes large accidents
The snowstorm grows into a whiteout blizzard	You cannot drive and do not reach work	Low	The area has not had whiteout blizzards in five years

TABLE 7.4 Severity table.

Term	Description
Significant	You cannot reach work at all
Moderate	You reach work late (>30 minutes)
Negligible	You reach work slightly late (<30 minutes)

TABLE 7.5 Tabulation of events, outcomes, probabilities, and severity levels.

Ways in which you do not get to work	Outcome	Probability of event happening	Rationale for the probability	Severity level
Slipping and falling while walking through snow to get to the car	You get a bruise, get first aid, and get to work late	Medium	You do not have snowboots	Moderate
Slipping and falling while walking through snow to get to the car	You break a bone and cannot go to work	Low	You have strong bones and will likely break the fall	Significant
Car does not start due to dead battery	You take a cab and arrive slightly late	High	You have not replaced the battery in a long time	Negligible
Car skids on icy roads but you control the car	You arrive at work slightly late	Medium	Roads are very icy and you have worn tires	Negligible
Car skids on icy roads and you are unable to control the car	You lose control and go off the road; you need to be towed and do not get to work	High	Your path has lots of iced-over bridges and you have worn tires	Significant
A minor accident on the road has slowed traffic	You arrive at work late	Medium	Icy roads can often cause minor accidents leading to slow but moving traffic	Moderate
A major pileup on the road halts traffic	You arrive at work late	High	The road has many bridges that ice over, traffic is usually fast, and this often causes large accidents	Moderate
The snowstorm grows into a whiteout blizzard	You cannot drive and do not reach work	Low	The area has not had whiteout blizzards in five years	Significant

TABLE 7.6 3×3 risk matrix.

Probability level		Severity level		
		Negligible	**Moderate**	**Significant**
	High	Reduce risk	Reduce risk	Reduce risk
	Medium	Acceptable risk	Acceptable risk	Reduce risk
	Low	Acceptable risk	Acceptable risk	Acceptable risk

Combination of the probability of occurrence of harm and the severity of that harm.[1]

In this vein, let's combine the probability and occurrence to find out the real risk of the harm of the events listed earlier. The easiest way to define this is through a key. Various ISO standards provide risk tables or risk matrices to accomplish this. The key in Table 7.6 is adapted from ISO 14971:2007.[2]

In Table 7.7 we finish our sample risk assessment based on Table 7.6.

Voila! We have now prioritized the items with the highest risk levels using a structured risk analysis such that targeted actions can be taken to reduce risk to an acceptable level.

When conducting risk analyses and evaluations, a major factor is stakeholder communication and consultation. In this case, I was able to come up with a few scenarios of potential failures, but they may not be all-encompassing. For example, if I had consulted your car mechanic in this exercise, she or he may have provided me with new information that could either add a failure mode or change the occurrence or severity of an already identified failure mode. If your mechanic had told me that your car's alternator belt was old and very susceptible to cracking in freezing conditions, I would have identified and added an event with significant severity. Conversely, if I had known that you just installed a state-of-the-art slip detection system in your car, that would make me reduce the probability of uncontrolled skidding of the car from high to low.

The following are benefits of stakeholder communication in the risk identification process:

1. Drawing from different areas of expertise to assign accurate severity and occurrence values
2. Using stakeholder expertise to cover all possible failures and consequences
3. Ensuring all stakeholders are aligned on assigned risk levels

---

1. ©ISO. This material is reproduced from ISO/IEC Guide 63:2019, with permission of the American National Standards Institute (ANSI) on behalf of the International Organization for Standardization. All rights reserved.
2. ©ISO. This material is reproduced from ISO 14971:2007, with permission of the American National Standards Institute (ANSI) on behalf of the International Organization for Standardization. All rights reserved.

TABLE 7.7 Tabulated risk assessment.

Risk	Probability of event happening	Severity level	Risk level
Slipping and falling while walking through snow to get to the car	Medium	Moderate	Acceptable
Slipping and falling while walking through snow to get to the car	Low	Significant	Acceptable
Car does not start due to dead battery	High	Negligible	Reduce risk
Car skids on icy roads but you control the car	Medium	Negligible	Acceptable
Car skids on icy roads and you are unable to control the car	High	Significant	Reduce risk
A minor accident on the road has slowed traffic	Medium	Moderate	Acceptable
A major pileup on the road halts traffic	High	Moderate	Reduce risk
The snowstorm grows into a whiteout blizzard	Low	Significant	Acceptable

Involvement of stakeholders is not only important for risk identification but is also critical post–risk assessment when risk treatments and communication plans have to be developed.

Another thing to consider is aggregate risk. In this case, the aggregate risk is the summation of risks that prevent the realization of the objective of reaching work on time. One way to show this graphically is as a consequence–time series chart, as shown in Figure 7.1.

It is important to consider the successive appearance of risks in time sequence or, in some cases, even the simultaneous occurrence of risks. In this particular example, since the risks occur sequentially, a chart like Figure 7.1 shows their progression and level of acceptability or unacceptability as they stand without any treatment. This shows the net position of the risks in terms of comparative acceptability. I know that the risk with the maximum footprint is the loss of control of the car on icy roads, which has the most severe impact, while risk of dead battery is also unacceptable but has a negligible impact on the objective. It also shows that we have three unacceptable levels of threats to our objective of reaching work. After attempts to reduce risks, this figure can be compared with the original levels to check net loss of risk.

Let us summarize three important definitions:

risk identification

The process of finding, recognizing, describing, and recording risks. Risk identification involves the identification of risk sources, events, their causes, and their potential consequences.

FIGURE 7.1 Consequence–time series chart for aggregate risks.

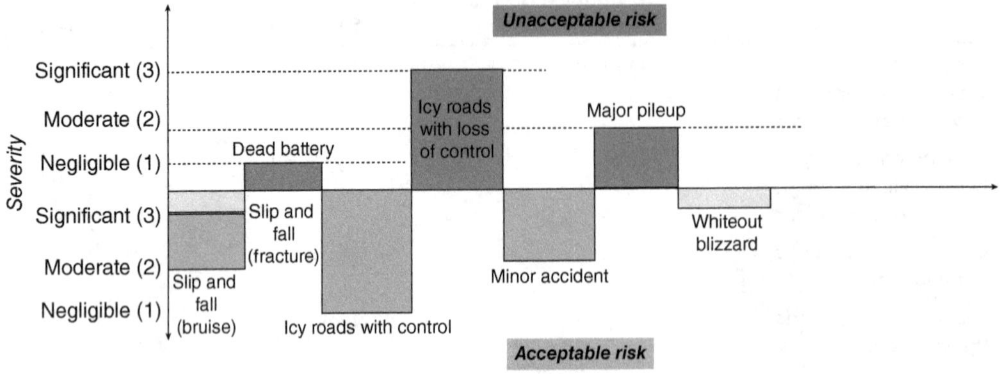

risk analysis

The process for comprehending the nature of risk and determining the level of risk.

risk evaluation

The final phase of risk assessment, where the results of risk analysis are compared with criteria and assigned a level of acceptability based on which additional actions to modify or maintain risk are determined.

CHAPTER 8

Events and Consequences

IN THE LAST CHAPTER, we used a simple and structured analysis to qualitatively assign risk levels to individual events. To correctly assess risk, one must understand what an *event* means.

ISO-31000:2018 defines an *event* as:

Occurrence or change of a particular set of circumstances.[1]

An event may have several causes and may or may not have consequences. It may be previously seen or experienced or may be just plain theoretical.

ISO 31000:2018 defines *consequence* as follows:

Outcome of an event affecting objectives.[2]

When we evaluated the list of possible events in the previous chapter, the severity was assigned based on the consequence. Table 8.1 clarifies this in regard to the previous example.

Consequence is simply the scale of severity we used earlier. It is, in fact, the measure of the impact.

It is critical that risk professionals understand event and consequence. Mistakes here could lead to the analysis being overly redundant and, in the worst case, incorrect. The following are common mistakes in this regard:

- The idea that one event can have only one consequence
- The idea that consequences must be certain
- Use of only the final consequence

---

1. ©ISO. This material is reproduced from ISO 31000:2018, with permission of the American National Standards Institute (ANSI) on behalf of the International Organization for Standardization. All rights reserved.
2. ©ISO. This material is reproduced from ISO 31000:2018, with permission of the American National Standards Institute (ANSI) on behalf of the International Organization for Standardization. All rights reserved.

TABLE 8.1 Tabulated risk assessment.

Risk	Probability of event happening	Consequence	Severity level
Slipping and falling while walking through snow to get to the car	Medium	Reach work late (more than 30 minutes)	Moderate
Slipping and falling while walking through snow to get to the car	Low	Cannot reach work at all	Significant
Car does not start due to dead battery	High	Reach work slightly late (less than 30 minutes)	Negligible
Car skids on icy roads but you control the car	Medium	Reach work slightly late (less than 30 minutes)	Negligible
Car skids on icy roads and you are unable to control the car	High	Cannot reach work at all	Significant
A minor accident on the road has slowed traffic	Medium	Reach work late (more than 30 minutes)	Moderate
A major pileup on the road halts traffic	High	Reach work late (more than 30 minutes)	Moderate
The snowstorm grows into a whiteout blizzard	Low	Cannot reach work at all	Significant

One event may lead to various different consequences, each with varying levels of probability. The consequence of the impact may be positive or negative. There arises a need to distinguish the level of impact so that the consequences can be compared and evaluated. This is usually done with the help of a ratings scale. In the previous example, the scale shown in Table 8.2 was used.

To classify the negative impacts, the term "severity" is commonly used. The severity measures the level of negative impact so that it can be classified as a category using a ratings scale as shown in Table 8.2.

In the earlier example, to keep it simple, we used only one consequence for most of the risky events. For slipping and falling, we used two consequences on purpose to demonstrate the various possibilities and probabilities of event outcomes. This event can be further expanded, as shown in Table 8.3. The need for detail must be assessed by the risk professional. In case you are conducting risk analysis for a complex system that has possibilities of multiple user or customer harms, you may want to explore the consequences in much greater detail.

TABLE 8.2 Severity scale.

Severity	Term	Description
3	Significant	You cannot reach work at all
2	Moderate	You reach work late (>30 minutes)
1	Negligible	You reach work slightly late (<30 minutes)

FIGURE 8.1 The consequence polygon.

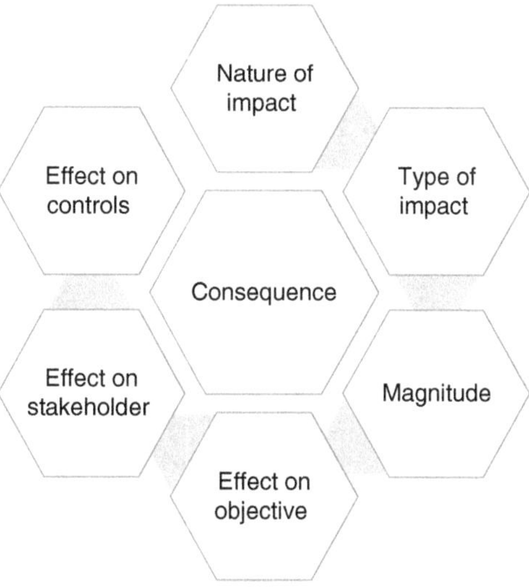

TABLE 8.3 Expanded risk assessment with immediate and final consequences.

Ways in which you do not get to work (sequence of events)	Probability of event happening	Immediate consequence	Final consequence*	Severity
Slipping while walking through snow to get to the car	Medium	Fall leading to a bruise	Reach work late (more than 30 minutes)	Moderate
Slipping while walking through snow to get to the car	Low	Fall leading to a broken femur	Cannot reach work at all	Significant
Slipping while walking through snow to get to the car	High	You regain balance and do not fall	Reach work on time	No impact / negligible

*Considering no other events occur after this event

The activity of drawing out consequences and analyzing them is known as *consequence analysis.*

A consequence analysis exercise can be done using the consequence polygon shown in Figure 8.1, which takes into account the following:

1. **Nature of impact**—chronic or acute
2. **Type of impact**—short or long term
3. **Magnitude**—scope of the impact (local vs. global, immediate vs. trailing)
4. **Effect on objective**—positive or negative
5. **Effect on stakeholder**—user, manufacturer, or layman effects
6. **Effect on control**—change in modification/mitigation strategy

One may choose not to include every section in the final risk analysis document, but it is important to have these points in mind during the consequence analysis activity.

CHAPTER 9

Basic Risk Modification

IN THE PREVIOUS CHAPTERS, we learned the basic concepts of risk identification, analysis, and evaluation. These are informative assessments that set the stage for modification of the assessed risk for organizational benefit. Risk modification, depending on the nature of risk response, can be called *risk treatment*, *risk mitigation*, or *risk control.*

Modification of risk is expected to reduce the adverse effects and, where possible, increase the beneficial effects of an endeavor such that the predetermined objectives are met with the fewest issues along the way.

In the previous example, we looked at the risk from driving in the snow. We identified certain unacceptable risks for reduction listed in Table 9.1.

The two obvious ways of reducing risks are to take actions to induce reduction in the probability and to take actions to induce reduction in the severity. In this example, it is much easier to effect a change in probability. The best way to approach risk modification is to modify the root cause of risk. Table 9.2 shows some modifications.

The addition of mitigation, in this case, is an anticipation to reduce the probability that an event will happen. Thus, we must update this register with the new anticipated probabilities and recalculate risk to confirm their acceptability. This is done as shown in Table 9.3.

In this case, we have reduced all risks to an acceptable level individually. Let us now look at the aggregate risks using the consequence–time series chart in Figure 9.1.

While we have reduced all unacceptable risks, we still need to be on the lookout for some high-severity risks as we embark on our objective to drive through the snow to reach

TABLE 9.1 Tabulated risk assessment.

Ways in which you do not get to work (sequence of events)	Probability of event happening	Severity level	Risk level
Car does not start due to dead battery	High	Negligible	Reduce risk
Car skids on icy roads and you are unable to control the car	High	Significant	Reduce risk
A major pileup on the road halts traffic	High	Moderate	Reduce risk

TABLE 9.2 Tabulated risk assessment with a column for risk modification.

Ways in which you do not get to work (sequence of events)	Probability of event happening	Severity level	Risk level	Modification
Car does not start due to dead battery	High	Negligible	Reduce risk	Check and replace battery when cold weather sets in
Car skids on icy roads and you are unable to control the car	High	Significant	Reduce risk	Change tires and check all systems as cold weather sets in
A major pileup on the road halts traffic	High	Moderate	Reduce risk	Use an app to find alternate routes with low-speed traffic

TABLE 9.3 Tabulated risk assessment with modified probability and risk levels.

Ways in which you do not get to work (sequence of events)	Probability of event happening	Severity level	Risk level	Mitigation	New probability	New risk level
Car does not start due to dead battery	High	Negligible	Reduce risk	Check and replace battery before winter	Medium	Acceptable
Car skids on icy roads and you are unable to control the car	High	Significant	Reduce risk	Change tires and check all systems	Low	Acceptable
A major pileup on the road halts traffic	High	Moderate	Reduce risk	Use an app to find alternate routes with low-speed traffic	Medium	Acceptable

FIGURE 9.1 Consequence–time series presentation of risk after mitigation (no unacceptable risks in this case).

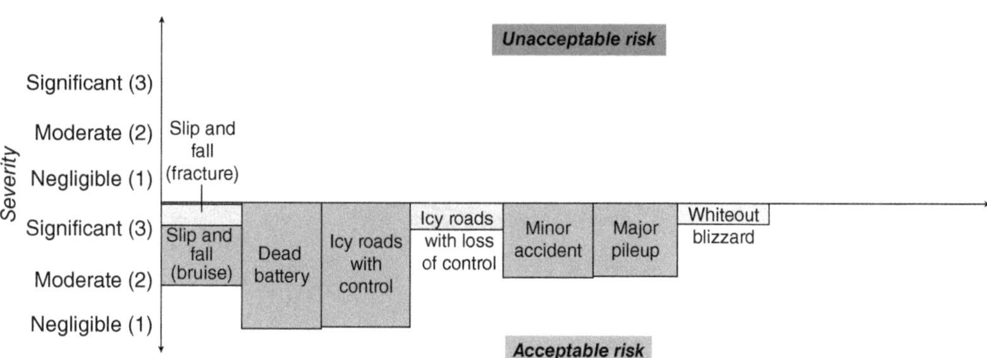

our office. One cannot be carefree as a result of this exercise, as there are many subjective factors involved in this assessment. It is easier to predict an impact or consequence than the probability. Since no one can predict the future with 100% certainty, there is always some error involved in prediction regardless of the rigor of the methodology used.

A monitoring and review phase is essential to continually assess the level of risk and to check whether the predicted profile is maintained. In this example, a driver will continually monitor the road and snow conditions. If the conditions worsen, one may decide to turn back. As objectives become more complex with the involvement of more processes and people, a need arises to structurally define the roles and responsibilities of the risk management process. There arises a need for understanding the stakeholders and planning the whole process to ensure it is inclusive, streamlined, and effective.

Risk modification, for example, should always be a balance between practicality and effectiveness. Outside the simple scenario we've been examining, this can translate into a lot of complex factors in an organizational context, including attitudes toward risk and the availability of the resources for modification. Therefore, a primary consideration before beginning organization-wide risk management activity should be to identify and engage stakeholders.

In this chapter, we focus on risk modification, which can be defined as:

risk modification (treatment)

The method of selection and implementation of options for addressing risk, which usually involves a measure that maintains and/or modifies risk.

CHAPTER 10

The Stakeholder

EVEN BEFORE WE BEGIN identification of the risks, we must begin the identification of the *stakeholders*. These are the cross-functional entities that have a stake in the product, process, or system for which the risk is being analyzed. ISO 31000:2018 defines a *stakeholder* as:

> *Person or organization that can affect, be affected by, or perceive themselves to be affected by a decision or activity.*[1]

Thus, any individual or organization that is directly or indirectly involved with, or is affected by, organization decision or activities can be a stakeholder. It is incumbent on the organization (and risk professionals) to identify the most relevant stakeholders based on their impact to the objectives.

The level of interest and influence a stakeholder has in the activity must also be noted. A structured method of doing this is through these two simple phases:

1. Identification
2. Engagement

In the *identification* phase, the interests, interdependencies, and "stake" of the stakeholders must be noted. It is important here to note the risk attitude of the stakeholder. They may have a risk-taking attitude or a risk-averse attitude. For example, an investment company with spare cash may want to invest in a high-risk, high-return market, while a maker of implantable medical devices may have a very conservative risk-averse attitude. Detailed discussion on risk attitudes can be found in Chapter 15.

In the *engagement* phase, the risk professional must foster positive engagement with the stakeholder, which leads to mutual benefit. This means managing the needs and expectations of the stakeholder and paying commensurate attention to their stake in the activity. Communication and cross-functional facilitation are key to success in this process.

---

1. ©ISO. This material is reproduced from ISO 31000:2018, with permission of the American National Standards Institute (ANSI) on behalf of the International Organization for Standardization. All rights reserved.

The level of engagement with a stakeholder is defined by the level of interest and influence (the *stake* of the stakeholder). Some stakeholders will eventually act as risk owners, and such identification is necessary early on to avoid confusion later in the risk monitoring phase.

The following are the levels of stakeholder engagement mentioned by the *Guide to Project Management Body of Knowledge*.[2] These can be leveraged during the risk management process for easy categorization:

1. **Unaware**—unaware of risks
2. **Resistant**—resistant to risk management efforts
3. **Neutral**—neither supportive of nor resistant to the risk management efforts
4. **Supportive**—aware of risk impacts and active participant in the risk management process
5. **Leading**—supportive and actively engaged in ensuring that the risk management plan is a success

Another method to categorize stakeholders is with the influence–engagement matrix. This is a variation of Mendelow's matrix, a tool that analyzes stakeholders on the basis of their interest in objectives and influence (power) in the organization. For risk management, engagement of important stakeholders is essential at each step, and this has been made evident on the x-axis in Figure 10.1. Instead of *interest* in objectives, we will plot the *impact* on the objective. This allows us to identify not only the stakeholders with the most skin in the game but also the ones who impact the "game" itself. Based on these two foundational parameters, the stakeholders can be classified into three categories:

1. **Key stakeholders:** These are the people whose engagement is crucial to the success of the risk management activities. For those key stakeholders with high engagement, maximum attention must be given, and efforts must be taken, to ensure that their engagement in risk management activities is sustained. For the key stakeholders who have low engagement in risk management activities, targeted efforts for reengagement must be taken to ensure that this is corrected. This starts with uncovering the root cause of disengagement and then gaining alignment, spending more resources, involving management, and so on.
2. **Active stakeholders:** These are the people who have low impact on the objectives but are actively involved in the risk management efforts. Such stakeholders must be shown consideration and their engagement must be sustained as long as doing so does not take resources away from the key stakeholders. Such stakeholders usually add value by uncovering issues that key high-level or executive stakeholders sometimes cannot due to their routine familiarity with the objectives. Involvement of the active stakeholders allows for a review by new and different sets of eyes.

---

2. Project Management Institute, *A Guide to the Project Management Body of Knowledge*, 5th ed. (Newtown Square, PA: Project Management Institute, 2013).

3. **Satellite stakeholders:** These are the people who have low influence on outcomes—and low engagement in risk management activities. These stakeholders are usually deserving of the least attention because not much value addition is expected of them. Still, their impact on objectives must be reassessed frequently. It is quite common for the influence/impact of some stakeholders to be misjudged early on, possibly leading to issues midway.

Throughout the risk management process or the product or service life cycle, if the expectation is that engagement and influence of stakeholders may change, then plan to redraw the chart in Figure 10.1 for different phases.

After the identification of the stakeholders is complete, chart various stakeholders as shown in Figure 10.2 such that a targeted determination can be made for their reengagement into risk management activities.

Once the stakeholders who need additional engagement have been identified, they must be approached with a proposition that ensures benefits and value creation for them arising from their participation in the risk management activities. While self-interest is the best motivator, at times, authoritative enforcement by top management is needed to ensure engagement, depending on the urgency and state of stakeholder participation.

After categorization of the stakeholders, it is useful to form an RACI matrix, which can help manage deliverables as the implementation of the risk management plan moves forward. RACI stands for responsible, accountable, consulted, and informed, which are defined as follows:

1. **Responsible:** This stakeholder is responsible for completing a risk management task or specific deliverable. The deliverables can be wide ranging and can encompass system, operational, functional, or document-creation-related

FIGURE 10.1 Influence–engagement matrix.

Influence on outcomes ↑	Low engagement	High engagement
High	*Key stakeholder: additional engagement efforts and maximum attention*	*Key stakeholder: maximum attention*
Low	*Satellite stakeholder: minimum attention*	*Active stakeholder: show consideration and meet their needs*

Low — Engagement in risk management → *High*

FIGURE 10.2 Influence–engagement matrix with stakeholder assignation.

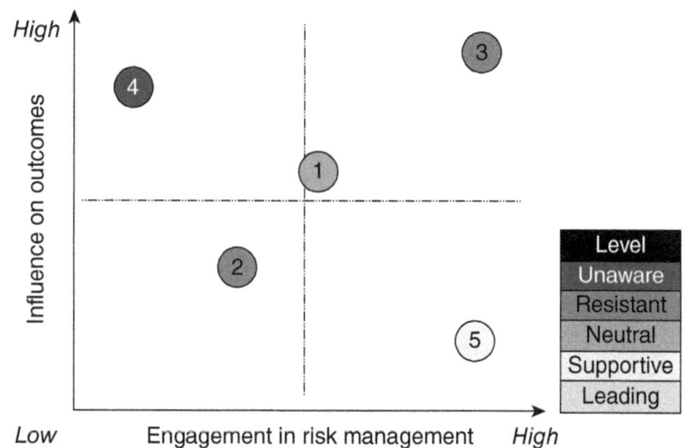

TABLE 10.1 An example of a RACI matrix.

Task	Risk manager	Stakeholder 1	Stakeholder 2	Stakeholder 3
Risk management plan development	R	R	C	I
Risk identification	A	R	R	C
Risk analysis	A	C	R	I
Risk response	A	C	C	I
Risk monitoring	A	C	C	I

tasks. The task will be completed by this stakeholder, and there can be more than one responsible stakeholder.

2. **Accountable:** This stakeholder is the person who owns the deliverable in terms of the completion liability and is the final approving authority. The accountable stakeholder may delegate the task and act as a reviewer or may also be the responsible party in some cases. It is a best practice to ensure that only one stakeholder is assigned the accountable status to avoid confusion.
3. **Consulted:** These are the stakeholders whose feedback is important by virtue of their expertise in the subject matter or routine association with the deliverable.
4. **Informed:** These stakeholders are periodically informed on the progress of the task or the deliverable. The communication is often one-way as opposed to two-way communication with the consulted stakeholders.

The RACI matrix can be created based on individual risk levels, at the level of hazards, or on the planning level, as shown in Table 10.1.

As we discussed earlier in the first example, engagement of the stakeholders leads to accurate identification, categorization, and classification of the risks. A lot of stakeholders will be the eventual risk owners, and they all must be on the same page in terms of escalation, action responses, communication, and documentation techniques.

CHAPTER 11

Upside of Risk: Opportunity

LOOKING AT ONLY THE DOWNSIDE OF RISK is akin to considering a coin to have only one side. Table 11.1 reproduces the dictionary definitions of the term "risk."

There is certainly a negative connotation of the term "risk." But let us dispel this falsehood early on.

We saw a few definitions of risk in earlier chapters, some with broader scope than others. Let us contrast two standard definitions and discuss their implications.

ISO 13485:2016 (*Medical Devices—Quality Management Systems*) defines risk as:

Combination of the probability of occurrence of harm and the severity of that harm.[1]

ISO 9000:2015 (*Quality Management Systems—Fundamentals and Vocabulary*), from which ISO 9001:2015 derives all terms and definitions, defines risk as:

Effect of uncertainty.
Note 1 to entry: An effect is a deviation from the expected—positive or negative.[2]

ISO 31000:2018 (*Risk Management—Guidelines*) defines risk as:

Effect of uncertainty on objectives.
Note 1 to entry: An effect is a deviation from the expected. It can be positive, negative or both, and can address, create or result in opportunities and threats.[3]

---

1. ©ISO. This material is reproduced from ISO 13485:2016, with permission of the American National Standards Institute (ANSI) on behalf of the International Organization for Standardization. All rights reserved.
2. ©ISO. This material is reproduced from ISO 9001:2015, with permission of the American National Standards Institute (ANSI) on behalf of the International Organization for Standardization. All rights reserved.
3. ©ISO. This material is reproduced from ISO 31000:2018, with permission of the American National Standards Institute (ANSI) on behalf of the International Organization for Standardization. All rights reserved.

TABLE 11.1 Dictionary definitions of risk.

Source	Definition of risk
Macmillan	"The *possibility* that something *unpleasant* or *dangerous might happen*"
Merriam-Webster	"*Possibility* of *loss* or *injury*"
Dictionary.com	"Exposure to the *chance* of *injury* or *loss*; a *hazard* or *dangerous chance*"
Cambridge	"The *possibility* of *danger, defeat,* or *loss*"
Oxford	"*Chance* or *possibility* of *danger, loss, injury* or other *adverse consequences*"

Sources: Macmillan Dictionary, s.v., "risk," accessed June 15, 2020, https://www.macmillandictionary.com/us/dictionary/american/risk_1; Merriam-Webster Dictionary, s.v., "risk," accessed June 15, 2020, https://www.merriam-webster.com/dictionary/risk; Dictionary.com, s.v., "risk," accessed June 22, 2020, https://www.dictionary.com/browse/risk?s=t; Cambridge Dictionary, s.v., "risk," accessed June 15, 2020, https://dictionary.cambridge.org/us/dictionary/english/risk; Oxford Learner's Dictionaries, s.v., "risk," accessed June 15, 2020, https://www.oxfordlearnersdictionaries.com/us/definition/english/risk_1?q=risk.

As we can see from the three separate definitions, the scope of risk and risk management went from negative to positive. So which definition is right? The answer is, all of them.

The context of the organization as detailed in Chapters 14 and 16 really defines the context of risk management. In the first definition, the negative aspect of risk is stressed since, in the context of medical devices, it makes sense to consider every possible failure of the device in detail from a safety and reliability standpoint. This one-tailed approach to risk arms the user with singlemindedness and specificity of scope (i.e., confined to failure and safety). But here too, one may argue that addition or deletion of design features may be opportunities that may well benefit from a risk and failure assessment. One can also argue that if one considers opportunities or upsides of risk right at the beginning, a more beneficial device can be manufactured.

ISO 9001:2015 and ISO 31000:2018 are more universal standards that take the two-tailed approach to risk, which includes positive and negative aspects. The benefits of this approach are apparent in system-level, operational, strategic, and enterprise risk management. But when we get to the product, process, or service level, as the risks tend to become more and more specific, many practitioners find it difficult and at times redundant to incorporate the opportunity side.

To simplify, let us define an *event*, which is full of uncertainty (i.e., full of risk), as follows:

A risky event is an event whose occurrence is uncertain,
but if it were to occur, it may have a negative or positive impact
on the product, process, or system.

This risky event may be turning a screw in a spinal implant or choosing a new indication for a drug or adding a new navigation feature to a car. A potential failure mode is still a risk event but only with negative risk.

Let us now look at an example that clarifies the concepts above related to risk, uncertainty, and positive and negative aspects. Let us consider a game where the

TABLE 11.2 Expected monetary value analysis for a $5 bet.

Outcome	Probability	Impact	Probability × Impact
Tails	50%	−$5	−2.5
Heads	50%	+$10	+5

correct guess on the outcome of a fair coin toss doubles your wager. We are aware that a fair coin toss has 50% probability of heads or tails. So here, the risky event is the coin toss, with a two-tailed risk.

If I flip a coin on a $5 wager and call heads, tails brings a 50% possibility of loss and financial injury to me, but heads brings a 50% possibility of profit for me. I could have chosen not to place the wager and not take a risk, but I decided that there was an opportunity for me to benefit by taking that risk. When such situations present themselves, how do you decide which path to take? Is the risk worth it?

A risk-benefit analysis can help drive a decision in such cases. Below is one that I performed on the fly for this simple two-outcome event by doing the following:

1. Assigning probability to the positive outcome
2. Assigning impact level to the positive outcome
3. Assigning probability to the negative outcome
4. Assigning impact level to the negative outcome
5. Comparing total risk between the two outcomes by using a risk equation

Table 11.2 shows my tabulated risk-benefit analysis.

Table 11.2, in fact, is known as expected monetary value analysis (commonly used in project management) and is often used to quantify aggregate risk by multiplying the likelihood of the outcome by the impact of the outcome. This multiplicative product gives an expected monetary value for each outcome, which can be added across all outcomes to give a final level of risk. The aggregate expected output here is $2.50, which does not mean I will earn $2.50 but if I play this game over and over again multiple times, I will probably end up with an average gain of $2.50.

So, the question I need to answer in this simple risk-benefit analysis is: Am I fine with the expected monetary value of $2.50? or Am I fine with a 50% chance of losing $5 for a 50% chance to gain $10?

The key concept here is that risk is involved for all outcomes borne out of uncertainty. Some of these outcomes are beneficial and have a positive risk or an opportunity associated with them. Risk-benefit analysis is mentioned in detail in Chapter 36.

CHAPTER 12

Detailed Risk Identification

BEFORE WE BEGIN THE RISK-IDENTIFICATION PROCESS, we must ask ourselves, Why do we perform risk management? Previously, we learned that all risk is the effect of uncertainty. Uncertainty is everywhere around us, and some of that uncertainty carries threats while some carries opportunities. And, some uncertainty just doesn't matter. That my car may or may not start when I leave for work today is an uncertainty that matters tremendously to me since the impact would mean that I would miss an important meeting. The number of red lights I encounter is an uncertainty that doesn't matter to me as I start my day well ahead of time to ensure stopping at red lights doesn't become a factor in arriving at work on time.

In the words of David Hillson, risk is "uncertainty that matters."[1] And why do only some uncertainties matter? Because they affect an end goal. In an organization, these end goals may be classified as outcomes, objectives, or outputs.

Risk identification is the process of determining which risks affect the end goals, intended uses, or objectives. This determination in the risk-identification phase involves finding, defining, and documenting these risks. Thus, the data and evidence gathering and consolidation within the organizational context (see Chapters 14 and 16 for details on organizational context) is most important to begin this process. On a high level, the data must:

1. Provide a comprehensive review of the function within the scope of risk management activities
2. Be verifiable and reliable
3. Be relevant to the context
4. Be inclusive of all relevant stakeholders
5. Consider internal and external sources
6. Take into account existing controls
7. Take into account past, present, and future states
8. Take into account all risk sources
9. Take into account all risk drivers

---

1. D. Hillson, ed., *The Risk Management Handbook: A Practical Guide to Managing the Multiple Dimensions of Risk* (London: Kogan Page Publishers, 2016).

Risk sources are defined by ANSI/ASIS/RIMS RA.1-2015 as:

A factor with the potential to create uncertainty in achieving objectives.[2]

Risk drivers are defined by ANSI/ASIS/RIMS RA.1-2015 as:

Event, individual(s), process, or trends having impact on the objectives of the organization.[3]

Risk sources have a large scope and include the tangible and intangible factors. ISO 31000:2018 describes risk sources as having intrinsic potential to engender risk. They are the true root originators of risk. These can be things as broad as political environments and as narrow as a small design feature in a product. Risk source is simply the source of the hazard. Risk drivers are actuators of the risks from the risk sources. These are specific events, individuals, processes, actions, sets of decisions, and so on that actuate the risk at its source and increase its probability of realization by giving rise to a hazard. Consequently, sometimes risk sources are also known as hazard sources. The relationship between risk source, risk driver, hazard, sequence of events, and hazardous situation is shown in Figure 12.1.

While it is great to know a risk or hazard source for mitigation purposes, in terms of risk assessment, hazard identification is where the traditional risk identification process begins.

The process of risk identification may start with identification of the hazards:

A hazard is a potential condition that, through a sequence of events, can cause a consequence.

Hazards can, and mostly do, exist without the occurrence of a failure. For example, the excessive vibration of internal components while driving a car on a dirt road is a hazard. It leads to a hazardous situation and failure only when some important component gets displaced and causes the car to stop or break down. Conversely, one may be able to drive the car for a long time without encountering any failures despite components being misplaced. This can be explained using the graphic in Figure 12.2.

In the example above, the dirt road is the risk source, and the risk driver is the need to traverse the dirt road (due to some objective, such as rural delivery). This leads to the appearance of a hazard, which is mechanical vibration. Overspeeding on a bad patch of road leads to magnification of vibration and dislodges a few components. This may lead to total stoppage of the car or may not lead to any event.

Thus, hazards are potential sources of risky events that may cause consequences (harmful, benign, or in some cases even beneficial).

---

2. *Risk Assessment*, ANSI/ASIS/RIMS RA.1-2015 (Alexandria, VA: American National Standards Institute, 2015), 3.1.
3. *Risk Assessment*, ANSI/ASIS/RIMS RA.1-2015 (Alexandria, VA: American National Standards Institute, 2015), 3.1.

FIGURE 12.1 From risk source to outcome.

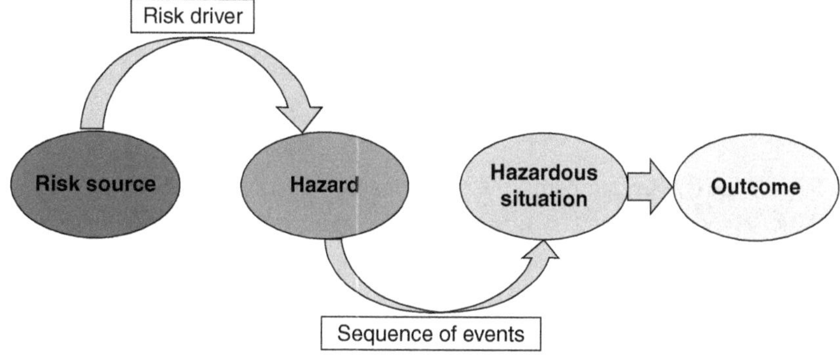

FIGURE 12.2 Dirt road as a risk source leading to vibration as a hazard and dislodged components as a hazardous situation.

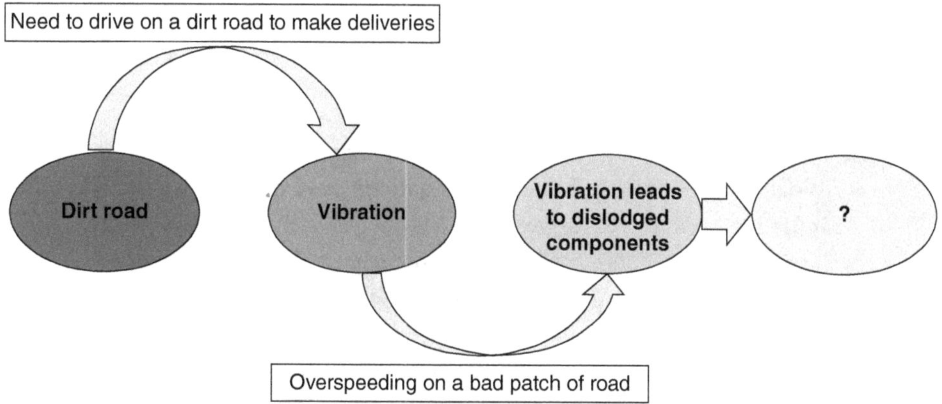

ISO 12100:2010 describes *safety hazard* as:

> *A potential source of harm.*
> *It can be ever present, or it can appear unexpectedly.*[4]

A *hazardous situation* is:

> *A circumstance in which the user or system is exposed to a hazard with possibility of an impactful consequence.*

---

4. ©ISO. This material is reproduced from ISO 12100:2010, with permission of the American National Standards Institute (ANSI) on behalf of the International Organization for Standardization.

In the example above, the hazardous situation is the dislodgement of the car's internal components due to exposure to vibration. This has the possibility of an impactful occurrence of total stoppage of the car.

Let us look at the full spectrum of events from risk/hazard source to outcome using the example in Figure 12.3.

Here,

Risk/hazard source: neighbor's rabbit farm
Risk driver: a gap in the fence enabling a rabbit to cross into my backyard
Sequence of events that lead to a hazardous situation: rabbit chews through the plastic fence of my vegetable patch
Hazardous situation: rabbit enters the vegetable patch
Harm: rabbit eats all the lettuce crop

For the product, process, or system, the risk professional should be able to classify the various hazards that surround the activities. During hazard identification, the following questions should be asked:

1. What is the hazard?
2. Is the hazard time dependent?
3. Is the hazard location dependent?
4. What events lead the hazard to become a hazardous situation?
5. What are the multiple hazardous situations caused by the hazard due to each initiating event or risk drivers?
6. Are there any events or risk sources that trigger the hazard itself?
7. Can the hazard be quantified? Does the quantification have an impact on the risk engendered by the hazard?
8. What are the consequences of the hazardous situations?
9. What the best- and worst-case scenarios of the hazardous situation, and what needs to be done to achieve or mitigate those?

FIGURE 12.3 Neighbor's rabbit farm as the risk source, rabbit as the hazard, rabbit's entry into the vegetable patch as the hazardous situation, and rabbit eating the lettuce crop as the negative outcome.

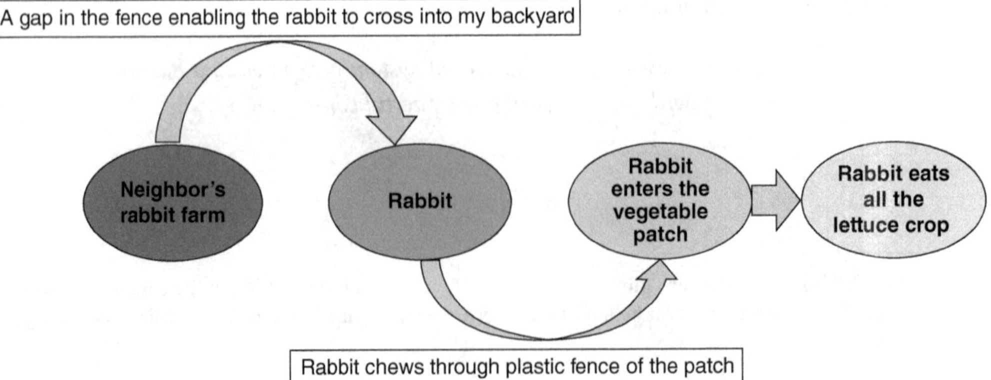

Sometimes there can be confusion between a hazard and a source or even a hazard and a hazardous situation. In such cases, it is most important to consider the context of the situation. Also important to consider is the definitions of terms themselves. Always remember that there can be many ways of doing the right thing. Different industries have different categories of hazards. For example, for medical devices, the following could be the hazards list:

1. Electromagnetic energy
2. Line voltage
3. Leakage current
4. Electric fields
5. Thermal energy
6. Mechanical energy
7. Gravity
8. Vibration
9. Biological agents
10. Bacteria
11. Viruses

For disaster management, a list such as the following could apply:

1. Drought/famine
2. Storms/floods
3. Heat/cold waves
4. Earth movements
5. Eruptions
6. Landslides
7. Biological events
8. Epidemics
9. Infestations

These hazard lists essentially act as prompts to guide the formulators of risk assessment to the potential failures that may manifest as threats or opportunities.

The questions we are trying to answer during the risk identification process are as follows:

- What could affect us?
- What could go wrong?

To answer these questions, the hazards list must be broken down into specific and sensible individual line items that may represent failures encompassing opportunities and threats. Here, we move from hazard identification into risk identification.

TABLE 12.1 Tabular organization of cause, risky event, effect, classification, and risk line item.

Hazard	Cause	Risky event	Effect	Classification	Risk verbiage
Icy road	Worn tires	Driving car on icy roads	Slippage and crash	Threat	Due to driving with worn tires on icy roads, the car can slip and crash

The key to the success of risk management lies here at this first step: *What level of specificity do you use to document the risk?* A simple technique for this is to follow the *risk metalanguage* described in the *Practice Standard for Risk Management*:[5]

Due to <cause>, <risk> can occur, which will lead to <effect>

The cause and effect loop must be clarified for the risk line to lend itself to proper usage. Another idea is to organize the cause, risky event, effect, and classification (threat, failure, or opportunity) in separate columns as in Table 12.1.

I have used neutral terms here to emphasize that there can be positive and negative aspects of risk. In certain industries, like medical devices, a risk may be specifically categorized in technical terms as *failure mode* and a negative effect may be a *harm*. It must be noted that there is a difference between *failure* and *failure mode*. This difference will be analyzed in more depth in Chapter 41 on failure modes and effects analysis.

As greater details are populated during the risk-identification exercise, it must be noted that some causes, effects, and risks will show up again and again. This is because one risk or failure may have more than one cause and, upon occurrence, could have more than one effect, which could be threats or opportunities. The cause and subsequent sequence of events can create the possibility of the negative or positive outcome through the activating agency of the risk.

WHERE DO THE RISKS COME FROM?

I mentioned that the lists of hazards act like prompts and help in targeted identification of risks from their very source. But to ensure that most of the risks are captured, engagement of the stakeholders is essential. The identification of the stakeholders precedes the risk identification and is extremely important since, many times, the success of risk identification depends on the success of cross-functional engagement of the stakeholders.

5. Project Management Institute, *Practice Standard for Project Risk Management* (Newtown Square, PA: Project Management Institute, 2009).

On an enterprise level, the high-level risks may be said to arise from volatility, uncertainty, complexity, and ambiguity (VUCA). The U.S. Army War College introduced the concept of VUCA to define the issues facing a fractured and weaponized world at the end of the Cold War. All systems and organizational challenges, on a base level, can be fit into the following four definitions:

1. **Volatility:** Volatility denotes the likelihood of changing rapidly and unpredictably. In risk contexts, volatility refers to the challenge of organizational control over the dynamics of change. In the risk-identification phase, we ask: *What rapidly changing liabilities does the organization face?* (stock market? consumer choice? etc.)
2. **Uncertainty:** While volatility looks at ups and downs, uncertainty looks toward problems faced due to lack of predictability. With anticipation comes awareness, understanding, and eventual evaluation of the issue in a risk management context.
3. **Complexity:** Complexity refers to the multitude of interwoven and interconnected risks that can confound their correct identification and defeat a risk response. Complex risks take effort to be defined through a simple causal nexus and can possibly lead to confusion. Using the risk metalanguage can diagnose such risks in the identification phase.
4. **Ambiguity:** Reality and outcomes are open to more than one interpretation; so are risks. Ambiguity regarding a risk impact or risk cause leads to incorrect risk evaluations.

VUCA is a good place to start risk identification as it has a very broad scope. Knowledge arms us against being victims of VUCA, and by looking through the VUCA lens, we may identify specific risks that may be more complex than they seem.

ISO 31000:2018 goes a layer deeper than VUCA and mentions general sources of risk, as shown in Figure 12.4.

In addition to the above items, a variety of sources should be scanned for potential risks. A few of them are listed below:

1. Design and development plan / project plan / action plan
2. Specification and constraints
3. Human resources management plan
4. Cost and schedule documentation
5. Assumptions
6. Stakeholder list
7. Quality management plan
8. Technical documentation
9. Supplier quality and procurement documentation
10. Academic and published studies
11. Quality checklists and forms
12. Standard operating procedures
13. Historical similar activities and their risk management plans

FIGURE 12.4 General sources of risk.

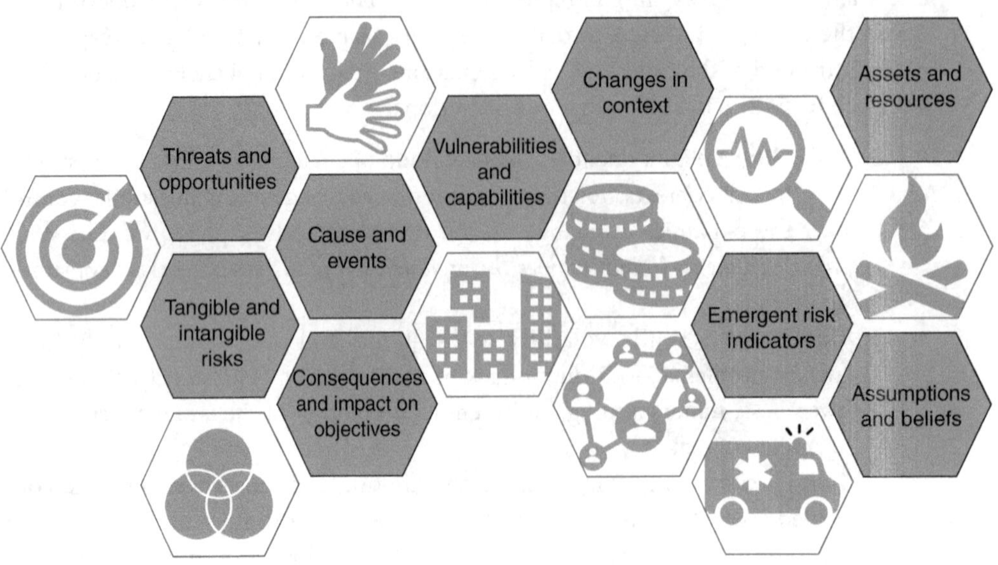

In this chapter we have learned how and where to identify risks. This is only the first part of the risk-identification process. In coming chapters we will see how to assign qualitative and quantitative probabilities to these identified risks.

It is important that the risk-identification process generate sufficient detail such that it may be properly qualitatively or quantitatively assessed and be assigned to a risk owner. In addition, the already identified risk may be updated as time passes and more knowledge becomes available; the risk-identification process must allow for such iterative identification. Most importantly, the process must allow for identification and proper documentation and assessment of emergent risks. New risks that were not identified during the initial identification phase should be prioritized for evaluation by quick formal identification supported by due process. This is summarized in Figure 12.5.

HOW DO WE IDENTIFY THE RISKS?

After the relevant cross-functional team has been identified and engaged, a comprehensive review of all the documentation stated above must be completed. The assumptions, requirements, and constraints must be tested, and a preliminary list of possible issues compiled.

As shown in Figure 12.6, for holistic risk identification, similar products, processes, or services must be reviewed in conjunction with assessment of relevant present conditions of the current product process or service under study. Finally, risks must be anticipated using an informed reflection about future states through the anticipated life cycle of the system.

FIGURE 12.5 Risk identification process: points to remember.

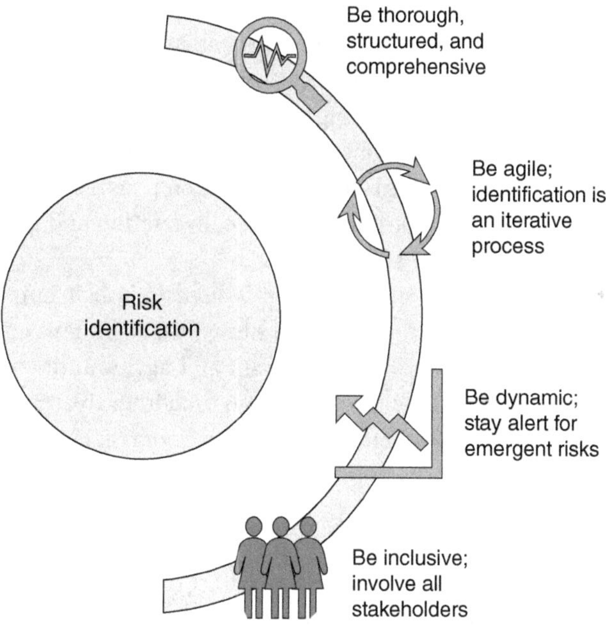
Be thorough, structured, and comprehensive
Be agile; identification is an iterative process
Risk identification
Be dynamic; stay alert for emergent risks
Be inclusive; involve all stakeholders

FIGURE 12.6 Risk identification: past, present, and future.

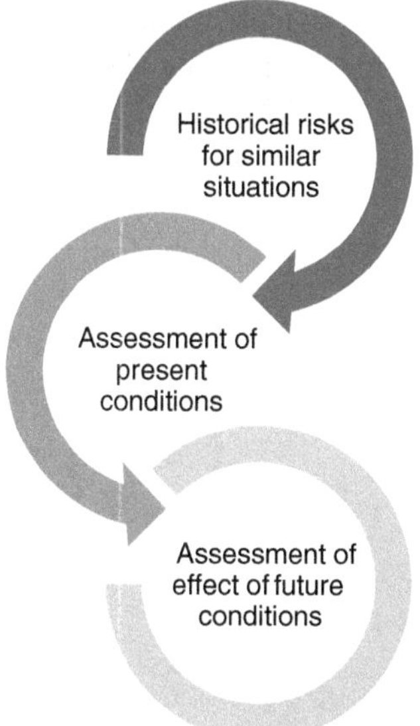
Historical risks for similar situations
Assessment of present conditions
Assessment of effect of future conditions

Information-gathering techniques are of immense benefit in this stage as they stimulate creativity. A few techniques are written below:

1. **Brainstorming:** Have a set of multidisciplinary experts who have good knowledge of the system essentially put the system through an imaginary pressure test that focuses on things going wrong and their consequences. This technique generates a lot of risk in a short amount of time and, if facilitated properly, can form the foundation of the risk-identification phase. A list of hazards can then be used as a starting point to generate conversation and automatically categorize the compiled risk list.
2. **Delphi Technique:** A questionnaire is used to solicit opinions on risk from various experts in the field, one at a time. These opinions are summarized and recirculated for further opinions, again and again, until consensus is reached on a list of risks. This technique, though time intensive, provides anonymity to the experts and allows them to finish the task of risk identification in their own time. This ensures that no one person dominates the discussion, and quashes the possibility of groupthink.
3. **Interviewing:** The risk manager takes on the role of an interviewer and summarizes the thoughts of the experts in a list of risks. This saves time but places more responsibility on the risk manager to ensure the efficacy of the process. Interviews can be coupled with surveys that include questions regarding survey takers' functional or departmental uncertainties and their perceived probability and impact rating of the risks.

For complex products, processes, and systems, root cause analysis may be needed at certain times to clarify the risk. This can be diagrammatically accomplished using the Ishikawa (fishbone) diagram and flowcharts.

CHAPTER 13

Chance and Possibilities

RISK, BY NATURE, IS BORNE OUT OF UNCERTAINTY. If there is a 100% probability of an event occurring, then that event is an actual hurdle or issue and no longer considered a risk. The probability of the occurrence of a risk is the likelihood of the occurrence of the risky event. While probability theory is an advanced subject in itself, for practical risk management purposes, we need only state some fundamentals.

An approach to probability is based on classical theory, which calculates the probability of an event based on favorability of the desired event over all events. This is given by the following equation:

$$\textit{Probability of an Event } E = \frac{\textit{Number of times Event } E \textit{ can occur}}{\textit{Number of all events}} \tag{13.1}$$

This formula can be used to calculate probability of a unique event from a set of events, where all events have similar probabilities, such as drawing specific cards from a full deck of cards or the probability of a number showing in the throw of a die. The total probability is always 1 (100%), and it is composed of the probability of the desired event plus the probability of the undesired events.

This can be written as:

$$\begin{gathered}\textit{Probability of final outcome}\\ = \textit{Probability of desired Event } E + \textit{Probability of all other events} = 1\end{gathered} \tag{13.2}$$

The key point here is that the probability of all (which includes each and every outcome) events totals one (1). Out of this, the challenge for us is to extract the probability of our outcome of interest under study.

The classical approach to probability is simplistic since it assumes that all outcomes have an equal chance of occurring. While this approach is great for certain tools like decision trees and fault tree analysis, in real-world business scenarios, we know sometimes this may not be the case.

A second approach to probability calculation is the *frequentist approach.* This approach depends on testing a sample size to gauge the relative frequency of occurrence of an event in the population. A small representative group is tested once or many times, depending on the need for statistical power, and the frequency of an event is ascertained. Many times, risk professionals do not have the luxury of conducting tests like these, and, often, the nature of risks under study does not lend itself to this approach at all (e.g., enterprise risks).

The last approach to probability accepts the fact that decisions regarding probability of risks are largely subjective, based on opinions, viewpoints, and beliefs grounded in available evidence. The probability is assigned according to the measure of degree of belief one has for the event. This does not mean ad hoc assignation, but a logical decision based on available facts that inform the belief.

An obvious drawback of the subjective approach is that it is more than likely to be off target. There are various methods to reduce subjective inaccuracy that will be discussed later in this chapter. A modern approach is to use Bayesian statistics, which I will discuss briefly.

The *Bayesian approach* gives us a mathematical formula to incorporate any new evidence into the old probability calculation so that the probability can be updated. The formula is as follows:

$$\begin{matrix}\textit{Probability of a risk } A' \textit{ knowing that} \\ \textit{an information } x' \textit{ is true}\end{matrix} = \frac{\begin{matrix}(\textit{Probability of information } x' \textit{ being} \\ \textit{true knowing that probability of risk} \\ A' \textit{ is true}) * (\textit{Probability of risk } A \textit{ being true})\end{matrix}}{(\textit{Probability of information } x' \textit{ being true})} \quad (13.3)$$

The Bayes theorem is an easy method to update previously assigned probabilities and iteratively arrive at an accurate probability level for any given risk as new evidence becomes available.

The foundational distinctions in assignation of probability for purposes of risk analysis have been summarized by Lt. Duane Boniface of the U.S. Coast Guard in Table 13.1.

As risk management professionals, we are continually challenged to ensure the correct assignation of probability. Many approaches exist to reduce errors by increasing objectivity in assignation. Use of structured methods by decomposing constituent scenarios and sequence of events, analyzing the causal nexus between events preceding

TABLE 13.1 Types of probability assignations.

Probability Interpretation	Description
Classical	The probability of an event is the ratio of the number of outcomes with the attributes of the event to the total number of equally likely and different ways.
Frequency	The probability of an event is given by the limit of its relative frequency as the number of samples becomes large.
Subjective	The probability of an event is a measure of the degree of belief that one holds for that event.

Source: Duane Boniface, Lt., U.S. Coast Guard, "Risk-Based Decision-Making Guidelines," accessed July 7, 2020, https://www.hsdl.org/?view&did=471178.

impact, and leveraging historical information is a good start, but we must be prepared to review and reassess the initially assigned probabilities as and when evidence emerges that may change our prediction. Depending on the risk methods, the probabilities assigned can be qualitative, semiquantitative, or quantitative.

The following five approaches for probability assignation are discussed in the rest of the chapter:

1. Expert opinion
2. Parametric analysis
3. Analogous analysis
4. Probabilistic analysis
5. Cause and effect analysis

In our first example, we assigned the probability based on an opinion, which though practical and obvious was subjective. A broken femur was a remote and unlikely-to-happen event, so the probability was assigned as low per Table 13.2.

Table 13.2 keeps things simple but does not allow us to assign a number to the actual rate of the events. To allow for such a detail, a table such as Table 13.3 may be used.

Now the question arises, How could one actually assign an exact value? The answer is that we don't. The table above has ranges instead of set exact values. The advantage of assigning a range is that we can capture a low estimate and a high estimate since pinpointing an exact value would be extremely difficult and have a high chance of being inaccurate. This is a semiquantitative method of assigning a range of occurrence to an event. Our aim is to use expert opinion to assign a measure to the randomness of the risky event. In realization of this goal, as far as possible, we should try to convert a qualitative assessment to a semiquantitative one using such tables. The range of the

TABLE 13.2 Qualitative probability and its description.

Term	Description
High	Occurrence is likely (often or frequent)
Medium	May occur but not often or frequently
Low	Rare occurrence (unlikely)

TABLE 13.3 Semiquantitative probability table.

Rank	Description
0	**≤0.001%** Extremely unlikely—up to 1 in 100,000 cases
1	**>0.001% and ≤0.01%** Occasional—up to 1 in 10,000 cases
2	**>0.01% and ≤0.1%** Moderately probable—up to 1 in 1,000 cases
3	**>0.1% and ≤0.5%** Reasonably probable—up to 1 in 200 cases
4	**>0.5% and ≤100%** Highest rank—inclusive of failure occurring in every case

values in the table can vary and should be set in accordance with the nature of risks encountered according to industry sectors. Keep in mind that the aim is to set a range of probability with about 90% confidence. The main fallacy is that people set the range too narrow, which is a behavioral bias of overconfidence or excessive optimism.

Likewise, I may have a previous activity that is similar to my current activity, and, thus, I may choose to assign similar values of probability. This combines past experience, historical information, and expert judgment. For example, a company may make valves and produce different product lines with minor modifications. If a new product line is introduced, the company may choose to leverage the risk probability information from the previous product lines to form a baseline performance based on probability of various failures of similar products. This method is known as *analogous estimating*. A major drawback of this technique is that it relies on heuristics of availability and representativeness—that is, some data may be easily available, leading them to be assumed to be more important, and some data may be easily stereotyped, leading to a narrow viewpoint.

Parametric analysis uncovers a statistical relationship between the subject activity and the previous activity to arithmetically calculate probability based on ratios in terms of failure rates, cost, or schedule. For example, if there are data that the valves of a certain product line fail at the inlet flap 1000 times per million opportunities, and if we know that the inlet flap is strengthened on the new product line by 50%, then we can assume based on the parametric relationship that the new valve will fail 50% less often. So, we will then assign a probability of failure as 500 per million. The drawback of this technique is that it is susceptible to the anchoring and adjustment heuristic (see Chapter 37). This occurs when a risk owner attempts to forcefully draw a parametric estimate from insufficient data. Thus, the nature of the data must be understood before drawing any inferential conclusion(s), however simple they may appear.

The *probabilistic analysis* combines the following three:

1. Historical data for same or similar product, or a product with similar features
2. A forecast based on cumulative or conditional probabilities of successive fault levels in a system
3. Subject matter expert opinion

An accurate way of calculating probability is by using *probability theory*. This method works the best for systems that can be represented by subsystems.

In Figure 13.1, the probability of the doorbell ringer being the mail carrier delivering the regular bills is 0.18, which translates to about one in five times, as opposed to the probability of the doorbell ringer being a violent neighbor throwing punches, which is one in a million. An important thing to keep in mind is that for each level of consequence, the probabilities must ideally add up to one, which means that you have considered all possible outcomes. In this case, the probabilities do not add up to one, which means there could be other consequences of the bell ringing.

In certain industries, use of quantitative methods such as the *Monte Carlo simulation* is common. This method provides estimates by incorporating the overall system

FIGURE 13.1 A causal probability tree for outcomes related to ringing of a doorbell.

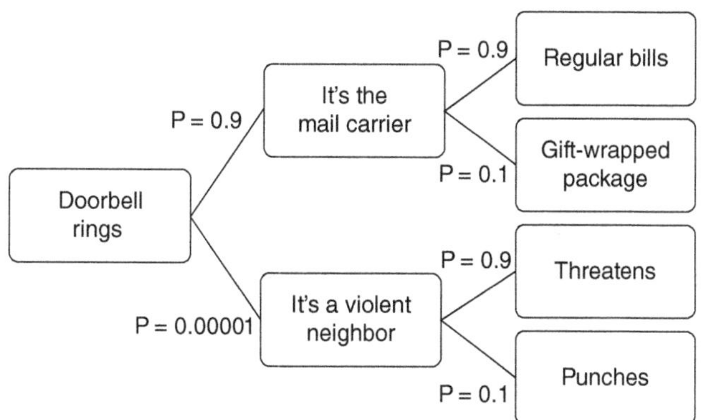

risk rather than just one individual failure mode. In this discussion, we will limit ourselves to risk analysis for specific individualized failures. Monte Carlo analysis is detailed in Chapter 46.

Usage of expert opinion should be formalized and not ad hoc. For example, if you are soliciting expert opinion on failure of a noncritical software feature on an airplane, different pilots may have different opinions depending on their technique, experience, and training. The software engineers may have a completely different viewpoint than the pilots, though they are both subject matter experts (SMEs). Similarly, in the health-care field, surgeons and doctors are often used as SMEs, but the onus is on the owner of the risk analysis to reduce subjectivity of the expert opinions. A few ways in which the objectivity of an SME opinion can be maintained are the following:

1. Pairing the opinion with historical data and investigating for gaps
2. Pairing the opinion with peer opinion and investigating gaps
3. Assigning weights to several factors and comparing weighted opinions among experts
4. Pairing the opinion with probability analysis methods discussed earlier

If there is a set causal nexus between events in a sequence, then the probabilities of preceding events can be multiplied to give the final consequence. Sometimes, events under study can be easily resolved into successive sets of causes and effects.

In Figure 13.2, a probability is assigned independently for every cause and effect pair in sequence. The final probability of lethal exposure to radioactivity due to the hazard of radioactive material storage in a chamber with poor sealant doors is $P1 \times P2 \times P3 = 0.00125$ or 0.125%.

This causal chain can be explained in terms of system, fault condition, fail-safe failure, and outcome, as shown in Figure 13.3.

The probability of harm in this case due to this specific causal chain is $P1 \times P2 \times P3 \times P4$. Care must be taken to not become narrow-minded in any step. One system may have several hazards, or there may be several fault conditions that lead

FIGURE 13.2 Causal probability chain related to storage of radioactive material in a sealed chamber.

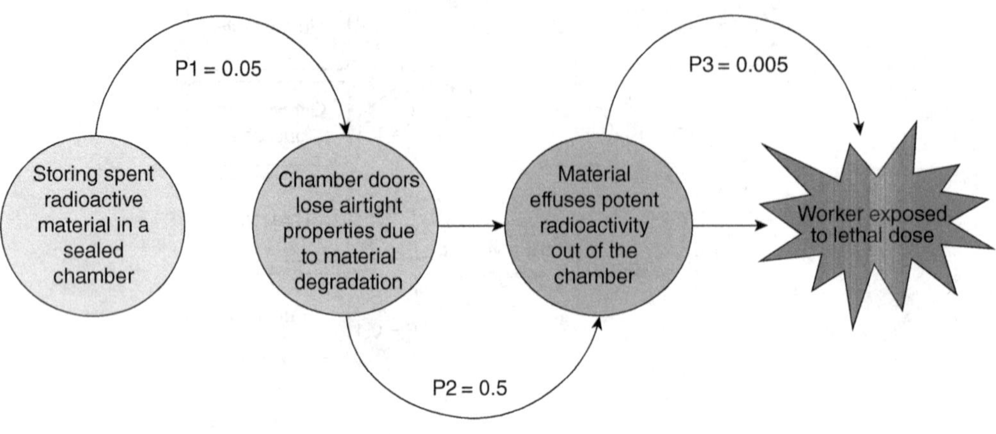

FIGURE 13.3 Causal probability chain template.

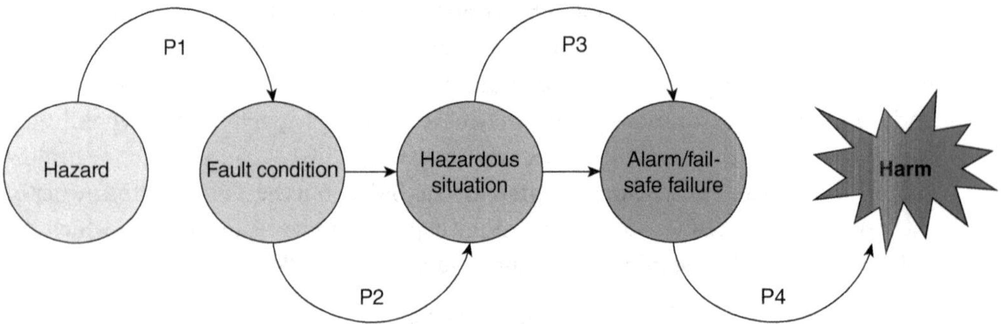

to different hazardous situations. This diagram, while being very applicable in this example, is not a universal standard, and the hazard may appear after occurrence of a fault condition depending on the system and the context. The actual assignation of step-wise probabilities can be accomplished by any of the estimating methods detailed earlier. The subjective aspect of these methods must be understood before using them.

The subjectivity of a probability estimate is based on the perception of the person assigning the estimate, which is in turn based on the person's knowledge and experiences in general. It is the risk professional's job to refocus this knowledge and experience toward the event under study. This can be done by supplying as much data and information as possible regarding the event and the system within which the event will occur. If it is common to hear, "Oh, that happens all the time. It's more than a 90% rate," then the risk management professional must uncover why and challenge the experts' assumptions by supplying the same nature of information on which the initial decision of >90% rate was made, to check whether the assumptions are still valid.

In this chapter, we learned the exercise of *likelihood analysis*, also known as *probability estimation*, which along with *consequence analysis* forms an important pillar of risk assessment:

probability estimation

The exercise of assessing likelihood of occurrence of risk and quantitatively, semiquantitatively, or qualitatively assigning a value to the assessed estimate.

CHAPTER 14

Organizational Context and Risk Management: The Working Details

THE VERY FIRST PHASE OF A FORMAL RISK management process is establishment of the context of risk management activities. ISO Guide 73:2009 defines *establishing the context* as:

> *Defining the external and internal parameters to be taken into account when managing risk, and setting the scope and risk criteria for the risk management policy.*[1]

The context thus has two components: external and internal.

ISO Guide 73:2009 defines *external context* as the following:

> *External environment in which the organization seeks to achieve its objectives.*[2]

The environment within which the organization operates is an important consideration in the risk policy adopted by the organization. For example, food production, medical devices, and pharmaceuticals are highly regulated sectors, and risk management policies in these sectors are strongly influenced by regulators such as the U.S. Food and Drug Administration, which regularly releases guidance on a variety of topics, including risk management expectations.

The external environment is also composed of one's competitors. A business cannot succeed if the risk profile of its products is significantly higher than that of its competitors. Industry benchmarking continuously calibrates the risk policies of businesses within a certain sector. For example, an aviation company would have to at least temporarily stop operations if it starts having frequent crashes. The industry benchmark

1. ©ISO. This material is reproduced from ISO Guide 73:2009, with permission of the American National Standards Institute (ANSI) on behalf of the International Organization for Standardization. All rights reserved.
2. ©ISO. This material is reproduced from ISO Guide 73:2009, with permission of the American National Standards Institute (ANSI) on behalf of the International Organization for Standardization. All rights reserved.

for 2017 was 0.39 fatalities per million flights. Thus, even one plane crash with more than two fatalities for a carrier would immediately be a perceived violation per the norms of the external business environment in which the aviation industry operates.

Of note is that as the external market environment changes, the risk management context should evolve accordingly. In the example above, the rate of aviation fatalities in 1970 was 6.35 per million flights. A company that still considers that rate acceptable per its internal risk management system will be unsuccessful since the external risk environment has evolved and standards have risen.

This underscores the need for benchmarking. Regardless of how structurally sound a risk management system is in a company, if it is incompatible with the context of the external business environment, it will fail.

The external context takes into consideration the views and perspectives of key stakeholders, which may be consumers or stockholders or clients. Their perceptions are molded by the market environment and their expectations are similarly calibrated. Per ISO 31000, the external context can include the cultural, social, political, legal, regulatory, financial, technological, economic, natural, and competitive environments, whether international, national, regional, or local.

ISO Guide 73:2009 defines *internal context* as the following:

Internal environment in which the organization seeks to achieve its objectives.[3]

The internal context is composed of the risk management framework (and its governance) of the organization and the skills, capabilities, perceptions, and expectations of the internal organizational stakeholders. A major internal stakeholder group is the top management or leadership that has the greatest influence over risk management direction. Enabling resources always flow from leadership decisions regarding the risk direction of risk management, and internal stakeholder alignment must start here. A risk manager may find himself or herself powerless if senior leadership is not aligned with the risk management structure.

The actual value addition by risk management is dependent on the level of accuracy and precision with which the risk management activities are carried out. This requires investment in human resources, skills development, physical assets, software assets, communication infrastructure, funds availability, and procedural efficiencies. Life-cycle risk management involves setting strategy and protocols and delivering results by continuous monitoring, control, and reevaluation. This is the most important organizational activity that falls under the internal context and must be harmonized with the external context.

Thus, a risk professional must consider devoting sufficient time to the establishment of the context of risk management activities before proceeding with risk

3. ©ISO. This material is reproduced from ISO Guide 73:2009, with permission of the American National Standards Institute (ANSI) on behalf of the International Organization for Standardization. All rights reserved.

assessment. This not only creates baselines but also establishes boundaries of future steps and helps the organization understand the scope of its risk policy.

ISO 31010:2018 mentions the following, which can be reviewed while setting the risk criteria:

- how it will be decided whether risk is acceptable;
- how the relative significance of risks will be determined;
- how risk will be taken into account in decisions on options, where each option is associated with multiple risks that might have positive or negative consequences, or both;
- how the relationships between risks will be taken into account.[4]

Specifically, the framework of the risk scoring system during risk analysis and risk evaluation phases should be decided while setting the context. The main task of the scoring system is to act as a measurement system that compares the identified risks with the baselines and checks/tests for acceptability per the organizational risk appetite and tolerance (see next chapter for details).

The scoring system will need definitions of the following four items:

1. **Constituent risk factors**

   The constituent risk factors are based on the very definition of risk. Usually, risk is characterized using the factors of occurrence and consequence. Sometimes, the factor of detection or detectability may be used. These three factors may be described using different words such as "likelihood," "frequency," or "occurrence" for probability and "severity" or "impact" for consequence. These distinctions must be noted and clarified since literal definitions of these words differ to an extent that can cause confusion among stakeholders. Some companies may choose to add additional risk factors such as vulnerability, reliability, duration, and effectiveness.

2. **Scales for constituent risk factors**

   All risk factors should have a scale on which they can be rated, such that different risk outcomes can be compared with one objective measure and assigned a rating. Common scales include levels ranging from 1 to 5 or 10 for increasing probabilities and/or consequences.

3. **Risk ranking and filtering**

   Once the risk factors have been assigned a rating, they should be combined to give a risk ranking. A risk matrix with graduated risk levels may be used that combines the risk factors to provide a risk level for a specific combination of risk factors. Sometimes, the rated values of risk factors can be

4. ©ISO. This material is reproduced from ISO 31010:2019, with permission of the American National Standards Institute (ANSI) on behalf of the International Organization for Standardization. All rights reserved.

multiplied to give a risk probability number (RPN) by which various risks can be compared.

4. **Risk acceptability**

   For certain combinations of risk factors, the output risk will be beyond the bounds of the organizational risk appetite or tolerance. While setting the context, these limits must be carefully decided and the tools being used should be aligned and validated. In the risk matrix, certain combinations of high values of risk factors may be deemed unacceptable, and such demarcation of the line between unacceptability and acceptability must be clearly agreed on by all stakeholders. If using an RPN, risk values above a certain number may be defined to be above the acceptable limit.

CHAPTER 15

Stakeholder Risk Attitude and Appetite

ORGANIZATIONAL RISK CULTURE IS AN AMALGAMATION of the risk culture of its internal stakeholders, which in turn is heavily influenced by the needs and capabilities of the external stakeholders. Among the internal stakeholders, the risk culture is influenced by a variety of factors, including considerations for reputation, leadership styles, regulatory context, competition, and economic pressures.

Risk culture can be defined as follows:

> *The way of thinking informed by a set of organizational values that determines behavior in the face of uncertainty; specifically, the decision making with regard to routine and nonroutine risk confrontation and associated risk identification, analysis, evaluation, modification, monitoring, and communication.*

To understand risk culture means to understand its three constituent and fundamental factors:

1. Risk attitude
2. Risk appetite
3. Risk tolerance

Risk attitude is defined in ISO Guide 73:2008 as:

> *Organization's approach to assess, and eventually pursue, retain, take, or turn away from risk.*[1]

This approach includes the perception of gain over loss or loss over gain for every risk and aggregate risk.

There are four kinds of common risk attitudes:

---

1. ©ISO. This material is reproduced from ISO Guide 73:2009, with permission of the American National Standards Institute (ANSI) on behalf of the International Organization for Standardization.

1. **Risk averse**

   A risk-averse stakeholder has a very low tolerance for high risk taking. There is increased sensitivity and aggressive reaction to threats and a hesitant attitude toward opportunities.

2. **Risk seeking**

   A risk-seeking stakeholder has a very high tolerance for risk taking. There is an aggressive drive to capitalize on opportunities and underreact to threats.

3. **Risk tolerant**

   A risk-tolerant stakeholder becomes inured to routine risks and considers many common operational risks acceptable. Unless an impactful event occurs, there is no change in this attitude. This may lead to underreaction to both threats and opportunities.

4. **Risk neutral**

   A risk-neutral stakeholder has a mature risk attitude, which seeks to consider long-term strategic and operational implications of risk management decisions. They focus on objective risk-benefit analysis as a basis for adoption of risk-seeking or risk-averse behavior.

Risk appetite is defined as:

> *The willingness of an organization to seek risk in anticipation of realization of opportunities.*

Risk appetite is a measure of aggregate organizational risk acceptance or risk-seeking behavior. Risk attitude is the organizational approach to risk, while risk appetite is more of an outcome of that approach. It must be noted that, per the definition, risk appetite pertains to "seeking risk." It means venturing out in uncertainty in "anticipation of opportunities." While the definition focuses on the upside of risk, we must not forget that risk can have two sides and can be negative as well.

ISO Guide 73:2009 *Risk Management—Vocabulary* defines *risk tolerance* as:

> *An organization's or stakeholder's readiness to bear the risk after risk treatment in order to achieve its objectives.*[2]

Risk tolerance may differ from stakeholder to stakeholder, and as individual risks are assessed, due consideration must be given to the risk tolerance of the stakeholder who may become the owner of the risk.

---

2. ©ISO. This material is reproduced from ISO Guide 73:2009, with permission of the American National Standards Institute (ANSI) on behalf of the International Organization for Standardization.

TABLE 15.1 An example of risk attitude and corresponding appetite and tolerance.

	Attitude	Appetite	Tolerance	Attitude appetite relation
Investment Banker A	Averse	$100,000	$5000 loss	Direct
Investment Banker B	Neutral	$1,000,000	$200,000 loss	Ad hoc
Investment Banker C	Tolerant	$1,000,000	$125,000 loss	Situational analysis based
Investment Banker D	Seeking	$10,000,000	$3,000,000 loss	Direct

Thus, risk attitude, risk appetite, and risk tolerance form the very basis of criteria for risk-level assignment (i.e., which risks the organization or stakeholder will pursue, retain, or turn away).

Table 15.1 clarifies this concept.

Risk-averse and risk-seeking stakeholders and organizations have an almost direct relationship to appetite—that is, more risk aversion leads to less risk appetite, and more risk-seeking behavior leads to greater risk appetite. Risk-neutral behavior is hard to predict since these stakeholders usually do not have a quick turnaround time for decision making. The risk-neutral stakeholder will often only take safer long-term risk decisions and be dormant or inactive to short-term risk unless it presents a consequence of very high magnitude. Risk-tolerant stakeholders and organizations will analyze the situation and moderate their behavior accordingly.

It is important to understand these concepts to ensure practical and realistic assignation of levels of risk acceptance or rejection during risk evaluation and risk treatment phases.

A more detailed look at risk culture involves further reconciling these factors of appetite, tolerance, and attitudes with their individual drivers. The drivers of risk appetite, tolerance, and attitudes may include the risk management competency of various people and departments, motivations for risk management in terms of incentives and intrinsic drivers, transactional relationships between various functions and persons, and, finally, the conduct of leadership and management and their cascade to junior members that is informed by values, ethics, and expectations accountability.

CHAPTER 16

Organizational Context and Risk Management 2: The Top View

IN CHAPTER 14, WE SAW HOW THE ORGANIZATIONAL context is defined and the role it plays in setting the risk criteria. In this chapter, let us take a broader view from an enterprise standpoint to truly understand the subcomponents of the organizational context in detail. The concepts listed in this chapter go to the very foundations of the context-setting exercise, which, if done with patience and diligence, can help ensure excellent alignment of the risk management program with the organizational objectives.

When beginning or embarking on a risk management program, it is important for the risk practitioner to understand the basic drivers of the organizational decision-making process. The architect of the risk management system can ensure its success by ensuring its relevance, which can be done by closely aligning the risk management system with the critical aspects of the following:

1. Organizational business model
2. Organizational culture
3. Value chain

Even if an organization does not have a mature risk management system, decisions on risk avoidance or acceptance are still made, and it is the job of the risk professional to understand an organization's source of decision making and the drivers of these decisions. This is done to understand the current risk culture and the governance model it stems from. This process of decision making in the face of risks can be as elaborate as a hierarchical risk committee with detailed quantitative analyses or as simple as the CEO or CFO making ad hoc decisions. Regardless, the risk manager needs to understand the environment in which the risk management activities will be carried out so that risk management structure can be adjusted or modified for maximum utility.

Let us investigate the three organizational aspects from above in more detail and learn their contributions to setting of the organizational context.

THE ORGANIZATIONAL BUSINESS MODEL

Every organization has a purpose and mission for which its functional apparatus is resourced, and a vision for which it is committed to expend resources in anticipation of returns. This forms the enterprise context of the organization from which flows the context of the risk management activities. The alignment of these two contexts is critical. No company will spend resources on managing risk on a product that minimally contributes to its mission and vision.

While the process to comprehend the business model starts by understanding the mission, vision, and values, the tangible flow of these statements from high-level policy to actionable objectives must be investigated to gain knowledge of the organizational context. Ideally, the business model should be based on the mission, vision, and values.

Understanding the business model in the context of risk management may not be an easy task. The risk professional must review both tangible and intangible sources of information. Tangible sources of information include reports on strategic planning and goals, reports from external agencies, public filings, media reports, sales reports, marketing reports, and operational results. Intangible sources of information come from the company culture and its historical outlook. The market environment informs the culture and the business model to a large extent and must figure as a parameter to be evaluated when setting strategic risk context. The goal of study of the above information is to uncover the strategic attitude of the organization toward opportunities and threats. In addition, if the organization is experiencing some emergent threats, analysis of the response to those threats can provide valuable information regarding risk governance structure and level of contingency response planning.

After the business model is understood, one must analyze the internal operations of the organization to verify their alignment with the strategic objectives. The level of disconnect between operational direction (goals and outcomes) and strategic objectives informs the probability of failure in meeting those strategic objectives. Any required calibration can potentially be managed through the risk management process. An analysis of internal operations also allows us to contrast the operational risk attitudes with the strategic attitude toward risk. Often strategic planning in a boardroom full of C-level personnel paints an optimistic picture that is either difficult or impossible for the ground-level organization to realize. If this schism is not addressed, it may lead to grave problems. If increasing sales aggressively is a strategic directive, but operationally the organization is hesitant because it has outdated manufacturing techniques that will be unable to meet the increased demand, there is a scope for risk management to provide targeted, prioritized solutions to mitigate the failure of a strategic goal. The rigor of risk management should match the strategic and operational priorities in order to deem serious attention.

ORGANIZATIONAL CULTURE

The risk manager must understand the organization's cultural environment, along with the accelerators of and obstacles to company goals, to ensure the fit of a risk management strategy with the organization. An aggressive, risk-taking CEO may reorient the financial organization's top purpose toward exploiting opportunities, but if the company historically has been known for risk avoidance and has it ingrained in its culture, then a mismatch between strategy and culture may occur that has potential to derail achievement of objectives. Application of risk management in such a situation may involve providing a realistic scenario analysis for the company to reassess its imperatives.

An organization's culture is the set of beliefs, assumptions, and values that informs its decision making. It is built slowly in social and psychological layers that affect internal and external interactions, perceptions, and collective identity.

Culture affects the risk attitudes, risk appetites, and risk tolerances to a large extent. If the strategic objectives and concomitant risk management activities are attempting to defy the culturally set norms, extreme caution must be taken to ensure reduction of disruption.

Risk culture is a subsystem of the organizational culture that includes sets of beliefs, assumptions, and values that inform the decision making in the face of uncertainty. Risk governance must recognize the risk culture as the foundation from which conventions, rules, and mechanisms arise for decision making with regard to risk.

Risk attitudes and appetites, detailed in the previous chapter, are the best indicators of the risk culture and its differences across functions and departments. Analyzing the risk culture by studying risk attitudes and appetites can not only arm the risk manager with critical information with regard to stakeholder resistance or resilience but also uncover the drivers and obstructers of risk-based thinking in the organization.

In a mature organization, the risk manager analyzes the risk culture and sets up a risk governance model, keeping the culture front and center. One may choose to modify the risk culture or even challenge it via the structured governance model, which allows for inclusive risk communication and consultation. The risk attitudes and perceptions of all stakeholders should be considered before setting risk acceptability or tolerance limits.

In an organization with immature risk management practices, the acceptable levels of risk are based largely on perceptions of risk and past personal and organizational experiences. In such organizations, risk governance is ad hoc and heavily dependent on the risk attitudes of a select few.

Objective assessment of risks, with due consideration to organizational risk attitudes, risk appetites, and risk tolerances of all stakeholders is a tactical approach that can lead to practical setting of risk acceptability levels.

THE VALUE CHAIN

Michael Porter, in the 1985 book *Competitive Advantage: Creating and Sustaining Superior Performance,* defines *value chain* as:

> *A set of activities that a firm operating in a specific industry performs in order to deliver a valuable product (i.e., good and/or service) for the market.*[1]

1. M. E. Porter, *Competitive Advantage: Creating and Sustaining Superior Performance* (New York: Free Press, 1998 [1985]), 84.

Since 1985, value chains have become much more complex and multifaceted due to outsourcing, offshoring, and multiple sourcing. The "set of activities" that make up a value chain are no longer sequential; they can be parallel and overlap across different locations.

A modern risk manager must be able to place the risk management efforts in the context of the value chain. The risk manager needs to understand this concept to ensure that the rigor of risk management efforts is in lockstep with the amount of value being added.

Value chain analysis will uncover the areas that add the most and least value, which will help the risk consequence analysis. Charting the inputs and outputs of value chains will help reveal the stakeholders who add the most and least value. It will also reveal resource distribution and associated imbalances.

A risk management framework that aligns itself with the value chain not only becomes automatically relevant but also sets itself as the barometer of value addition such that it can be an effective value monitor and control tool. The risk professional must ask the following questions:

1. Where does the organization add the most value?
2. Where in the value chain are the most resources spent?
3. Is the perception of value addition by management in line with the actual value chain?
4. What uncertainties affect the value chain?
5. What are the threats to the value chain?
6. In which steps lie opportunities to increase value in the value chain?

Looking at the value chain in the context of the business model and structuring the risk management framework in synchrony with the value chain will not only make the framework relevant but also synchronize it with the strategic and operational goals.

CHAPTER 17

Comprehensive Risk Management Maturity (CoRMM) Model

THE ORGANIZATIONAL RISK COMPETENCY MUST BE ASSESSED, and the current state must be acknowledged. The current state must then be compared with the desired future state, and corresponding improvements must then be systemically carried out.

The Comprehensive Risk Management Maturity (CoRMM) model, detailed in this chapter, is based on the maturity of the following parameters:

1. Risk leadership
2. Risk management knowledge, skills, and abilities (KSAs)
3. Risk governance
4. Risk process inclusivity
5. Risk process pervasiveness
6. Value creation

Table 17.1 identifies and defines the varying levels of the above attributes and assigns a score per the attribute's maturity. An organization may assess its maturity by choosing a level along the scale for each of the six attributes and summing the final score.

Based on the total score, the maturity of the organization can be classified into one of the following four levels:

1. **Minimal (0–8)**

   With minimalistic maturity, there is either nil or basic risk management knowledge (present only because of compliance, legal, or regulatory requirements). At this stage, most knowledge needed to manage risk is undocumented and tribal. The organization has not devoted resources to any structured risk management activities and has made ad hoc decisions in the face of uncertainty.

2. **Developing (9–18)**

   There is some framework for risk management activities, although their governance is not well defined across a full spectrum of operations. There are likely some areas where risk management is driven by specialists, but this is not holistic and has narrow functional or departmental relevance. While there is a certain level of risk awareness, stakeholder involvement is not efficient and

TABLE 17.1 CoRMM attributes and scoring key.

Attribute/score	5	3	1	0
Leadership	Full and sustained support of the top leadership of the organization for implementation and sustenance of a successful risk management process	Infrequent support of the top leadership in some aspects or some departments	Changing leadership leads to changing priorities and risk policies, which leads to ad hoc support and risk process implementation issues	No support from top management for risk management
Knowledge, skills, and abilities (KSA)	Employees involved with the risk management process are experienced and accomplished experts who carry out comprehensive and structured risk assessments using customized tools that perfectly apply to the organizational need (and context) on a frequent or predetermed basis.	Mature risk professionals who have sufficient knowledge of risk processes and tools to carry out risk management activities using standard tools which mostly apply to the organization needs on a regular basis.	Some employees are knowledgeable but most are novices in risk management methods and tools. The processes and tools used the organization are not customized and only vaguely apply to the needs of the process. Risk management process is often not on time and ad hoc.	No employees involved with the risk management process can be considered as subject matter experts and without rigorous training will not be able to complete simple risk assessments.
Governance	A mature structural framework that governs the processes that dictate the organizational risk management activities and related decision making encompassing policies, procedures, and processes which that dictate risk management approaches, methods, and oversight is present. An appointed employee oversees the system and any gaps are promptly acted upon.	A structural framework governing the risk management activities exists but is not completely aligned with the organizational needs, leading to some gaps in approaches, procedures, and mechanisms pertaining to risk management effcetiveness. There are a few opportunities present to better integrate risk management with operations and other organizational functions.	A skeleton framework for risk governance exists but has multiple gaps. Procedures and mechanisms for risk management exists in isolation in some departments but an overarching policy is not present. In some cases risk processes may be well aligned with the organizational needs but they are a function of interest and KSA of departmental process or product owners.	There is no framework for organizational risk governance, and no policies, procedures, or directives exist that dicatate risk management approaches.

Inclusivity	All stakeholders are assessed for inclusion, and all appropriate stakeholders are a part of the risk management process; and their knowledge, views, and perceptions are given due consideration in all aspects and stages of the risk management process.	Most of the stakeholders are included in the risk management process. There is no set inclusion criteria, and sometimes a few lower level stakeholders are missed. Some fringe stakeholders are, at times, not communicated the results of the risk management process.	Only the most responsive stakeholders are part of the risk management process. An attempt is made to include all stakeholders, but the process is not contingent on their involvement. Usually, stakeholders who are busy are not included in the process but just notified. Fringe stakeholders are not involved at all.	Most of the stakeholders are not part of the operational aspects of risk management process. Only a small team of one or two people completes the whole process and communicates the final output to their supervisor.
Pervasiveness	Risk management is optimized at every level and includes set processes for product or process risk management, operations risk management, and strategic or enterprise risk management.	Some elements of risk management are present at all levels (product or process risk management, operations risk management, and strategic or enterprise level risk management) but they are not harmonized well. There is some transfer of information, knowledge, and data that lead to learning but this integration is limited.	The risk management process is not present at all levels and is mostly limited to either products or process or operations. When strategic or enterprise risk management is present, it exists in isolation and does not feed into lower level decision making.	There is only limited, very specific, or low level risk management activity, which does not holistically affect the organization's output in any large measure.
Value creation	Risk management is a proven process which contributes to high value creation. Risk is consistently monitored and re-assesed, which leads to actions that add value to organizational products, processes, and services.	Risk management adds a reasonable amount of value to the organization. Some processes are redundant and result in deliberation, but most processes lead to well-defined actions which enrich organizational outputs.	While risk management is a set process, it is largely a mandated paper exercise. At very infrequent intervals, some actionable changes occur but are a function of other driving factors in addition to risk management.	Risk management is done since it is required. Some paperwork is generated and the risk is infrequently updated but no actionable changes occur.

inclusive, leading to a few risks falling through the cracks. There are poor or nonexistent linkages among product- or service-level risk management, operational risk management, and enterprise risk management. Documented risk assessments feature in some decisions, but the stakeholders' trust in risk assessments is low since the assessments are usually either overestimates or underestimates due to incomplete stakeholder participation and insufficient skills in the risk assessment process.

3. **Managed (19–25)**

   In a managed setting, preventive thought is prevalent and enforced by structured and collaborative risk assessments and modifications. The departmental risk governance is sound and has some level of top management support. There is a high level of repeatability in the risk process and large potential for scalability. Risk information from the product/service level is communicated to many relevant stakeholders and at times does feed into strategic planning. Risk-based decision making is common, but the negative side of risk is much more pronounced, and upside risk (i.e., taking advantage of opportunities) is often not considered.

4. **Optimized (26–30)**

   In cases of optimized maturity, risk is front and center from the beginning of the strategic planning process down to the system, product, and/or process design levels. Decisions are made based on risk, and risk-based thinking is prevalent for problem solving. The risk information from the product/process level flows efficiently to the top enterprise level and is taken into consideration when conducting enterprise risk planning and strategic risk planning. Risk is seen as a proven tool for value creation and sustenance and is often used to objectively classify threats and opportunities in order for their value-driven treatment. Risk governance is mature, and risk process systems are scalable and repeatable.

CHAPTER 18

Risk Management Planning and Risk Management Plan

***RISK PLANNING* IN AN ENTERPRISE CONTEXT** is an important piece in priming the organization for risk management activities. Planning begins with a *gap analysis*, which is a comparison of the current state with the desired future state. This activity flows from the setting of organizational context, discussed in Chapters 14 and 16. The answers to investigations during the risk management planning phase can be obtained through the information uncovered during context setting, also described in Chapters 14 and 16. Assessment of risk management maturity, such as that done by the CoRMM model (described in Chapter 17), is a good way to assess the current state of organizational risk management capability and capacity.

For tactical, process-specific risk management planning, the following questions could be asked to uncover gaps:

1. Are the current risk planning, risk identification, risk assessment, and risk treatment and response processes enough?
2. Are the current risk processes inclusive?
3. Do the current risk processes add value?
4. What is the risk competency of the organization?
5. What process steps could be improved or added?
6. Are the resources enough for the present state?
7. What resources will be needed for the future state?

The tactical plan for risk management must be decided on with the organizational risk maturity in mind. This plan should include common consent on the following:

1. Scope and context of the risk process in its entirety throughout the life cycle (inclusions and exclusions must be listed), especially on the following:
   a. Methods of data gathering and risk identification
   b. Methods of risk assessment
   c. Criteria for risk evaluation and prioritization
   d. Criteria for risk acceptability
2. Resources (human and financial) and resource development
3. Team member and stakeholder roles and responsibilities

4. Reporting structure and cascading levels of decision making
5. Timelines of deliverables
6. Risk repository (or risk register) and its document controls
7. A general idea of the risk appetite and attitude
8. Risk review methods (periodic and ad hoc)
9. Risk escalation pathways
10. Contingencies

When conducting risk assessments for complex products, processes, and systems, a separate document must be prepared that defines how the activities of risk management will be conducted. This document is not generic and specifically details the approaches, methodologies, and tools used.

The following should be considered for inclusion in the risk management plan:

1. **Stakeholder roles and responsibilities**

   As stressed multiple times earlier in this book, the clarity of responsibilities of the stakeholder is critical to ensure the success of risk management. Stakeholder roles and responsibilities should be defined by phases to ensure that there are no gaps in understanding of the roles in pre-completion, post-completion, and sustenance phases. Some stakeholders will be risk owners, while some will be approvers; others may just need to be informed and kept in the loop. This clarification is important and must be referred to in the plan. A RACI matrix (see Chapter 10) may be used for this purpose.

2. **Definition of probability and severity (impact)**

   Tabulation of different levels of probability and severity per a standard or customized scale is preferable. There are various scales available for qualitatively or quantitatively classifying probability and impact. These scales are discussed in detail in upcoming chapters.

3. **Risk acceptability criteria**

   See Chapters 25, 26, and 27 for more details.

4. **Hazard categories**

   Categorization essentially means grouping the risks. A hazard-based categorization lends itself to easy grouping in terms of expected failures and also in terms of causes of failure. In the project management discipline, a risk breakdown structure is sometimes used to satisfy this criterion. In other sectors, product-, commodity-, or service-based groupings may be used.

5. **Budget, including proposed cost reserves and approval chain for usage**

   The monies needed to realize risk management activities must be properly budgeted to ensure timely and effective responses. An estimation must be made early on in the process and approved by the management such that a cost baseline is established. As the risk management process progresses, realistic and practical changes must be made to this estimate. For the foreseeable risks for which no mitigations have been performed and which may prove to be a financial burden if they are realized, a contingency reserve must be set. The trigger and approval chain for such reserves must be established in the plan.

6. **Stakeholder tolerances**

   Stakeholder tolerances are important to assess since the risk responses will be based on risk thresholds, which, in large part, are essentially stakeholder risk thresholds. More risk means more opportunity but may also mean more chances of loss (financial or reputational). Depending on the industry, these thresholds may differ, but they also may change based on maturity and outlook of the organization or company. Therefore, a note should be made in the plan regarding this since this sets the baseline for risk mitigations and responses.

7. **Frequency of tracking, reporting, and review**

   Risk management is an iterative process and relies on effective feedback and feedforward loops of information and data sharing. The data have to be analyzed, and usable information must be disseminated to risk owners and other stakeholders. The frequency of review meetings and templates for tracking must be decided in the plan.

In addition, depending on the organization's need, the plan should consider methods for determining aggregate risks (at various hierarchical levels of risk management as defined in Chapter 1) and measures to verify the effectiveness of implementation of risk treatments and modifications.

The following is a sample risk management plan:

1. Description of the system
   a. Objectives / intended use / characteristics
   b. Dependencies
   c. Stakeholder analysis
2. Risk management scope and objectives
   a. Prioritization of objectives/characteristics
   b. Scales for probability and severity
   c. Definition of risk and risk trigger conditions
3. Risk management methodology
   a. Interface with organizational methods of risk management
   b. Risk taxonomy and metalanguage
   c. Key deliverables
4. Risk management organization
   a. Roles and responsibilities
   b. Rules of escalation
   c. Budget

   d. Schedule
   e. Reporting
5. Tools and techniques
   a. Description of tools and techniques for risk identification
   b. Description of tools and techniques for risk analysis
   c. Description of tools and techniques for risk monitoring and control
   d. Documentation and storage requirements
   e. System requirements
6. Communications
   a. Dissemination of information
   b. Pre-launch reporting
   c. Post-market/post-launch surveillance
   d. Audience and nature of communication
7. Criteria for success

INTEGRATION OF THE RISK MANAGEMENT PLAN AND THE QUALITY MANAGEMENT PLAN

The quality management plan of an organization lists the key quality deliverables, objectives, and goals. The risk management plan must be aligned and be in synchrony with the quality management plan as much as possible. As quality objectives are closely tied to the strategic objectives, the risk management process can leverage the quality deliverables, measures, metrics, and processes. Since the quality management plan applies to the same system or subsystem for which the risk management plan is intended, the risk process can use it to ensure that the system objectives, dependencies, assumptions, constraints, and outcomes are aligned. The risk management plan, by nature, complements and supplements the quality plan.

Of note are the monitoring and measurement aspects of the quality plan. If for specific quality objectives or metrics a risk occurrence rate and thresholds are defined, the risk process becomes an evidence-based proactive monitoring tool that can help plan preventive action and correct deviations. Depending on the level at which the quality planning is done, several risk management plans can act as feeders into one high-level quality plan.

CHAPTER 19

Risk Process Facilitation

A COMPANY'S RISK PROCESS is central to most of its decisions and practices. Companies may state something like "every situation is unique," but on closer review, employees and management are still using a process whether it is written or unwritten. The risk facilitator must understand this first and foremost. Complete risk analysis must look at both producer/provider and consumer factors when determining issues with a product or service. Furthermore, the analysis must incorporate different viewpoints from inside and, if available, outside the company.

We will define *risk facilitation* as:

The art of helping a stakeholder group deal with any phase of a risk process or reach an agreement or solution without offering dictatorial subject matter expertise.

Oftentimes, various stakeholders will have different perceptions of an identified risk based on multiple qualitative forms of data relating to the severity or the probability of the risk. An output of risk management is the conversion of these multiple viewpoints and perspectives into one qualitative, semiquantitative, or quantitative parameter. While realizing this is challenging, it does add significant value by ensuring the accurate identification of issues.

Risk teams should be diverse, with multiple people with different skills and experiences, and, where possible, should include an independent reviewer. An independent reviewer is necessary since this person is not a part of the formulation phase of risk deliverables and can provide unbiased feedback on the output. Inclusivity in the risk process will result in more accurate and more realistic risk assessments, but it also leads to challenges in cross-functional agreement and team dynamics.

A facilitator must navigate these challenges to ensure that the risk teams function properly and stay on track. Too often, disagreement among team members during the risk assessment phase leads to incorrect assignation of risk values, which leads to the failure of all downstream processes, including risk treatments and modifications. Thus, it is critical that all voices be given enough weight. The loudest person in the room could be wrong, for example, while the right answer rests with the quietest person in the room.

A risk facilitator should have the following:

1. Knowledge
   a. Facilitation tools and techniques (brainstorming, SWOT [strengths, weaknesses, opportunities, threats], etc.)
   b. Team-building phases
   c. Conflict management
2. Skills
   a. Communication
   b. Active listening
   c. Group dynamics management
   d. Time management
   e. Cheering and encouragement of participation
   f. Ability to bring about consensus
3. Attitudes
   a. Flexibility
   b. Responsiveness
   c. Empathy
   d. Altruism
   e. Neutrality/impartiality

Tuckman identified four stages of team performance, as shown in Figure 19.1.

The risk facilitator must understand these stages of team performance and adjust her or his behavior accordingly when a risk team is expected to be assembled to provide results. In the initial forming and storming stages, when the team may be more prone

FIGURE 19.1 Four stages of team performance.

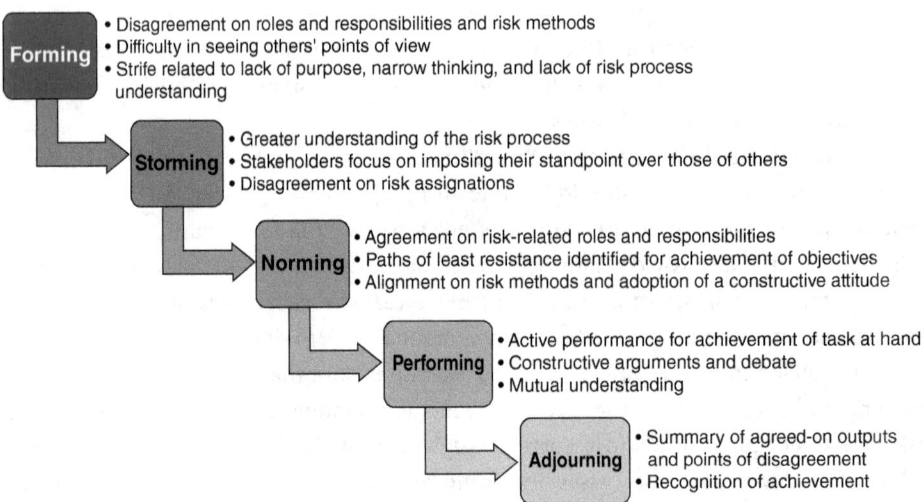

Forming
• Disagreement on roles and responsibilities and risk methods
• Difficulty in seeing others' points of view
• Strife related to lack of purpose, narrow thinking, and lack of risk process understanding
Storming
• Greater understanding of the risk process
• Stakeholders focus on imposing their standpoint over those of others
• Disagreement on risk assignations
Norming
• Agreement on risk-related roles and responsibilities
• Paths of least resistance identified for achievement of objectives
• Alignment on risk methods and adoption of a constructive attitude
Performing
• Active performance for achievement of task at hand
• Constructive arguments and debate
• Mutual understanding
Adjourning
• Summary of agreed-on outputs and points of disagreement
• Recognition of achievement

Source: Adapted from B. W. Tuckman, "Developmental Sequence in Small Groups," *Psychological Bulletin* 63 (1965): 384–399.

toward nonconstructive disagreement, the risk facilitator must be firm in setting the agenda and ensuring that disagreements do not turn into lingering discord and animosity. Here the facilitator may have to interject often, break up monologues or arguments that do not add value, and continually remind the team of the collaborative objective.

In the norming stage, the actual value-added process begins and the facilitator, after setting the stage, must slowly allow the team members to take over ownership of moving the process forward. The facilitator should interject only intermittently when the team gets off track in their discussions or begins straying from objectives.

In the performing stage, the team works well together since the objective of the risk management phase, abilities of the members, and constraints of time and resources are amply clear. At this stage the facilitator must support the discussions to accelerate results and only very rarely will need to redirect the group.

At the adjourning phase, the facilitator must conclude the discussion by summarizing main decisions and outputs. Points of disagreement, if any, and future actions to resolve should be stated as well.

All risk teams are different, and so the facilitator must continually gauge the group dynamics to check for the need for intervention. David Hillson has described three zones of facilitator behavior as it applies to risk management, as shown in Figure 19.2.

In the first zone, the facilitator has a slight authoritative and dictatorial tone. This is necessary to overcome initial resistance in the forming and storming stages. Such disposition is helpful in establishing boundaries of conduct, disciplining misbehavior, and setting rules. It is important that this phase be completed as quickly as possible. In the norming stage, the facilitator enters the second zone where they move into a collaborative style where the group is allowed autonomy to steer itself and find its footing. In the performing stage, the facilitator moves into the third zone and must withdraw further and watch the group perform per its intent without being overtly involved in routine tasks. Here, the facilitator must be supportive of group decisions but must not "guide" the group in any specific direction. The adjourning phase is where the most versatility is demanded of the facilitator. As the group starts performing, time often becomes a secondary aspect, and lack of time is viewed as a hurdle. Especially with well-performing groups, time seems to

FIGURE 19.2 Zones of risk facilitation.

Description	Zone 1	Zone 2	Zone 3
Style	Directive	Collaborative	Supportive
Title	Boss	Partner	Friend
Position	In front	Alongside	Behind
Verbalization	"Do this!"	"Shall we ... ?"	"How can I help?"

Source: D. Hillson, *Risk Facilitation Made Easy*, paper presented at PMI Global Congress 2015—EMEA, London, England. Reproduced by permission from Project Management Institute, Newtown Square, PA.

be in short supply as they pay good attention to detail. The facilitator must balance performance delivery with the constraint of time and move from being a passive supporter to active collaborator to finish the tasks at hand. If needed, the facilitator may need to assume the directive style to ensure all tasks are completed per schedule.

Hillson also matches the risk facilitator's behavior with the group behavior, as shown in Figure 19.3.

While the above trend line may vary considerably, the onus is on the facilitator to check the pulse of the team and change his or her attitude and assess the need for course correction.

Risk teams should be assembled to review risk at set intervals and ensure that the company's risk assessments are continually updated. Smaller companies are sometimes unable to pull together a diverse team due to lack of resources or even employees. While it would be most objective to bring in an outside firm to assess risk, often this is done in-house and the danger of bias always exists as the creators of a product, process, or system will tend to evaluate it in a positive light. When the risk team is assembled in-house, an independent reviewer must always be present to counter any bias. The

FIGURE 19.3 Facilitation styles as team progresses through Tuckman's four stages.

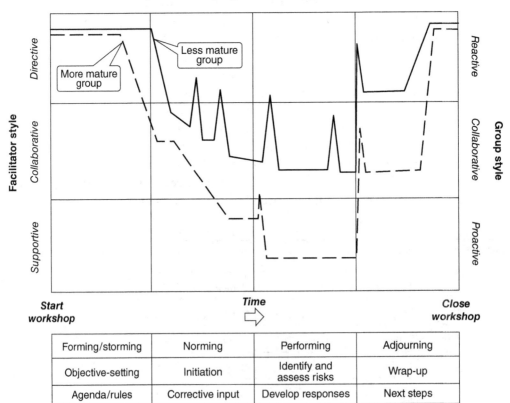

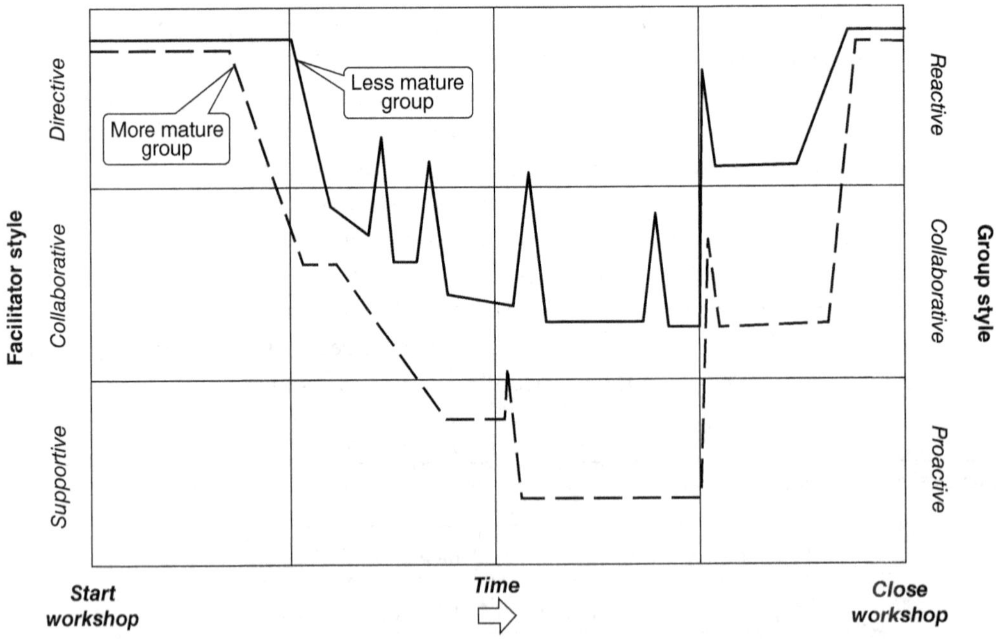

Forming/storming	Norming	Performing	Adjourning
Objective-setting	Initiation	Identify and assess risks	Wrap-up
Agenda/rules	Corrective input	Develop responses	Next steps

Source: D. Hillson, *Risk Facilitation Made Easy*, paper presented at PMI Global Congress 2015—EMEA, London, England. Reproduced by permission from Project Management Institute, Newtown Square, PA.

risk facilitator must be cognizant of these biases and engage the independent reviewer accordingly. Risk intervals should be tightened to properly assess the severity and/or probability of a foreseeable event occurring. The facilitator and team members should also recognize any shortcomings of the team and keep an open mind during the brainstorming and review process. If specific shortcomings or gaps are identified, the team should be augmented with subject matter experts or stakeholders as needed.

Data relevant to the product or service that come from external sources are also important in a full holistic review. Information on how other, similar products behave in the field, and how other companies handle certain issue/control points is vital to the risk team's ability to accurately conduct risk identification and assessments. An example of external information on a medical product could be searching the U.S. Manufacturer and User Facility Device (MAUDE) database prior to a risk assessment for any potential failures of similar devices (or the same device).

A company's attitude toward risk (as defined as averse, seeking, tolerant, or neutral in the previous chapter) must also be considered when conducting risk analysis meetings and facilitating the overall process. A successful risk manager identifies how these attitudes may affect a company's ranking of perceived risks, and should pose theoretical questions, press for deeper explanations, and try to force the group to think in a different mindset to reach a proper goal. An example of this could be a company not wanting to list or analyze a clear risk to the user or company. This could be because the company is risk averse and simply doesn't want to acknowledge the issue, or the company could be risk tolerant and deems the issue as not serious enough to warrant a discussion. In both situations the risk manager must find diplomatic ways to reach a consensus with the team. The risk must be recorded even if the team feels it is a low rank. The main goal of initial meetings is to list as many risks as possible so that over time they may be better understood and tracked. Failure to do so handicaps the risk review process, making it harder to gather meaningful data—which in turn could jeopardize the company's operations and future.

A risk facilitator must utilize both inductive and deductive methods to fully realize the foreseeable events, hazardous situations, and risks to a business or a consumer. Inductive reasoning draws conclusions only after assembling all the data and facts and systematically categorizing them to identify patterns (like a science experiment). By contrast, deductive reasoning looks at something that is known (such as a failure point) and works backward to use those data to justify the conclusion (such as a detective solving a murder). Both approaches are acceptable; however, a hybrid approach utilizing tools from both styles of thinking is most helpful. Inductive reasoning tools such as fishbone analysis diagrams help with brainstorming and discover new and unique control/risk points. On the opposite spectrum, deductive tools such as the failure modes and effects analysis (FMEA) are best at enumerating risks, ranking them accordingly, and showing which situations and risks should be addressed first and checked most often.

A risk facilitator should be aware that the risk should be managed throughout the life cycle of the service or product. For a product, the process should address the design and testing, distribution, usage, and eventual disposal. For a service, the process should encompass pre-planning, customer acquisition, the service itself, and any post-execution activities. These risk points should be reevaluated regularly at planned intervals. Attention should also be paid to the length of these intervals, making sure they are not too short or too long. Short intervals can lead to an oversampling of data and localized distortion of data. Likewise, longer intervals could miss important key details or lead to a system that is slow and unable to effect change and maintain product quality or customer loyalty. Risk reviews should be meaningful with clear objectives and goals to motivate the group and keep everyone on topic. It is very easy for groups to move to tangential conversations and drift away from the risk itself. The risk facilitator must center the conversation and, when it strays, gently lead the group back to the analysis.

In conclusion, to facilitate the risk process in an organization, a risk professional must be resourceful and conduct multiple reviews in planned intervals. These reviews must encompass all parts of a product or service. During implementation, risk review meetings are paramount and require a commensurate team with diverse backgrounds. Teams may also need an independent reviewer to maintain partiality. Tools should be used frequently to create patterns from the data, and a successful process will draw on both inductive and deductive reasoning to tease out a comprehensive list of risk and control points to maintain product quality and high customer service expectations.

RISK MANAGEMENT TEAMS

There can be one team or various teams for risk management as the demands of the risk management process change. In the first phase, risk identification, the team may include a larger number of stakeholders as the intent is to identify as many risks as possible. The risk manager or facilitator must balance team size and expertise per the nature of the risk identification task at hand. For example, if a brainstorming session is being held to identify gross numbers of risks, then a larger group size may be suitable; but if the Delphi technique (as detailed in Chapter 12) is being used, then a select number of experts must be chosen.

In the risk analysis and evaluation phase, the focus is on using methods and tools to characterize the risk qualitatively or quantitatively. All the team members and stakeholders from the risk identification phase may not be needed in this phase. Here, the nature of the work is more intense, and the facilitator plays a key role in this phase to keep the team on track in terms of deliverables and ensuring interpersonal collaboration. Sometimes, questions may arise regarding methods or tools being used, and an expert must be engaged periodically to ensure correct application of these tools. The assignation of occurrence and impact rates is a challenging task, and care must be taken to involve the stakeholders who own the data or data management systems from which data are extracted to ensure that mistakes are not made in the interpretation of the data.

In the risk treatment phase, the identified and assessed risk is used to plan and formulate actions to modify the risk. Team members in this phase must include stakeholders with responsibility and authority to own the actions being determined. If an action is agreed upon without the presence and consent of the concerned stakeholder who will be the eventual owner, it may not be followed through in the manner expected by the risk team. In this phase, the team must also define the indicators to monitor and review risk and stakeholder responsibility in that regard. Finally, the risk communication structure should be defined. As a risk is about to be realized, decisions regarding its modification are very time crucial. These decisions rely on correct and sufficient information about the upcoming risk, its precursors and indicators being disseminated to the right stakeholders who can prepare future actions. A RACI matrix, detailed in Chapter 10, can be used to assign responsibilities to the list of stakeholders through the life cycle of the risk management process.

CHAPTER 20

The Risk Repository (Risk Register or Hazard Log)

THE STORAGE OF RISK INFORMATION in a secure and retrievable location is critical to the success of risk management. The vehicle for risk repository should be addressed in the planning phase itself to suit the methods of and the tools for risk assessments. This repository can be a physical paper or virtual document, but it must be a revision-controlled manuscript that is able to be continually updated and approved. These documents are sometimes referred to as risk registers, risk tables, or hazard logs.

The documentation starts in the risk identification phase, where the list of identified hazards or risks or failure modes is created. This is usually the first column of the risk register or table. Since this is the first building block of the risk documentation process, it may be of value to identify, along with the risk, certain accompanying information, such as the "date identified," "identified by," "current oversight," "ownership," and so on. Along with the identification of the risk, the expected outcome of the risk must also be documented in words.

With identification of the risk, the brainstorming team can be challenged with identification of the cause of the identified risk. This is important information and must be documented for two reasons:

1. There might be disagreement among stakeholders regarding the root cause in later stages of risk management
2. This information is critical for risk modification / risk treatment

Then, the information regarding the risk assessment itself in terms of occurrence and impact should be documented. The expected outcome of the risk in the risk identification stage can be used to judge the impact of the risk. Specifically, the results of risk analysis and evaluation should be documented in separate columns. As required, the risk levels (and accompanying priorities) must be documented as well.

The resulting modification of the risks, each by line item, should be identified and documented for every identified risk. The risk response action should be documented next to the modification.

Finally, the owner of the risk (and the associated response) should be identified and documented for future reference. There must be one more column to document the actual outcome or effect of the risk upon realization for future assessment purposes.

Thus, a simple risk repository should contain the following:

1. List of risks, failure modes, or hazards (and expected outcomes)
2. Causes of risks
3. Probability of occurrence
4. Impact or severity or consequence
5. Priority or risk levels
6. Risk response
7. Risk owner
8. Actual outcome, if and when available

It is always useful to document the reassessment of risk after risk modification in terms of new modified probability, occurrence, and risk level. Separate columns can be added for this activity.

Specific tools like FMEA, hazard analysis and critical control points (HACCP), and hazard and operability study (HAZOP) have a risk register inherent in their respective worksheets. We will review these in the upcoming chapters.

To conclude, it is important to have a documented and centralized risk repository to ensure the following:

1. Agreed-upon risks, responses, and owners are documented
2. The documentation is readily available to all stakeholders
3. The documentation can be referred to in case of disagreements
4. The documentation can be referred to in order to review modifications and associated actions
5. New emergent risks can be documented and assessed as needed
6. To add to body of knowledge of organization risk management for reference in the future

While the risk repository can be physical or virtual, it is important to ensure good documentation practices in the following regards:

1. The document is easily retrievable with properly defined protocols for access
2. The document has appropriate change-control precautions and safeguards in place
3. Approval authority in case of changes is identified in the risk management plan along with method of electronic or physical signatures
4. A document with built-in calculations (e.g., MS Excel sheet) has its calculations validated during design
5. The document is revision controlled with revision history available to relevant users

CHAPTER 21

Detailed Risk Identification Tools

ISO 31000:2018 DEFINES THE PURPOSE of the risk identification process as:

To find, recognize and describe risks that might help or prevent an organization achieving its objectives. Relevant, appropriate and up-to-date information is important in identifying risks.[1]

To accomplish this, a range of techniques can be used. A few of these techniques are listed below.

RISK BREAKDOWN STRUCTURE

The Risk Breakdown Structure (RBS), introduced by Hillson,[2] provides a good structural framework to begin the risk identification process. A big problem in the risk identification process is lack of *systemic* understanding, which oftentimes leads to unstructured, narrow, and ad hoc risk identification. This in turn misleads the risk prioritization and mitigation efforts, thereby, which leads to the failure of risk management efforts. Before the individual risks undergo a qualitative or quantitative assessment, they should be mapped out with regard to their workflow within the system. Based on Hillson's definition, the RBS can be defined in a generic way as:

A source-oriented hierarchical grouping of risks that organizes the total risk exposure. Each descending level represents an increasingly detailed definition of sources of risk.

1. ©ISO. This material is reproduced from ISO 31000:2018, with permission of the American National Standards Institute (ANSI) on behalf of the International Organization for Standardization. All rights reserved.
2. D. Hillson, "Use a Risk Breakdown Structure (RBS) to Understand Your Risks," *Proceedings of the Project Management Institute Annual Seminars & Symposium* 10 (October 2002), https://www.pmi.org/learning/library/risk-breakdown-structure-understand-risks-1042.

The most important accomplishment of RBS is that it provides the scope of the risk management activities in a single snapshot. The universal utility of RBS lies in the fact that it can be used with the desired level of detail. For example, the RBS in Table 21.1 is for the development of an implantable medical device.

It must be understood that the versatility of RBS makes it available to be used for the same purpose from different standpoints. In the example above, we focused on the

TABLE 21.1 Example of Risk Breakdown Structure (RBS).

RBS level 0	RBS level 1	RBS level 2	RBS level 3
Device risk	Implantable component risk	Biocompatibility risk	Cytotoxicity
			Intracutaneous reaction
			Pyrogenicity
			Systemic toxicity
			Hematocompatibility
			Genotoxicity
			Carcinogenicity
			Reproductive toxicity
			Etc.
		Interface risk	Functional interface
			In situ interface with physiology
			Interface with delivery device
		Dimensional risk	Sizing
			Connectivity
			Tolerancing
			Design vs. manufacturing specifications
		Performance risk	Implant stability
			Reliability
			Delivery performance
			Material choice
			Usability
		User risk	Human factors
			Usability
			Training
			Qualification of user
			Patient selection
	Delivery device	...	...

TABLE 21.2 Another example of RBS.

RBS level 0	RBS level 1	RBS level 2	RBS level 3
Design risk	Implant design	Design scope risk	Requirements gathering Users/customers Design inputs Design deliverables Use/usability risk
		Development process risk	Specifications formation Verification plan Schedule Cost Resources Validation plan
		Product realization risk	Functionality In situ interface Delivery performance Stability Dimensional requirements Biocompatibility Material choice Interface with other components Reliability Manufacturability

risk from the standpoint of the components, but we could also look at the risks from the standpoint of the design phase, as shown in Table 21.2.

The principal advantages of RBS are the following:

1. Acts as the first step in systemic and holistic risk identification
2. Allows the discovery of redundancies and gives a bird's-eye view of dependencies
3. Provides an easy and handy tool to track risk linkages

STRUCTURED WHAT-IF TECHNIQUE (SWIFT)

The structured what-if technique (SWIFT) is another versatile tool that is compatible with popular risk assessment techniques. It is a prospective systems-based technique that imbibes more structure to the traditional brainstorming technique. True to its acronym, SWIFT can be conducted more quickly than detailed step-level analysis since it is used to examine risks and hazards on a systems or subsystems level. It can be used as the first phase of methods such as HAZOP, HACCP, or FMEA, which are detailed later in the text.

FIGURE 21.1 SWIFT process.

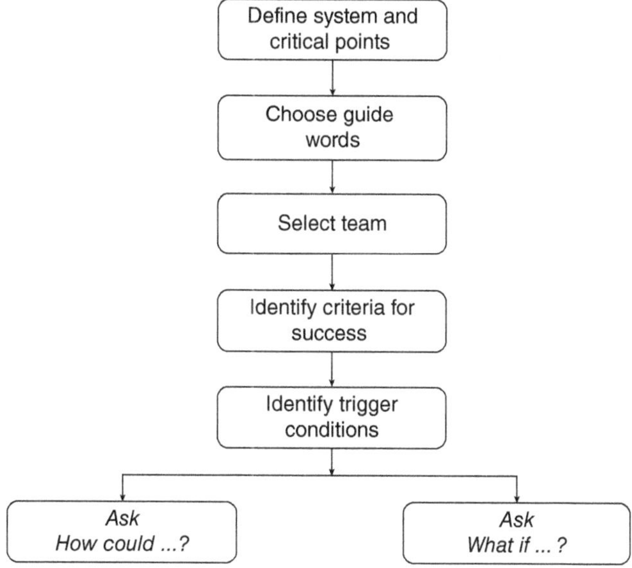

SWIFT has two major steps:

1. Failure (risk) identification: by asking *What if?*
2. Cause identification: by asking *How could?*

Figure 21.1 shows the SWIFT process sequentially. The process begins by defining the system, its key elements, and its critical points. Based on this knowledge, a set of guide words is chosen, which will challenge the critical points of the system.

Common guide words are the following:

- Material problems
- External events or influences
- Operating errors and other human factors
- Analytical or sampling errors
- Equipment or instrumentation malfunction
- Process upsets of unspecified origin
- Utility failures
- Integrity failure or loss of containment
- Emergency operations
- Environmental issues
- Timing
- Process
- Amount
- User

The guide words are chosen by the facilitator and may include any relevant words that would be applicable for the brainstorming session. With the aid of the guide words and the system and trigger conditions, the relevant questions could be asked.

The SWIFT process relies not only on the knowledge of the facilitator but also on his or her choice of SWIFT team members. The team should comprise stakeholders who have detailed knowledge of the system under study, including its internal and external context, and have proper competencies to participate in a creative brainstorming session where they will be asked "what if" questions.

With the team, the facilitator must state and document the desired output, objective, or criteria for success that are being challenged in the analysis. Based on this, the team must answer the following:

1. "What if" questions based on a combination of guide words and criteria of success
2. "How could" questions to identify any missing hazards and confirm root causes of any identified risks

For example, Figure 21.2 shows a risk identification process that may be used for a car tire.

ASSUMPTIONS AND CONSTRAINTS ANALYSIS

A large percentage of issues, losses, and failures occur due to flawed assumptions and poorly understood constraints. By understanding these two terms, we can leverage them to conduct a risk identification process that can help uncover hidden unapparent risks.

An assumption is a belief that is expected to hold true for an expected amount of time. Assumptions can be small, big, obvious, or not so obvious. The belief in the assumption should be directly proportional to the empirical evidence related to its validity, but this is often not the case. We often assume things are "too big to fail" and that "it has always been this way," only to find the opposite.

For example, I assume an hour's drive to work each day and plan my meetings accordingly. I have never timed my drive, neither averaged times nor considered common or extreme traffic conditions. Thus, this assumption could eventually prove false and cause me to miss one of my early morning meetings.

Assumptions are inherent in a lot of activities, and so questioning these assumptions is a good way to identify hidden risks. In the SWIFT example above, we could have chosen to assume that the tire pressure sensor will light up if the tire was low on pressure. We still could have carried out an analysis, but questioning that assumption gives a much more robust grasp on all risks. Thus, assumptions can add significant risks to any endeavor.

A constraint is simply a limitation. All businesses have limitations of time, resources, money, and so forth. There can also be limitations on outputs of product or process or service. Most often constraints are out of our control, and thus the scope of work has to be defined to ensure it does not exceed the organizational constraint.

A simple method for assumptions and constraints analysis is shown in Figure 21.3.

FIGURE 21.2 SWIFT process example (car tire).

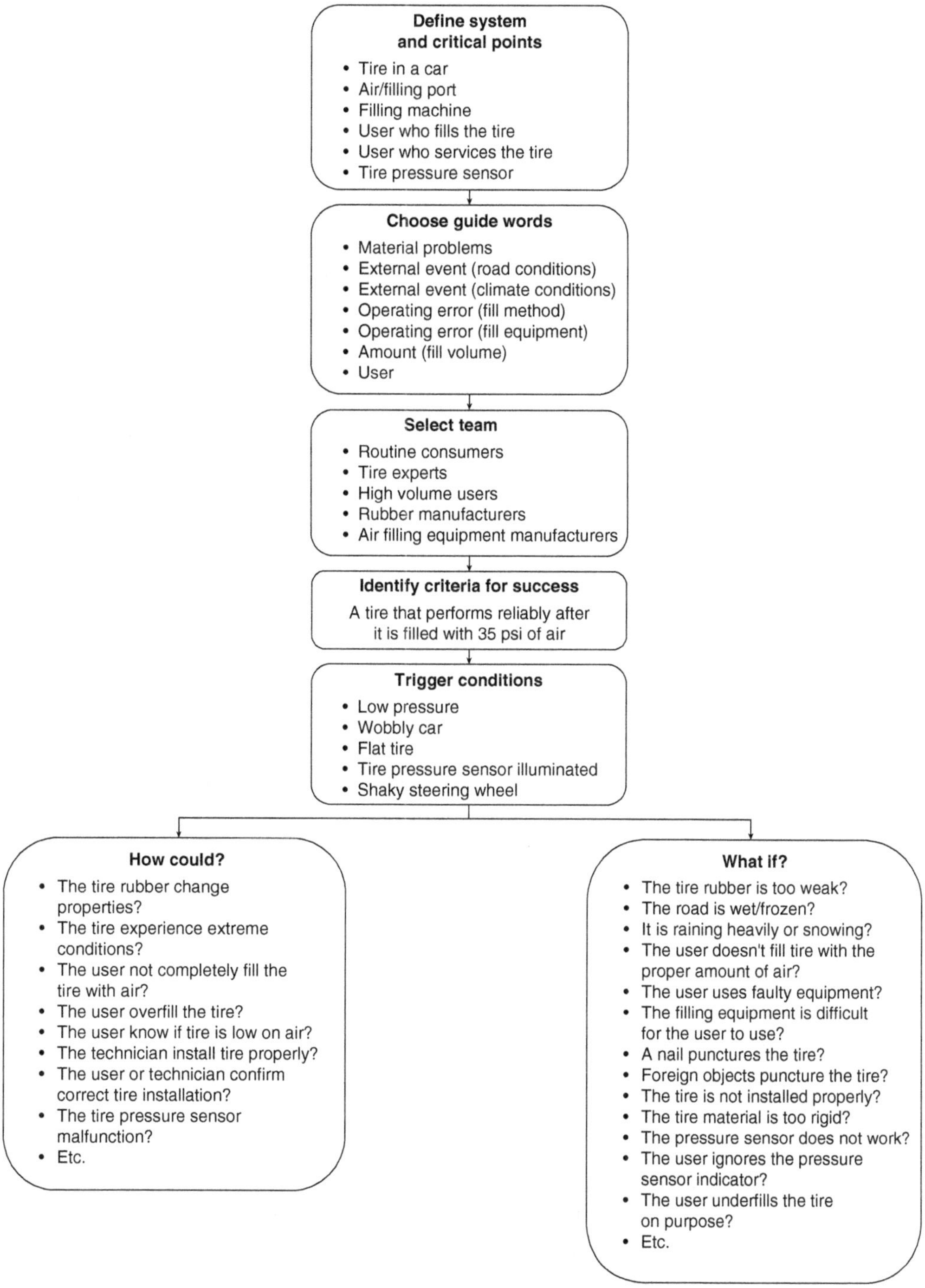

Define system and critical points

- Tire in a car
- Air/filling port
- Filling machine
- User who fills the tire
- User who services the tire
- Tire pressure sensor

Choose guide words

- Material problems
- External event (road conditions)
- External event (climate conditions)
- Operating error (fill method)
- Operating error (fill equipment)
- Amount (fill volume)
- User

Select team

- Routine consumers
- Tire experts
- High volume users
- Rubber manufacturers
- Air filling equipment manufacturers

Identify criteria for success

A tire that performs reliably after it is filled with 35 psi of air

Trigger conditions

- Low pressure
- Wobbly car
- Flat tire
- Tire pressure sensor illuminated
- Shaky steering wheel

How could?

- The tire rubber change properties?
- The tire experience extreme conditions?
- The user not completely fill the tire with air?
- The user overfill the tire?
- The user know if tire is low on air?
- The technician install tire properly?
- The user or technician confirm correct tire installation?
- The tire pressure sensor malfunction?
- Etc.

What if?

- The tire rubber is too weak?
- The road is wet/frozen?
- It is raining heavily or snowing?
- The user doesn't fill tire with the proper amount of air?
- The user uses faulty equipment?
- The filling equipment is difficult for the user to use?
- A nail punctures the tire?
- Foreign objects puncture the tire?
- The tire is not installed properly?
- The tire material is too rigid?
- The pressure sensor does not work?
- The user ignores the pressure sensor indicator?
- The user underfills the tire on purpose?
- Etc.

FIGURE 21.3 Assumptions/constraints analysis decision tree.

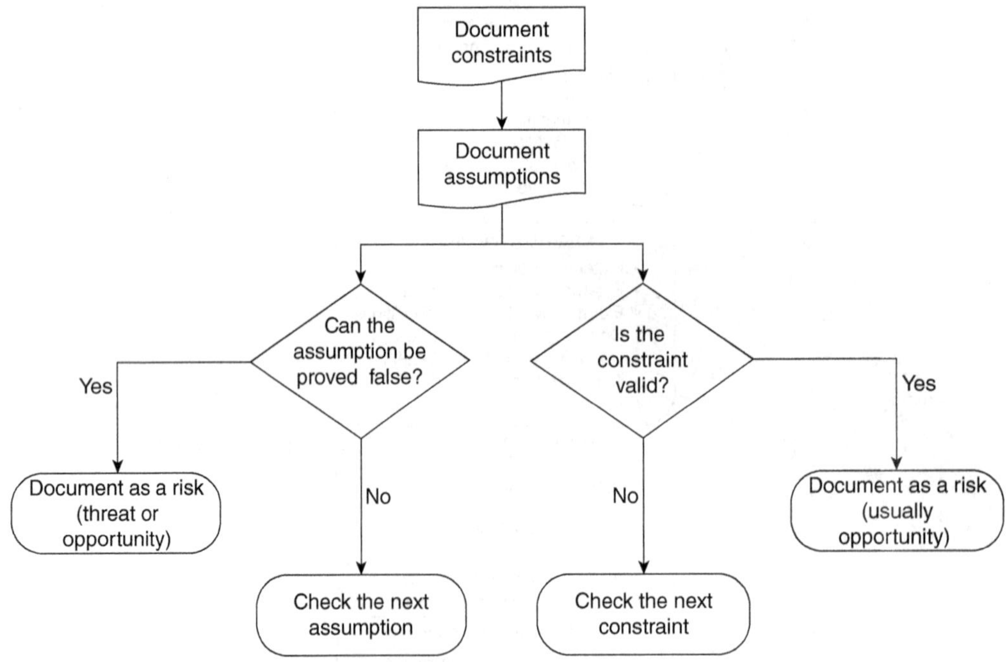

SWOT ANALYSIS

A strengths-weaknesses-opportunities-threats (SWOT) analysis can help set the initial tone in a risk identification process by focusing on both threats and opportunities. While this is only a starting point (since it produces only generic high-level risks), it does focus on both internal and external risks and broadens the contextual scope of any brainstorming session.

A simple SWOT matrix as shown in Figure 21.4 is used for this exercise.

An exhaustive list of strengths and weaknesses of a system, product, process, or service must be created first. The strengths provide a list of opportunities based on a brainstorming session with stakeholders who can predict outcomes upon organizational leveraging of the relevant strengths. Similarly, weaknesses can correspond to threats. The use of risk metalanguage can help tailor this exercise to the risk identification phase.

As stated earlier, the risks generated by SWOT analysis tend to be high level and thus must undergo detailed review to ensure sufficient detail for an effective evaluation process. Each SWOT risk will likely lead to multiple individual-specific risks.

There are various other methods of risk identification, and any of them could be used as long as care is taken to:

1. Ensure that most consequential risks are properly identified
2. Ensure cross-functional participation of all stakeholders

FIGURE 21.4 SWOT analysis.

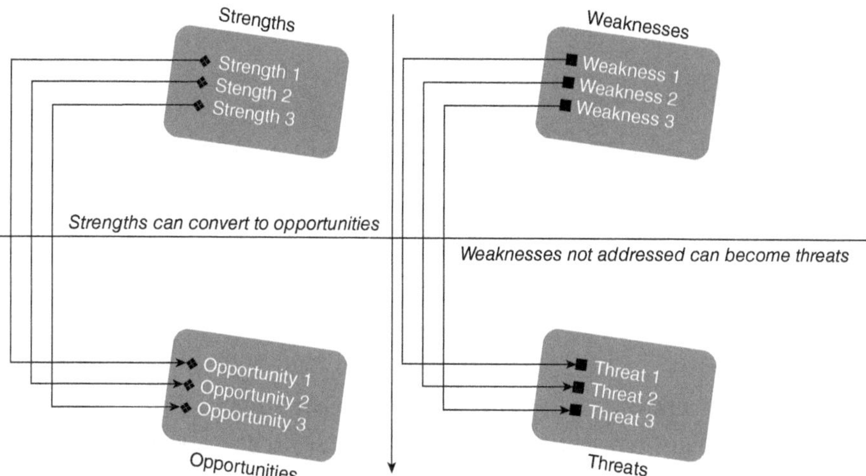

3. Ensure that consideration is given to the nonapparent risks
4. Ensure that a present situational analysis is conducted along with a futures analysis
5. Ensure that previous risks associated with similar projects are considered

Usually, a separate brainstorming session for risk identification is not held. It is assumed to be a part of the consequence analysis and risk assessment. In coming chapters, we will see many more tools for consequence analysis, which can also function as risk identification tools. Indeed, ISO 31000:2018 specifically guides us toward investigating the following factors and the relationships between those factors for risk identification:

- tangible and intangible sources of risk;
- causes and events;
- threats and opportunities;
- vulnerabilities and capabilities;
- changes in the external and internal context;
- indicators of emerging risks;
- the nature and value of assets and resources;
- consequences and their impact on objectives;
- limitations of knowledge and reliability of information;
- time-related factors;
- biases, assumptions and beliefs of those involved.[3]

3. ©ISO. This material is reproduced from ISO 31000:2018, with permission of the American National Standards Institute (ANSI) on behalf of the International Organization for Standardization. All rights reserved.

CHAPTER 22

Checkpoint: Risk Assessment—a Macro View

IN THE PREVIOUS CHAPTERS, we started with delving into the basics of risk by understanding probability and severity in detail. We identified and prioritized risks and conducted a basic risk analysis. We have armed ourselves with some very effective knowledge of the first phase of any risk assessment process by understanding not only the tools and methods but also critical aspects such as organizational context, stakeholder involvement, team dynamics, risk planning and facilitation, and risk attitudes and appetites. In the coming chapters we will embark on an even deeper study of the next phases of the risk management process, which include hazards and consequence analysis, risk evaluations, risk treatment, and different aspects of monitoring risk.

Before we move on to even more detailed theory, methods, and tools, it is important to extract ourselves out of the details and take a bird's-eye view of the risk assessment process. In this chapter, we take a slight step out of the trees to glance at the forest and calibrate ourselves to the greater structure of the risk management process and the role of risk assessment within it.

ISO 31000:2018 divides the risk assessment process into three distinct and sequential phases:

1. Risk identification
2. Risk analysis
3. Risk evaluation

At all levels of risk management, the risk assessment is an activating phase that is the crux of the risk management process and that will require significant resources.

The risk identification process, as discussed earlier, deals with finding, recognizing, and describing the risks. The risk analysis process deals with understanding the risk in terms of its constituent factors, which are usually probability and consequence. The risk evaluation process deals with comparing the results of the risk analysis process with the predefined criteria to check acceptability of the risk.

Figure 22.1 is from ISO 31000:2018, which clarifies the interaction of these three processes with other risk management processes.

Once a preliminary design of a product, process, service, or system is finalized, the first risk assessment can be started. It is important not to wait for the final design

FIGURE 22.1 Risk management process per ISO 31000:2018.

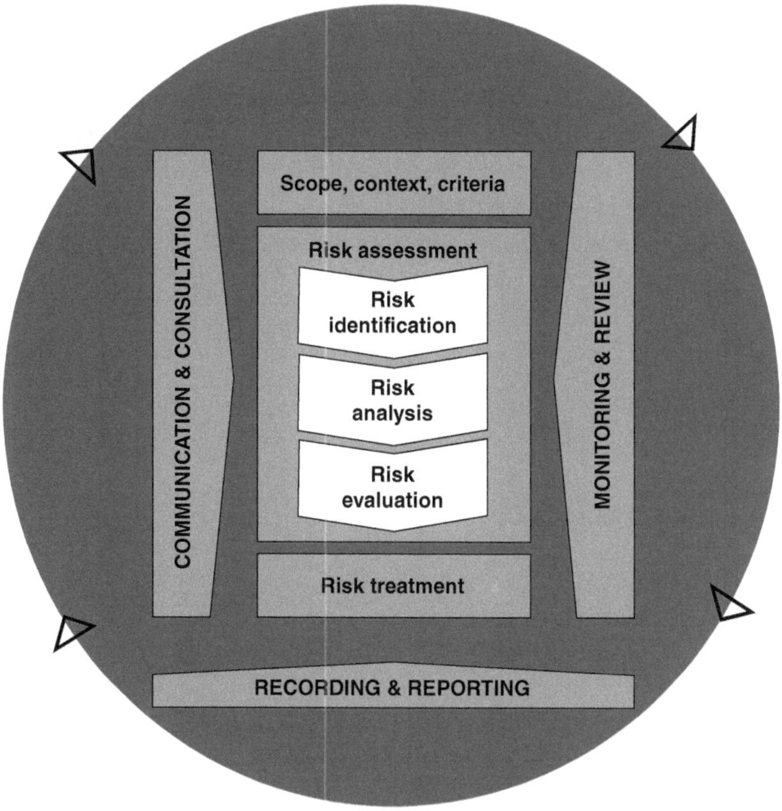

Source: ©ISO. This material is reproduced from ISO 31000:2018, with permission of the American National Standards Institute (ANSI) on behalf of the International Organization for Standardization.

freeze but perform preliminary risk analysis early on. The closer to the requirements-gathering phase the risk analysis is performed, the easier and cheaper it will be to implement risk modification measures. The concept of risk-based thinking is to have not only the designers thinking about potential hazards and their consequences from the first stroke of their pencils but also the process owners and the finance, marketing, clinical, engineering, operations, and other relevant functions thinking the same way. The goal is to inculcate risk-based thinking among all stakeholders from design stage 0, which starts with requirements gathering.

To ensure successful risk management, risk professionals must holistically view the process at all times and not narrow their focus on one specific aspect. A common mistake is detailed analysis and documentation in the design phase followed by change of ownership in the live production phase where the threads of risk monitoring and control are lost. The root cause of this problem is a defect in the risk management plan that often does not identify interfacing, crossover responsibilities and does not empower the owners with correct guidance and information to realize efficient risk management practices. Such interfacing problems can also arise in the risk assessment process between the identification, analysis, and evaluation phases. Thus, sufficient clarity in terms of responsibilities and outputs of various stakeholders must be provided in the risk management plan.

As seen in Figure 22.1, risk assessment, which we talked about at length in earlier chapters, is only a subsystem of the whole risk management process, which includes *communication and consultation* with relevant stakeholders and *monitoring and review* of the identified and evaluated risks.

Let us begin by understanding the fundamental path of risk from conception to impaction by describing the hazards and their outcomes in the next chapter.

CHAPTER 23

Hazard, Hazardous Situation, and Benefit and Harm

THE WORD "HAZARD" HAS BEEN ASSOCIATED with risk in the English language for at least 900 years. It traces its roots to the Middle English word "hasard," which was a dice game. This word itself comes from the Arabic word "az-zahr," referring to dice. Through the ages, the word "hazard" has come to describe a source of uncertainty and danger. Even Shakespeare used the phrase "hazard of the die" to describe the unsafe and dangerous condition of Richard III being on the battlefield without his horse.[1]

The very source of risk is the hazard, and it is necessary to analyze this concept for fundamental understanding of how risk emanates from its antecedents. The sequential concept of hazard, hazardous situation, and consequential outcomes is not new and is referenced in risk management standards such as ISO 12100:2010, ISO 14971:2019, and guidance documents by the International Atomic Energy Association (IAEA).

Hazard is defined in ISO 12100:2010 and ISO Guide 51:2014 as:

The potential source of harm.[2]

Hazard is the enabling state that can lead to the possibility of harm, while risk is the probability of harm from a situation triggered by the hazard. Consider the following situation:

1. A bottle of pesticide is a hazard since it is a potential source of harm (Figure 23.1). There are numerous possibilities one may think of involving this bottle of pesticide, which may end in a harmful scenario. For example, a person may drink it, mix it with food, or spill it into a water supply.
2. A hazardous situation is the activating scenario that converts the many random possibilities into a foreseeable probability. ISO 12100:2010 defines *hazardous situation* as follows:

---

1. B. Zimmer, "'Hazard': From Medieval Dice to the Risks Faced by Frontline Workers," *Wall Street Journal*, May 14, 2020, https://www.wsj.com/articles/hazard-from-medieval-dice-to-the-risks-faced-by-frontline-workers-11589481761.
2. ©ISO. This material is reproduced from ISO 12100:2010, with permission of the American National Standards Institute (ANSI) on behalf of the International Organization for Standardization.

Circumstance in which a person is exposed to at least one hazard.[3]

An example of a hazardous situation would be a baby playing near the bottle of pesticide (Figure 23.2). Now we have a bona fide hazardous situation from which specific scenarios of harm can result.

3. Risk is the attempted estimation of one such pair of probability and severity. For example, in Figure 23.3, the bottle has been knocked over and caused a spill. The knocking over of the bottle by the baby was the triggering event that caused a hazardous situation of the spill.

Harm, which here is eponymous with *consequence*, is defined as follows:

A physical or psychological damage, a deleterious consequence on health or human life, property or environment.

The hazardous situation is often not defined in traditional risk management in non-health and non-safety sectors, but the addition of this extra step in the process can provide considerable guidance in resolving the complex connection between hazard and consequence. ISO Guide 51:2014 expands on the definition of hazardous situation in ISO 12100:2010 as follows:

FIGURE 23.1 Bottle of pesticide: a hazard.

3. ©ISO. This material is reproduced from ISO 12100:2010, with permission of the American National Standards Institute (ANSI) on behalf of the International Organization for Standardization.

Circumstance in which people, property or the environment is/are exposed to one or more hazards.[4]

A hazard need not affect a specific person or group of persons; it can potentially impact property, commodities, or the environment.

Once the hazards are identified, the risk reviewer can determine a sequence of events that will lead each hazard to one or more hazardous situations, and each hazardous situation could lead to one or more harms (Figure 23.4).

For further clarity of the concepts stated in this example, see Table 23.1.

The hazardous situation does not always lead to a negative consequence. An organization may choose to take risks in anticipation of realization of an opportunity. In such a case, instead of a harm, we have a *benefit*, which is defined as follows:

An advantage or profit realized from a risky activity.

FIGURE 23.2 Baby near the bottle of pesticide: hazardous situation.

FIGURE 23.3 Baby hurt by the spilled pesticide: harm.

4. ©ISO. This material is reproduced from ISO/IEC Guide 51:2014, with permission of the American National Standards Institute (ANSI) on behalf of the International Organization for Standardization. All rights reserved.

FIGURE 23.4 Hazard to harm.

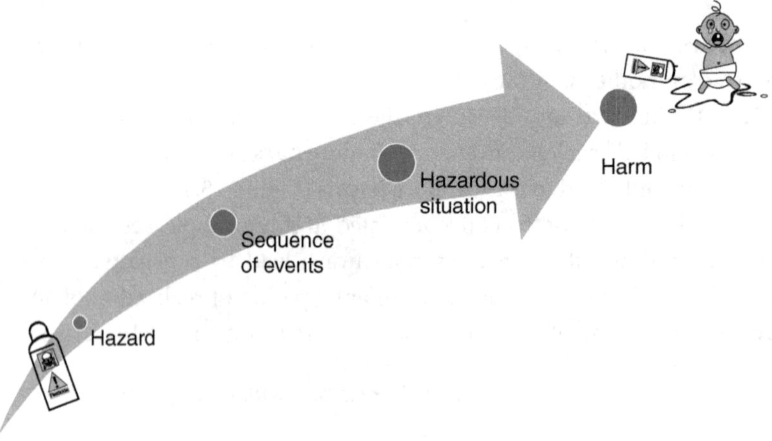

TABLE 23.1 Tabular representation of hazard to harm.

Hazard	Sequence of events	Hazardous situation	Harm
A bottle of pesticide	Baby topples over the bottle without the cap opening	None	None
		Bottle hits the baby	Bruise
			Cut/bleeding
	Baby topples over the bottle in a direction away from him	Spill away from the baby	None
	Baby topples over the bottle and it rolls away without opening	None	None
	Baby hits the bottle and it doesn't topple over	None	None
	Baby hits the bottle and it topples over in his direction	Spill near or on the baby	Skin irritation
			Skin blisters
			Burns
			Eye irritation
		Bottle hits the baby	Bruise
			Cut/bleeding

FIGURE 23.5 Hazard to benefit.

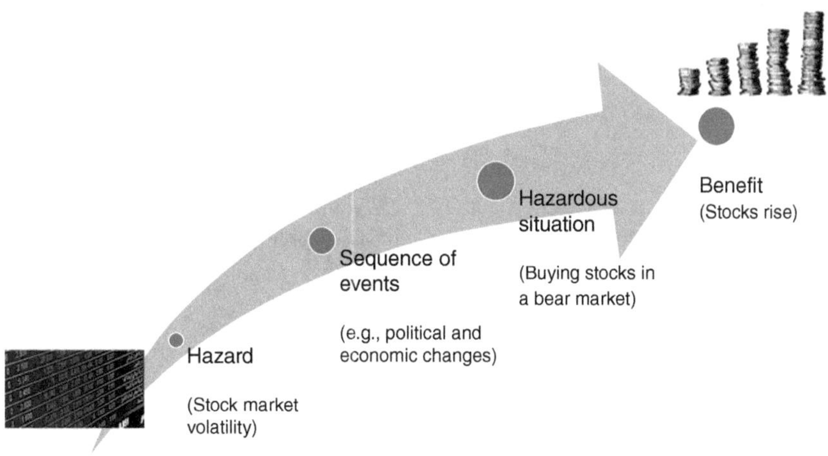

FIGURE 23.6 Spectrum of events that lead from hazard to hazardous situation on the left and spectrum of consequences on the right.

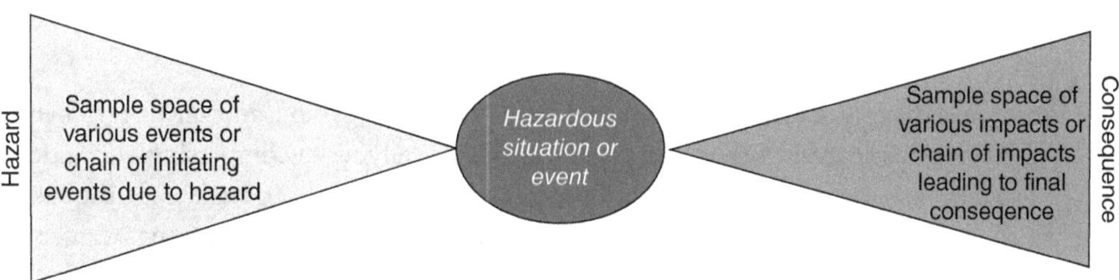

Figure 23.5 provides an example to clarify this and show the importance of correctly gauging the sequence of events and the hazardous situation.

As can be seen, to make a benefit, one must correctly predict two probabilities: a hazard leading to a hazardous situation and a hazardous situation leading to a benefit.

One must also be cognizant of the various different initiating events from the same hazard that lead to a hazardous situation and the chain of short-term impacts that lead to the final consequence. There might be best-case and worst-case consequences depending on the chain of events. This is illustrated in Figure 23.6.

The Society of Risk Analysis defines *hazard* as:

> *A risk source where the potential consequences relate to harm. Hazards could, for example, be associated with energy (e.g., explosion, fire), material (toxic or eco-toxic), biota (pathogens) and information (panic communication).*[5]

Commonly, hazards have been associated with forms of energy such as mechanical energy / kinetic energy due to moving parts, acceleration, and friction; nuclear energy

5. T. Aven, "SRA Glossary," Society for Risk Analysis, June 22, 2015, https://www.sra.org/sra-glossary-draft.

FIGURE 23.7 An example of harm and benefit (negative and positive consequence) resulting from the same hazard.

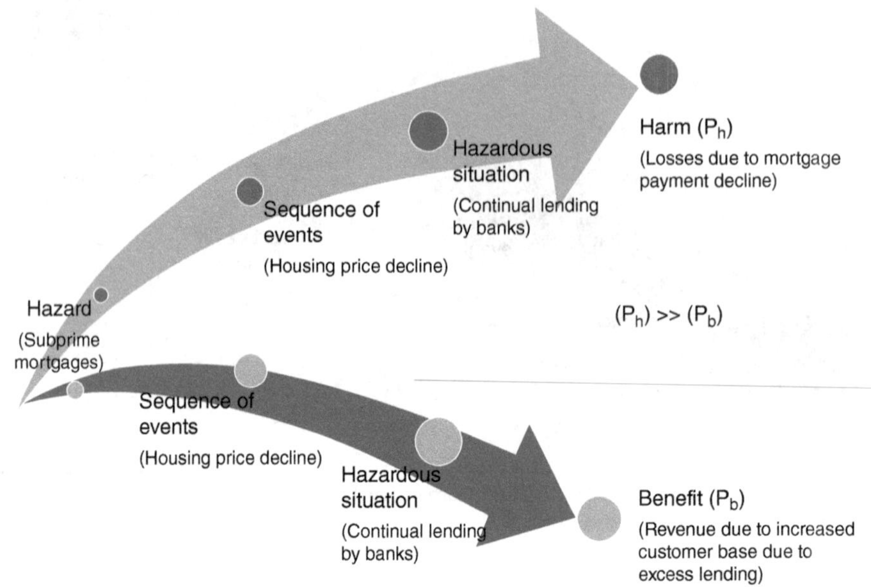

such as radiation; electrical energy such as wattage or current; and chemical energy. While this fits manufacturing sectors, hazards are really all-encompassing and indeed include a vast and disparate variety of potential sources of danger, such as earthquakes, storms, dangerous materials, stock market swings, icy roads, cyber-hacking, terrorism, and so on. For a system under study, it is important to understand its environment of operation and list all possible hazards that could cause a measurable impact for analysis.

In the 2008 U.S. subprime mortgage housing crisis, numerous risk managers did not consider the two-part probabilities. Addition of the "sequence of events" stage clarifies the linkage between hazard and hazardous situation and separates the hazardous situation and benefit/harm pair. In Figure 23.7, the same hazard and hazardous situation could lead to harm or benefit based on the assigned values of probability. But when broken down in this way, there is much more clarity in the calculation of probability than just using a simple cause and effect relationship.

The difference between benefit and harm is commonly known as risk-benefit analysis, which essentially is a comparison of two sets of risks: risk of threat versus risk of opportunity. This will be explained in detail in the chapter on risk-benefit analysis.

CHAPTER 24

Detailed Consequence Analysis

***CONSEQUENCE ANALYSIS* IS AN EXERCISE** in "futures thinking" where the nature and type of impact of a probable risk are determined. One event may have a plethora of impacts of varying magnitude and thus varying consequences for the organization.

Consequence analysis focuses on discovery of the most likely consequences by using cause and effect relationships. Figure 24.1 shows a cause that may have multiple effects. The exact effect is not known due to the uncertainty surrounding the future path. During the risk analysis phase, of which the consequence analysis is a part, a list of plausible effects is chosen for consideration. These effects or consequences are then assigned probabilities of occurrence and magnitudes of consequence and the risks are calculated and evaluated. In the figure, four effects were analyzed and assigned risk values, but only one effect (A) actually materialized. This effect led to Risk A, for which this particular team was prepared since correct analysis had already been done.

To assign consequences with greater accuracy and precision, the theory on hazard, hazardous situation, and harms and benefits, discussed in the previous chapter, prepares us to correctly assign these differing magnitudes and ensure proper resolution within the eventual harms and benefits. This is clarified in Figure 24.2.

This method forces the user to delve into details and chart a causal nexus through the structure afforded by the path of hazard to consequence by attempting to qualitatively and quantitatively assess uncertainty.

Consequence analysis further involves ensuring that all contributory factors toward a risk are taken into consideration. It also involves looking at secondary consequences that may cascade into other risks and that may appear after passage of a set amount of time. Most importantly, the consequences must be tied back to the original objectives of the system for them to be meaningful and add real value.

Usually, risk analysis makes us prioritize the consequences by factoring in the following:

1. Magnitude of impact (severity)
2. Probability of impact

All of the tools listed earlier for risk identification inherently use consequence analysis. A few more tools are discussed in the following sections.

FIGURE 24.1 Effects analysis in light of uncertainty.

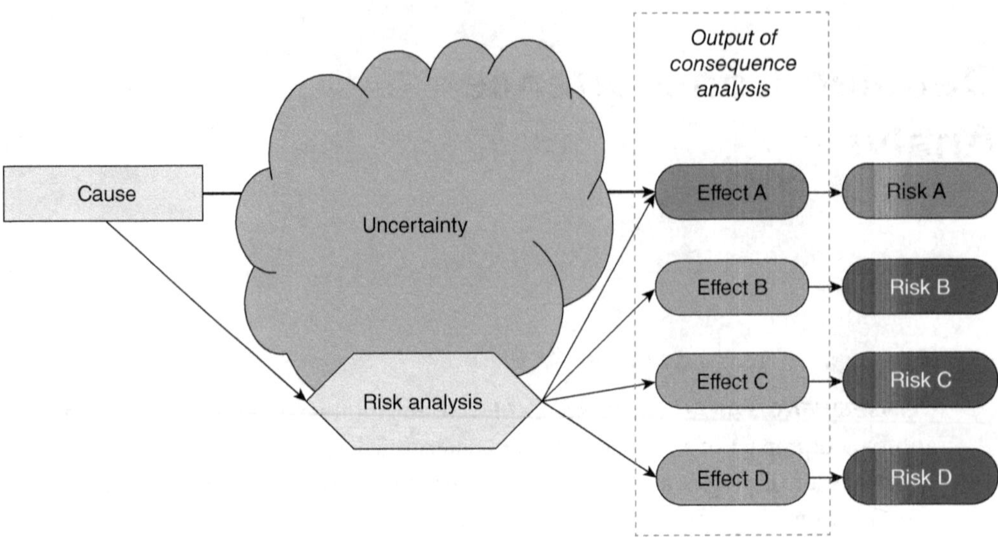

FIGURE 24.2 Consequence analysis as a part of structured risk analysis.

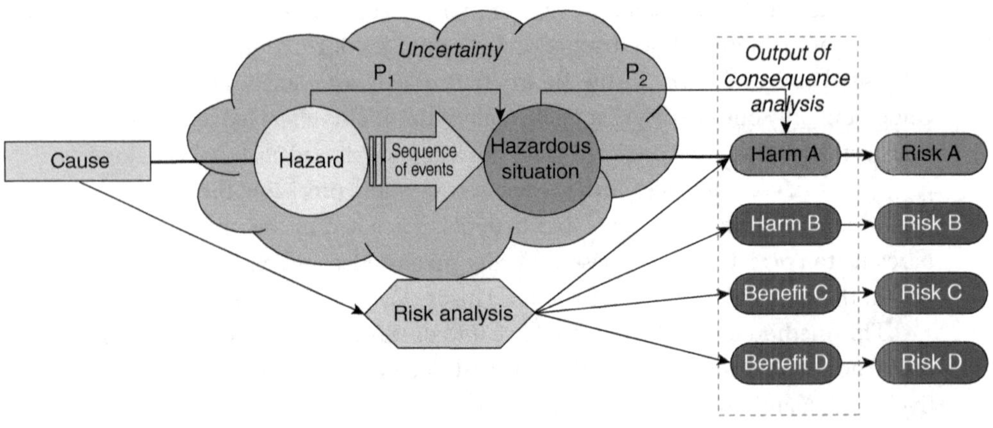

FAULT TREE ANALYSIS (FTA)

Fault tree analysis (FTA) uses Boolean logic to analyze a single fault event in a deductive top-down manner. FTA starts with the top-level failure and uses logic gates to construct a relationship between the top-level event and the descending level causes.

The top event is the critical system event and is the effect for which the causes are being investigated. The immediate faults are the next level events, which precede the top event. The necessary faults are the activating condition necessary to begin the cause and effect relationship.

FIGURE 24.3 FTA example with top event of car sliding off the road.

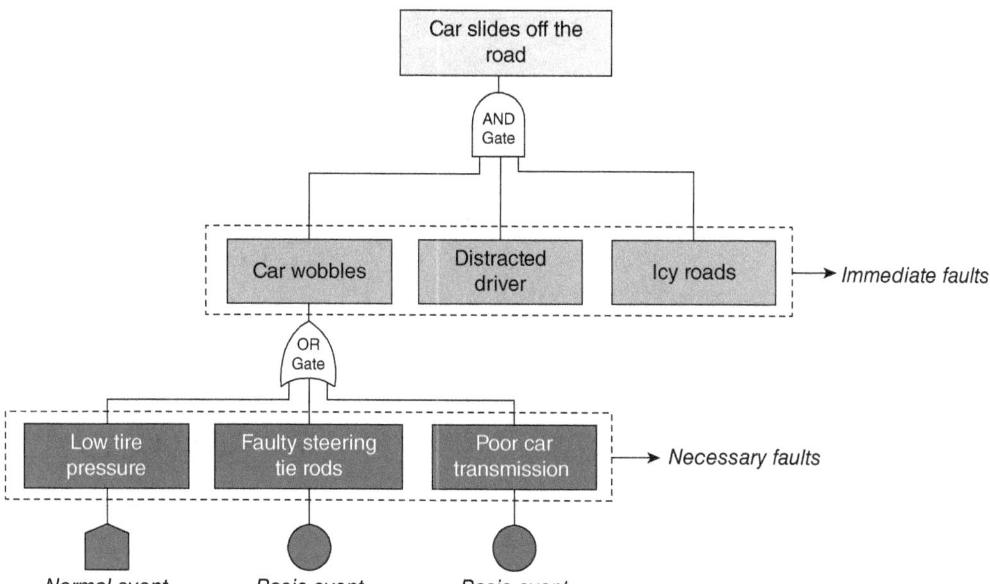

FTA is really a method to draw out all possible sequences of events within the cause and effect relationship. The minimal set of events (lower-level faults) needed to make the effect occur is known as the minimal cut set.

Another nomenclature of importance is the basic event and the normal event. *Basic event* is the initiating faulty condition, and *normal event* is a routine condition expected to occur during normal operation.

Figure 24.3 illustrates these concepts.

The scope of this analysis is very specific, and hence it is unable to be used for generic events since the tree would become very unwieldy. FTA can also become byzantine when a large number of system conditions exist leading to numerous hazardous situations. This analysis is more suited to a system that has a few intricate consequences where a cause and effect relationship is complex. Nevertheless, this basic technique provides a logical method of consequence analysis by levels or causes in a diagrammatic representation.

DECISION TREE ANALYSIS

A decision tree is a decision mapping tool that uses tree branches to map possible alternatives and consequences. It is a great tool to lay out options and evaluate them by consequence.

A simple structure of a decision tree is shown in Figure 24.4. The black square denotes a decision point, and a black circle is a chance event. To construct a decision tree, the point of decision and multiple alternatives at that point must be identified. The outcomes of alternatives must be assessed for further decision points or final outcomes.

FIGURE 24.4 Decision tree analysis.

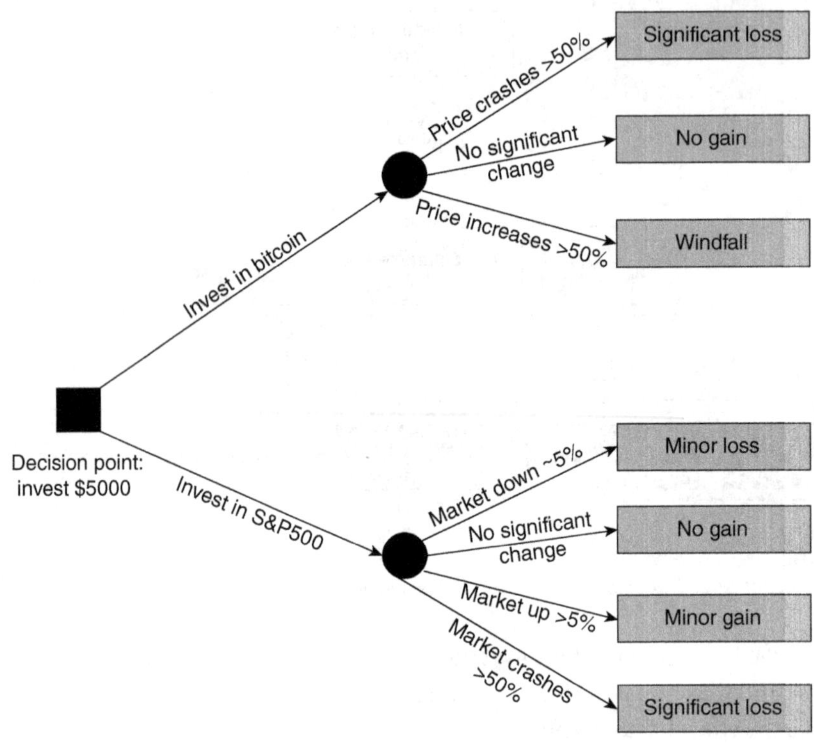

Once the basic tree is constructed, each outcome from a chance node is assigned a probability value. The outcomes must be assigned a quantitative value as well. In this example, the actual rise and fall of investment can be easily converted to a dollar value as shown in Figure 24.5.

The next step is to calculate the value of the chance node. This is done by multiplying the quantitative consequence value by the probability of the consequence and adding all the values as shown in Steps 2 and 3. In the final step, the value of the chance node is subtracted from the value of the investment to give the total value of the decision.

Further decision nodes can be included once the preceding consequences are either realized or seem certain, as shown in Figure 24.6.

EVENT TREE ANALYSIS (ETA)

Event tree analysis (ETA) is an inductive technique that uses a bottom-up approach to trace eventual consequences of an initiating event. ETA often uses binary logic and assigns two probabilities to a set of succeeding second-level consequences. Depending on the situation, more than two probabilities can be assigned if more than two succeeding level consequences are present.

FIGURE 24.5 Chance node and final quantitative outcomes of decision tree analysis.

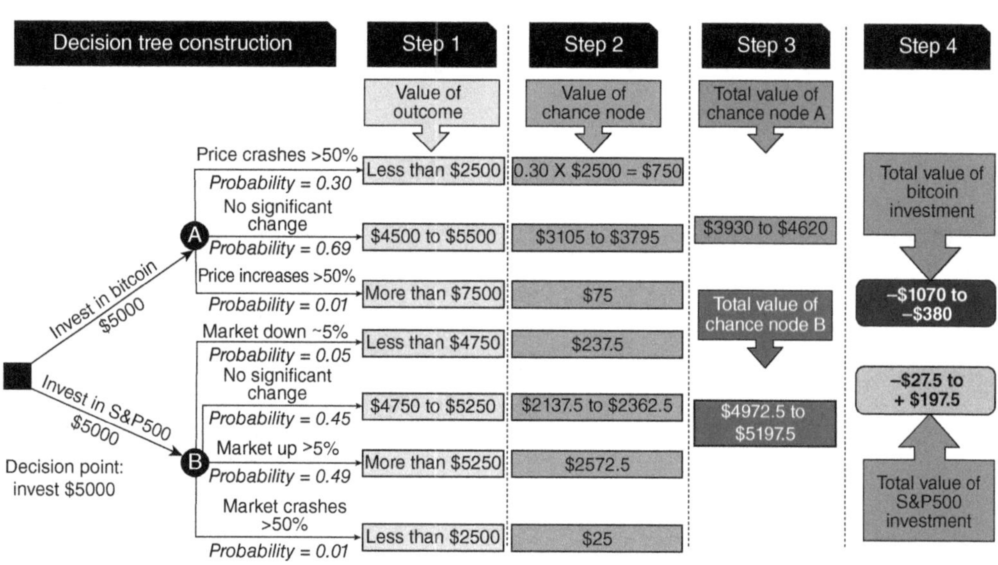

FIGURE 24.6 Expanded decision tree analysis.

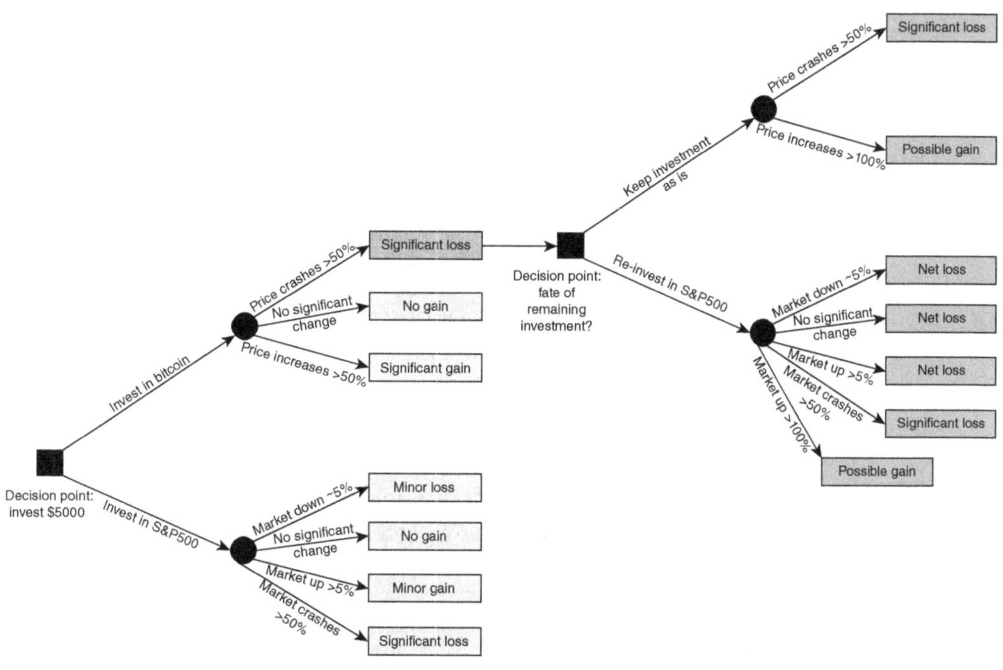

In Figure 24.7, the short circuit condition *may or may not* lead to a fire. This is the first link in the causal chain. In case of fire, the sprinkler system *may or may not* work. This is the second link. The third link is the activation of the fire alarm system. The fire alarm system *may or may not* work.

FIGURE 24.7 ETA for initiating event of a short circuit.

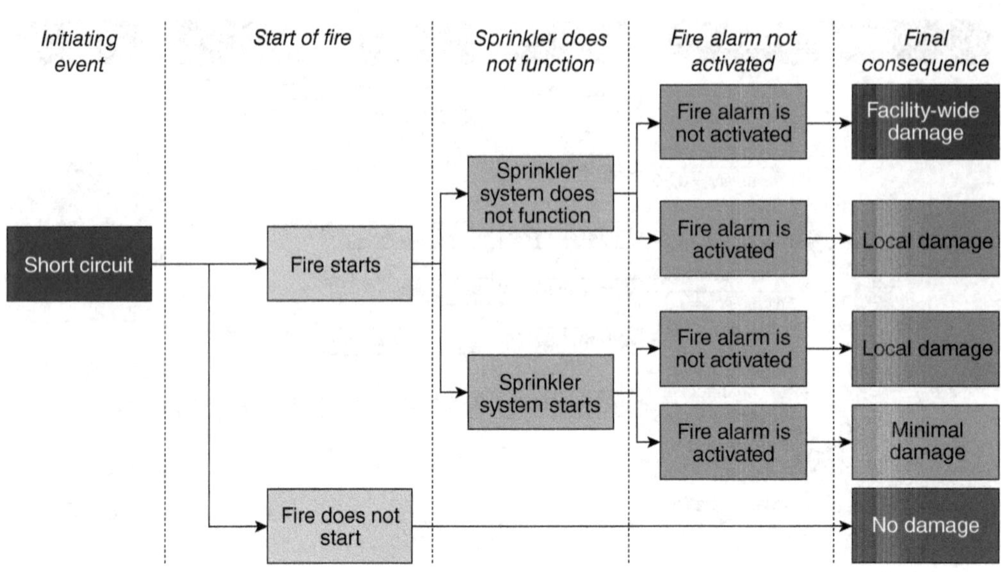

These three causal chains are sufficient to describe the causal nexus between the short circuit and its potential consequences.

Owing to its binary logic, ETA can be easily quantified into probabilities, as shown in Figure 24.8. Each event is assigned a probability, and the successive probabilities of the causal chain are multiplied to give the probability of the consequence. Here, the probability of uncontrolled fire with no alarm leading to facility-wide damage is $0.80 \times 0.01 \times 0.001 = 8 \times 10^{-8}$.

Thus, the steps for ETA are as follows:

1. Define system and boundaries
2. Identify initiating event
3. Consider mitigations in place for the initiating event
4. Assign first-level outcome of the initiating event
5. Assign probabilities to all first-level outcomes based on the mitigations in place
6. Based on second-level outcomes, create the succeeding outcomes and assign probabilities
7. Continue to increase causal chain until a final consequence is obtained
8. Multiply all preceding probabilities (assigned in steps 5 and 6) for one event and consequence set to obtain probability of consequence

BOW TIE ANALYSIS

A bow tie analysis can be defined as a diagrammatic method of displaying the cause and consequence relationship of a specific hazard to its varied impacts together with system mitigations along the sequential causal chain.

FIGURE 24.8 Frequency calculation of fire due to explosion.

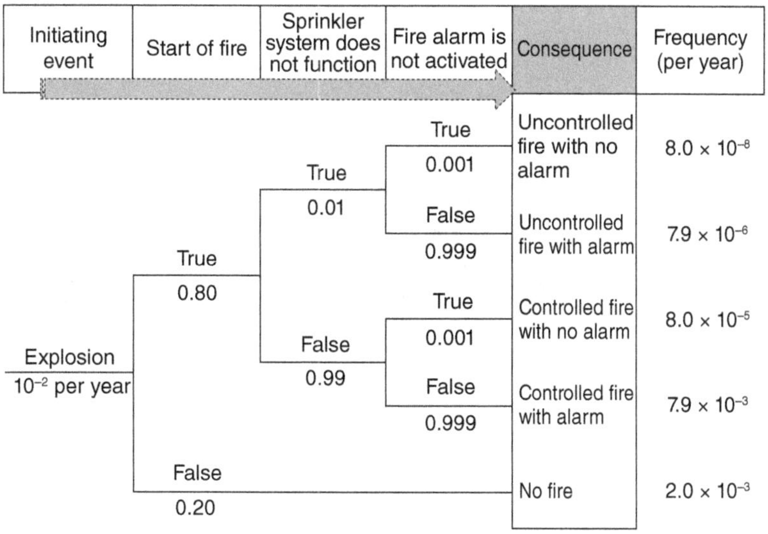

Initiating event	Start of fire	Sprinkler system does not function	Fire alarm is not activated	Consequence	Frequency (per year)
Explosion 10^{-2} per year	True 0.80	True 0.01	True 0.001	Uncontrolled fire with no alarm	8.0×10^{-8}
			False 0.999	Uncontrolled fire with alarm	7.9×10^{-6}
		False 0.99	True 0.001	Controlled fire with no alarm	8.0×10^{-5}
			False 0.999	Controlled fire with alarm	7.9×10^{-3}
	False 0.20			No fire	2.0×10^{-3}

Source: Reprinted by permission from *Risk Management: Part 3 Guide to Risk Analysis of Technological Systems*, IEC 60300-3-9, ed. 1.0 (Geneva, Switzerland: International Electrotechnical Commission, 1995), figure A.3.

FIGURE 24.9 Simplified fundamentals of bow tie analysis.

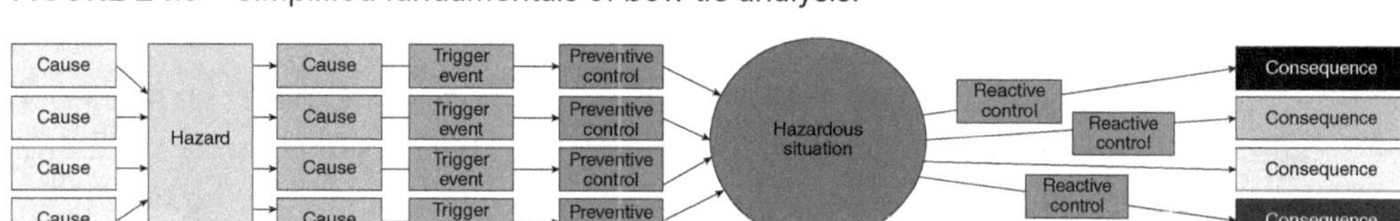

The construction of the diagram begins by placing the event in the center and listing the sources of risks or hazards toward the left. In Figure 24.9, both the causes of the hazard and the causes engendered by the hazard that lead to trigger events are shown. This allows us to analyze the source of the risk from the very source of the hazard.

A hazard transforms into a hazardous situation due to a triggering event or sequence of triggering events. These events are not impactful failures but red flags that are harbingers of the hazardous situations ahead. These triggering events act like signals, upon which, when activated, preventive controls can be placed to preclude the hazardous situation.

If there is no preventive control or the control fails, the hazardous situation is live. At this point, an adverse event can still be prevented if reactive controls exist in the system that can catch the hazardous situation and mitigate it. If no reactive controls exist or the controls fail, then there is a consequence.

FIGURE 24.10 Simplified bow tie analysis for hazardous event of release of radioactive substance from a chamber.

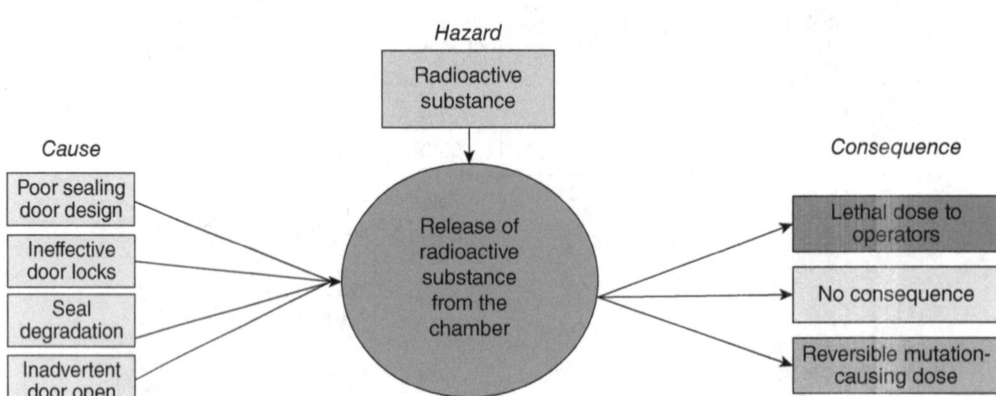

ISO 31010:2019 defines a bow tie diagram as follows:

> *A bow tie is a graphical depiction of pathways from the causes of an event to its consequences. It shows the controls that modify the likelihood of the event and those that modify the consequences if the event occurs. It can be considered as a simplified representation of a fault tree or success tree (analysing the cause of an event) and an event tree (analysing the consequences).*[1]

In a general bow tie diagram, the sources of risk, which due to certain triggering causes lead to the event, are listed on the leftmost side. Barriers or controls are shown by vertical bars, along with the escalation factors that cause the controls to fail. At the very bottom, management activities that support the controls are shown as horizontal bars (see example in Figure 24.11).

The simplest form of the bow tie diagram is shown in Figure 24.10, which lists the event under study, its causes, and consequences. As can be seen, depending on the nature of the event under study within the system under study, the diagram can be modulated to best fit the need to show the path from cause to consequence.

This illustration is nascent in its current form since it is missing the safety barriers of preventive and reactive controls. The causal path detailed in this diagram can be used to identify specific controls that may already be in place or that need to be implemented. If the controls are already in place, then the bow tie diagram can help us determine the sequence in which more than one control were to operate, and assess the adequacy of control in light of specific consequences. Figure 24.11 is a completed diagram with preventive barriers shown as dark gray rectangles on the left and reactive barriers as light gray rectangles on the right.

1. *Risk Management—Risk Assessment Techniques*, IEC 31010:2019 (Geneva, Switzerland: International Electrotechnical Commission, 2019), B.4.2.

FIGURE 24.11 Complete bow tie analysis of release of radioactive substance from a chamber.

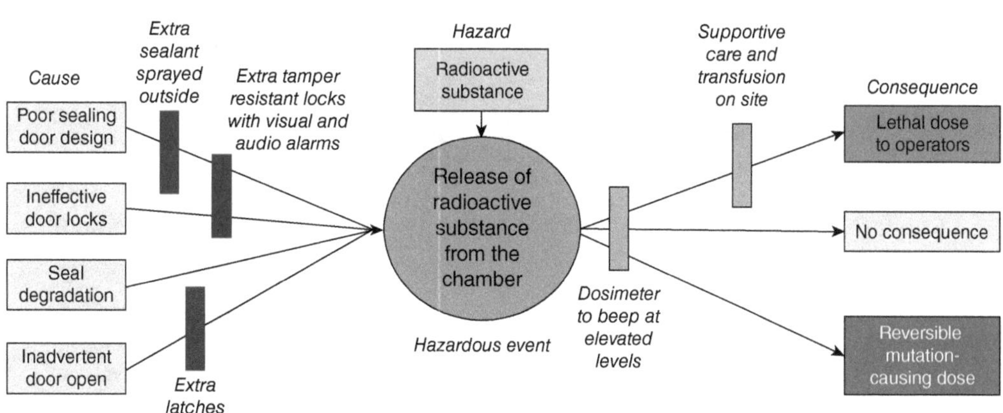

CAUSE AND CONSEQUENCE ANALYSIS (CCA)

Cause-consequence analysis (CCA) uses the logic of FTA to depict conditions necessary for the critical event and then uses conditionality to chart differing consequences. The occurrence of conditionalities (yes or no) can be further depicted as the output of more fault trees as needed. Figure 24.12 shows the CCA in a diagrammatic format.

The following example, shown in Figure 24.13, clarifies this concept. After satisfaction of the lowest-level actuation events, here shown with an OR gate, the causal chain moves to the conditional event. Here it is "Will Brexit occur unplanned?" If yes, then the consequence is listed. If no, we could have listed another consequence, but for accuracy, we have added a sequential logic for the "no" answer to occur. The reason for doing this is to clarify the sequence of events for the "no" answer, which lead to another conditional event. If unplanned Brexit does not happen, then a new election will occur and its mandate may or may not be for Brexit. If an overwhelming majority of "no Brexit" candidates are elected, then the answer to the condition "Is new election mandate for no Brexit?" will be yes—there will be no Brexit.

If the answer to this condition is no, then the consequence of "Brexit with minimal economic impact" will occur only if the elected anti-Brexit government reaches an acceptable deal with the European Union (EU).

Since the CCA relies on logic gates and binary conditional logic to chart the causal nexus, like event tree analysis, it is easy to assign probabilities and add or multiply them.

Despite being a bottom-up approach unlike FTA, CCA still leverages the mathematical simplicity afforded by logic gates and combines it with a structured analysis of the causal chain to diagrammatically display causes and effects. CCAs can also be more realistic than FTAs and ETAs since they can also incorporate time dependencies and conditionalities better than FTA.

CCAs do require intensive effort and can become complex and large. Thus, they should be used for very critical events where such efforts are justified.

FIGURE 24.12 Basic logic of CCA.

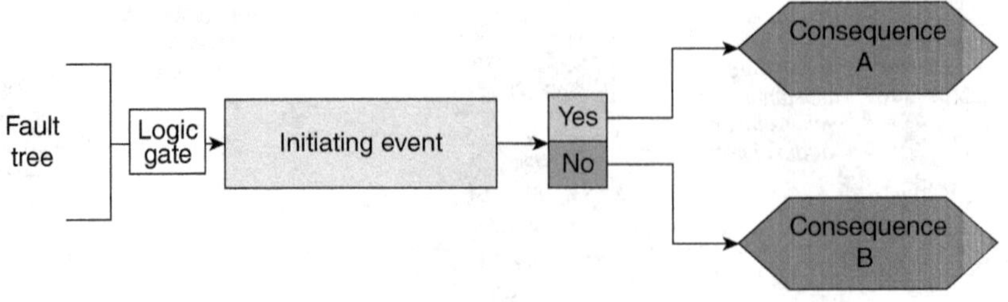

FIGURE 24.13 Example of CCA: Brexit.

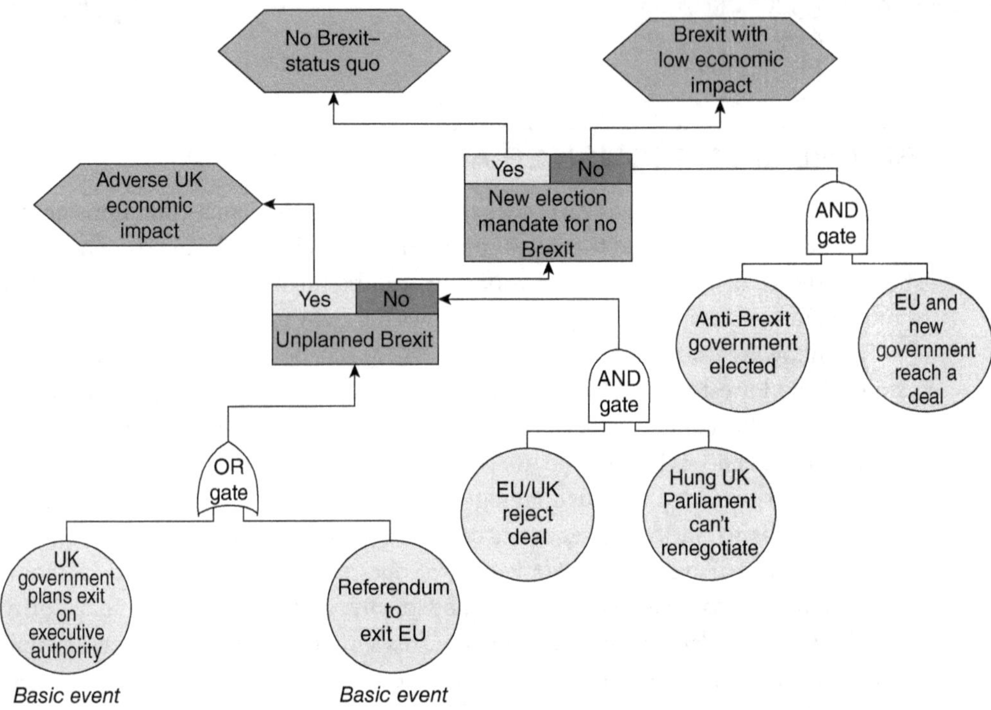

SCENARIO ANALYSIS

Scenario analysis is a predictive technique for analyzing aggregate future outcomes. It can be used for high-level prediction and tracking of critical risks to measure their deviation of expectation and analyze causes and consequences.

In Figure 24.14, a major corrective change was effected and the decrease in the number of complaints is predicted with a downward slope. The dotted line is the predicted rate of decrease. The green area is the most likely rate of decrease with

FIGURE 24.14 Scenario analysis.

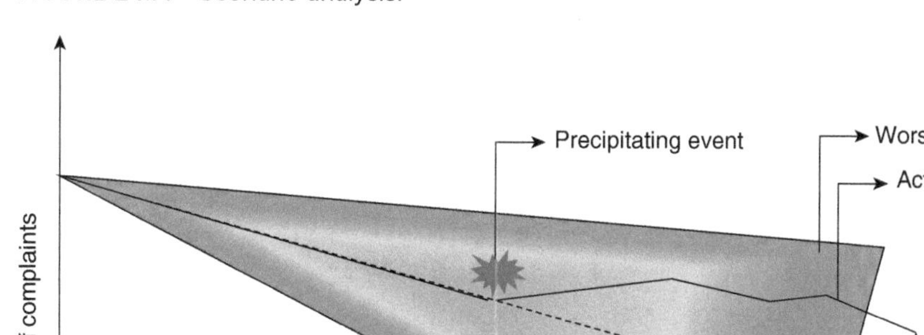

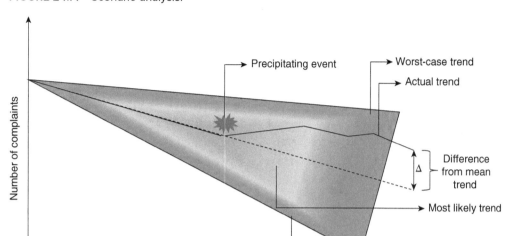

consideration for medium- to high-impact events. The blue bands on the sides are on the edges of trend analysis and represent the worst and best possible trends. Any significant change in trend beyond statistical common cause variability (usually three sigma) can be said to be effected by a precipitating event, and investigative analysis is needed in such cases.

This tool can also be used to continually measure deviation from predicted values to consider proactive course corrections. Scenario analysis focuses on monitoring lead indicators of change and takes into account a multitude of future scenarios with respect to the situation at hand. This tool is best suited for time-varying high-level strategic or operational risks, which are indicators of organizational performance.

ROOT CAUSE ANALYSIS (RCA)

Root cause analysis (RCA) is the process by which a cause of a problem is investigated and verified. Most of the time there is a tendency to quickly solve the problem rather than identifying the root cause and fixing the issue. Most often the symptom of the problem is mitigated rather than the root cause of the problem, leading to repeated problems. Identifying the root cause is an important step to eliminate repeated problems. The main steps involved in the RCA process are defining the problem, understanding the process, identifying possible causes, collecting data, and analyzing data to confirm the identified root cause. These steps are sequentially shown in Figure 24.15.

FIGURE 24.15 Steps of RCA.

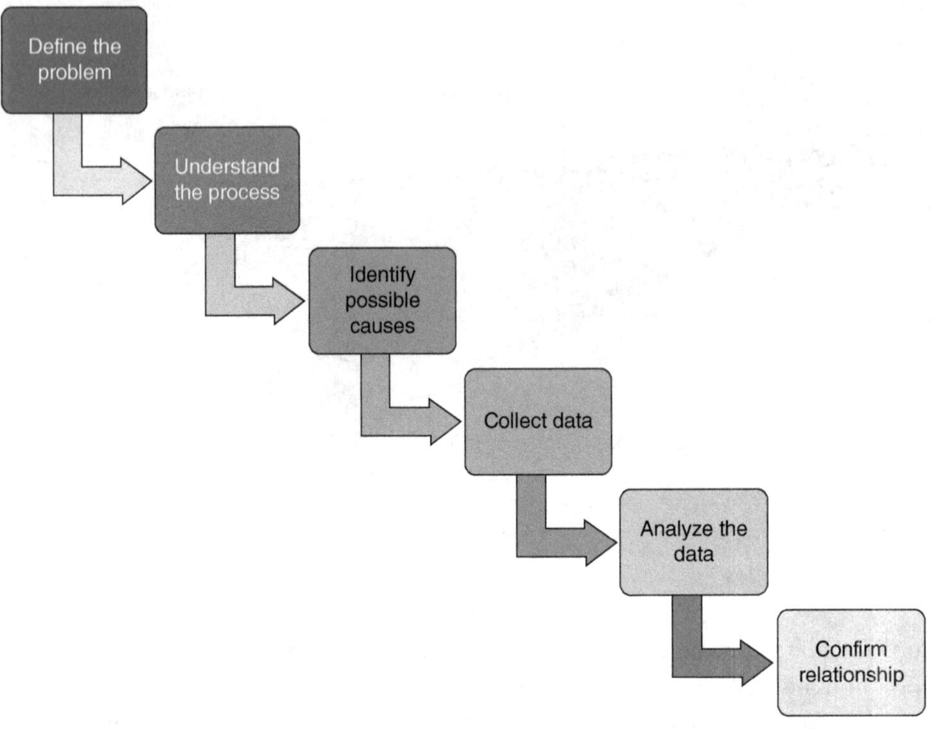

Defining the problem: The problem statement should be clear, concise, and complete. Without a good understanding of the problem, the root cause identification will fail. The following are elements of a good problem statement:

What: what is happening?
Where: where is the problem found?
When: when was the issue noticed?
How much: what is the frequency or magnitude of the problem?
Who: who was impacted by the problem?

Understanding the process: Define the steps involved in a process. This will help identify where the problem occurs. This can be achieved by creating a flowchart with the major steps.

Identifying possible causes: Different techniques are used to identify the possible root cause. Some of the major ones are the following:

- Brainstorming
- 5 Whys
- Fishbone diagram (Ishikawa diagram)

Collecting data: Data are collected to analyze and confirm the identified causes. The following are some of the tools used in data collection:

- Interviews
- Observation
- Check sheet
- Pictogram

Analyzing the data: The collected data are analyzed to confirm and eliminate the incorrect root causes. A flowchart is often used for analyzing the data.

Failure Analysis and Confirming the Relationship

Fishbone Diagram

The fishbone diagram, also known as the Ishikawa diagram, is a pictorial representation of cause and effect. The salient feature of this method is categorization of the potential causes by preidentified main elements, such as "people," "machine," "environment," "method," and "material," which can potentially contribute to the hazardous situation under study.

The seven steps for RCA using a fishbone diagram are listed in Figure 24.16. These include slight modifications from the general RCA process listed earlier. This tool focuses on categorization of the causes to enable targeted investigations. These factors can be further resolved into subfactors by increasing the "bones" on the fish as shown in the figure.

The holistic approach of the Ishikawa diagram forces us to consider all aspects of the system that may contribute to the failure and extracts us from narrow, one-lane thinking. Oftentimes a cross-functional team brainstorming causes will come up with causes and interrelationships that a single process expert will not be able to uncover.

5 Whys

The 5 Whys process is another tool that takes the opposite approach to RCA. Instead of holistically looking at the system and then driving to the root cause, this approach

FIGURE 24.16 Steps for creation of a fishbone diagram.

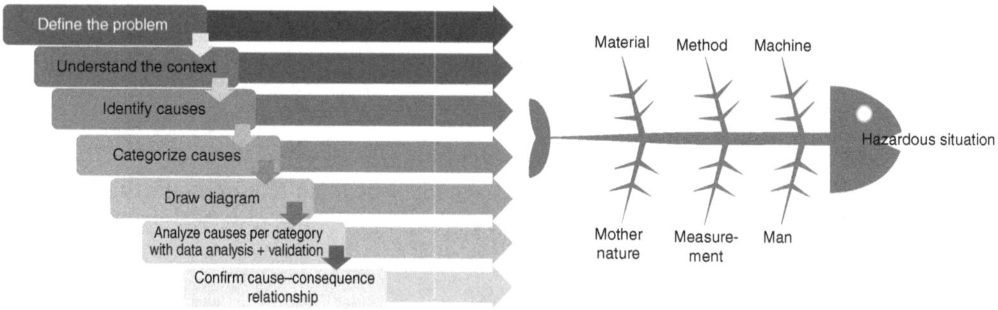

FIGURE 24.17 Example of 5 Whys tool.

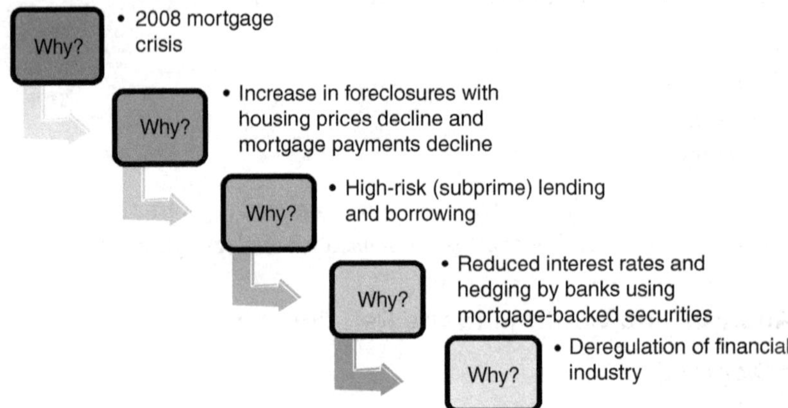

looks at the problem and dives deeper into its reasons. It relies on successive iterations of interrogation (as many times as needed) to uncover the root cause of an observed effect. The 5 Whys tool was developed by Sakichi Toyoda of the Toyota Motor Corporation and is a critical success factor of the much-acclaimed lean Toyota Production System.

With this tool, an investigator of an issue asks the question "Why?" five times, or as many times as necessary until a deeper cause cannot be found. This is illustrated in Figure 24.17.

PRELIMINARY HAZARD ANALYSIS (PHA)

Preliminary hazard analysis (PHA) begins in the initial design/development stages, hence the name "preliminary." This analysis mainly focuses on the hazards and their control measures. PHA was developed by the U.S. Army, and the method was published in the MIL-STD-882 standard. Per this standard, the following should be accomplished in the PHA study:

- Determination of initial risk assessments of identified hazards
- Evaluation of hazards associated with design or function for severity
- Evaluation of hazards associated with design or function for probability
- Provisions, alternatives, and mitigation measures to eliminate hazards or reduce associated risk

PHA is performed in the initial stage to assess systemic hazards that affect the functioning and thus provides an opportunity to modify the main requirements that will help avoid safety issues in the design. The many steps of PHA are summarized sequentially in Figure 24.18.

FIGURE 24.18 Steps in PHA.

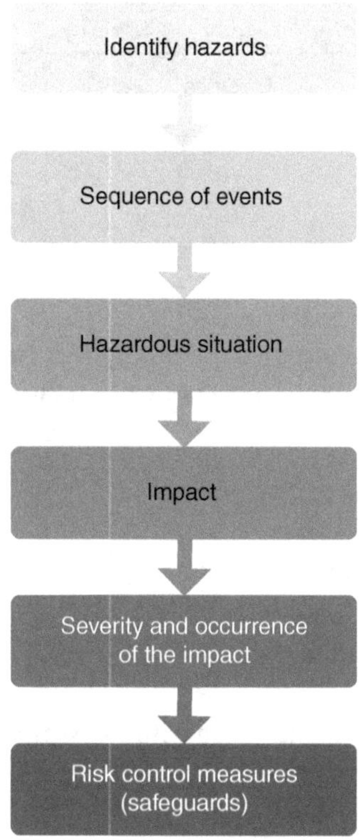

FIGURE 24.19 From hazard to a variety of harms.

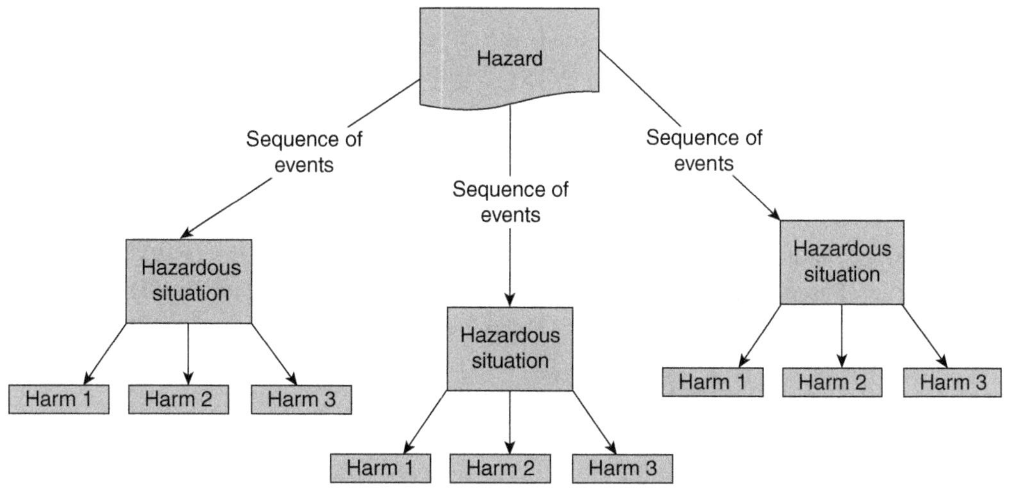

TABLE 24.1 PHA example.

Hazard	Sequence of events	Hazardous situation	Harm	Severity	Occurrence	Risk	Risk control
Electric power	The switchboard is damaged and user trying to switch on	The live wire is exposed	Electric shock	3	2	M	A fuse will be used to break the circuit

The hazards are identified by considering their impact on the design in use-case scenarios. The following from MIL-STD-882E can be investigated to list potential system impacts due to hazards:

1. System components
2. Energy sources
3. Hazardous materials
4. Interfaces and controls
5. Inadvertent activation
6. Software
7. Operating environment (along with its assumptions and constraints)
8. Modes of operation
9. Environmental impacts
10. Usability and human factors
11. System or component malfunction

It is important to understand that when the system operates, it may operate in an environment of hazards or create hazards by its operation itself.

Once the hazards are identified, the sequence of events that leads from each hazard to various hazardous situations is identified. For every sequence of events we identify one or multiple hazardous situations that are related to each hazard. For each hazardous situation, one or multiple outcomes (or harms) are identified. Based on the identified outcomes or harms, the severity is determined. An occurrence or probability value is determined based on each sequence of events that leads from the hazard to the hazardous situation and onward to the outcome (or harm). Figure 24.19 clarifies this concept. Based on the risk level, the risk control measure is applied. These risk control measures may help the design team create new requirements that will drive the risk-based design.

An example of PHA is shown in Table 24.1.

Once the hazard analysis is complete, a documented study must be done to determine the impact of these hazards on the design requirements, and, where needed, modifications must be made.

CHAPTER 25

Risk Analysis

THE RISK ANALYSIS PHASE ENTAILS QUALITATIVE, semiquantitative, or quantitative impact analysis of the risks identified in the risk identification phase. It is the second part of the overall risk assessment process of identification, analysis, and evaluation (see Chapter 22).

ISO 31000:2018 defines the purpose of the risk analysis phase as follows:

> *To comprehend the nature of risk and its characteristics including, where appropriate, the level of risk.*[1]

This phase requires an understanding of the nature of the risk such that it can be profiled in terms of probability and consequence (severity or magnitude) and eventually be assigned a risk level. Each and every risk must undergo this process. Risk evaluation that follows the analysis phase uses this analyzed nature of risk and considers it in the context of the organization's willingness to accept the risk.

Risk analysis consists of two main things:

1. Defining the risk in usable terms—this usually means in terms of probability and consequence
2. Measuring the risk for relative comparison

In this book, we will focus on carrying out the analysis by resolving the risk into its constituents of likelihood and consequence. Consequence analysis and assessment of likelihood by assignation of probability or occurrence rating together comprise the risk analysis phase as shown in Figure 25.1. Sometimes, factors such as detection, duration, exposure, vulnerability, and volatility are added depending on the organizational and product/service context.

While consequence analysis ensures accurate assignation of the impact of the risk, and probability assessment ensures assignation of a probabilistic occurrence value, both of these operations cannot be conducted in isolation. Sometimes the identified

1. ©ISO. This material is reproduced from ISO 31000:2018, with permission of the American National Standards Institute (ANSI) on behalf of the International Organization for Standardization. All rights reserved.

FIGURE 25.1 Consequence analysis and occurrence assignation together compose the risk analysis.

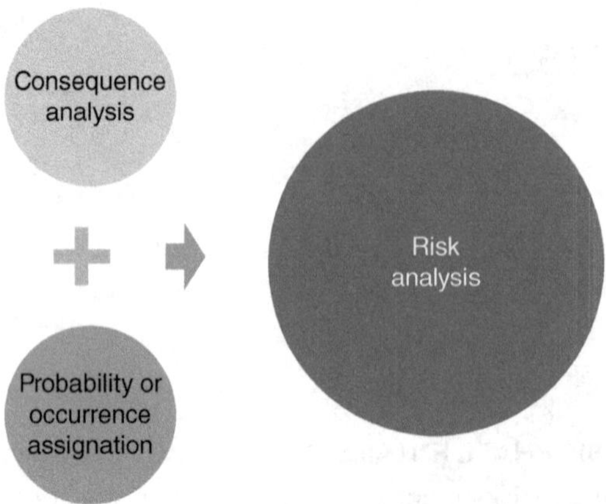

risks may lead to one or multiple consequences. The probabilities of these consequences will mostly be different and must be assessed accordingly.

We can use two methods to analyze the identified risks:

1. Use the risk metalanguage as discussed in Chapter 12
2. View the identified risk first as a condition caused by a hazard that leads to one or multiple harms

Let us look back at the risk metalanguage used in the risk identification phase:

Due to <cause>, <risk> can occur, which *will* lead to <*effect*>

High-level enterprise risks, some financial risks, compliance risks, and project and portfolio risks benefit from using the first method. Let us look at the metalanguage in Figure 25.2.

Depending on the context within which the organization, system, or product or service operates, various root causes may give rise to various conditions. These conditions may mature into multiple effects or consequences with differing probabilities, thus giving rise to risks. While we have considered the probability and consequence, risk analysis must also consider the complexity of the situation at hand and interconnectivity of risk factors.

The second method to analyze risk leverages the theory of hazard and hazardous situation detailed earlier. This is clarified in Figure 25.3.

In this case, the context is a little more narrowly defined in terms of hazards. This may not always be true for a business, but in sectors like automotive, healthcare, medical devices, and manufacturing, this leads to structured and targeted risk analysis by reducing uncertainty up front. By charting the progression from hazard to hazardous situation by a sequence of events and subsequently from hazardous situation to single or multiple consequences, the risk professional is afforded a lean path that reduces

FIGURE 25.2 Illustration aid for usage of risk metalanguage.

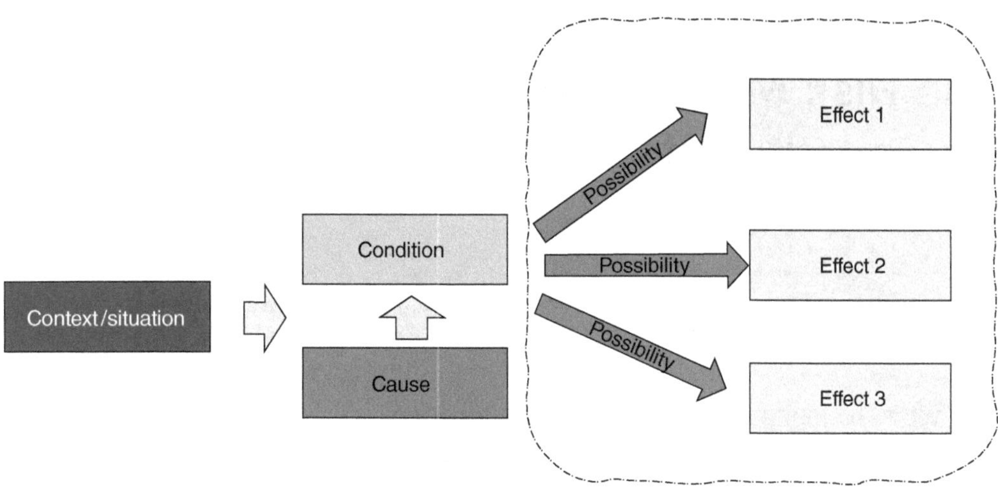

FIGURE 25.3 Flow from hazard to effects (outcomes).

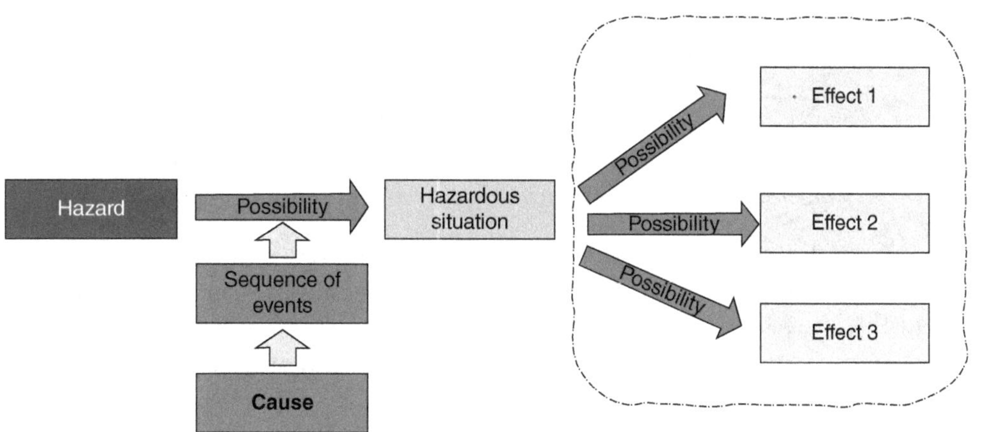

divergence of opinions, hidden assumptions, and biases and brings forward any system constraints.

Regardless of the method used, the aim of the risk analysis phase is the following:

To analyze the nature of risk by breaking it down into its constituent consequences and probabilities and comparing it with an objective baseline in absolute or relative terms.

The most common method for doing this is to use a probability and impact matrix. This is discussed in the next chapter.

CHAPTER 26

The Risk Matrix and Its Constituents

WE DISCUSSED THE DEFINITIONS OF PROBABILITY, consequence, and impact or severity earlier, but I will restate them as we review the concept of risk matrices.

probability

It gives the likelihood of occurrence of an event.

consequence

It refers to the end effect (outcomes) of risk.

impact or severity

It refers to consequence or at times, specifically, to the magnitude of consequence of the risk usually defined on a scale for relative comparison.

For each risk, the probability and consequence (impact) are assessed. An example is shown in Figure 26.1. The risk of an earthquake has a consequence of destruction, which is assessed per the Richter Mercalli scale. The likelihood of an earthquake is dependent on the location under analysis. It is more likely at regions near fault lines and less likely at other places.

The scale of consequences shown here is the Richter Mercalli scale of earthquake effects shown in Figure 26.2.

The scales can be custom made or be adapted from standardized guidances, but the important thing is that they should be relevant to the organizational context and should range from the minimum to the maximum realistic imaginable impact to the achievement of objectives at hand. For example, the Mercalli scale ranges from no damage by a minor earthquake that barely registers on sensitive instruments at level I to total damage at level XII.

Figure 26.3 shows the generic idea of an impact/consequence table. The magnitude of consequence is placed on a scale of varying discrete levels of increasing impact.

The ratings may be numbers or phrases and can thus be qualitative, semiquantitative, or quantitative. The scale can show negative or positive impact as appropriate. The impact can increase or decrease from top to bottom or vice versa.

FIGURE 26.1 Risk as a combination of severity of earthquake impact and likelihood of earthquake occurrence.

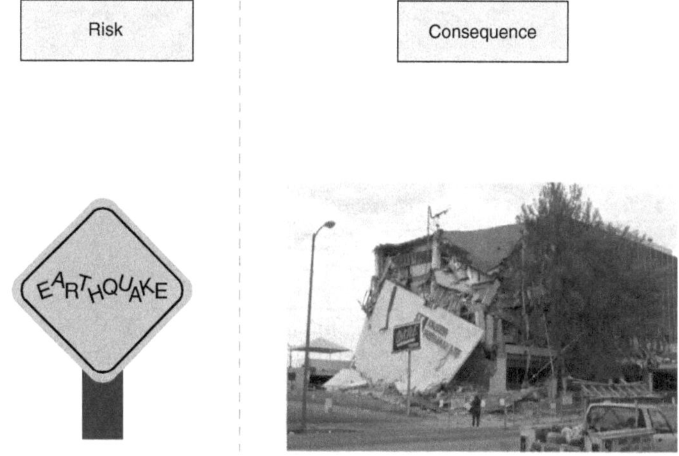

Magnitude of impact (severity)

Richter	Mercalli	Earthquake effects
2	I	**Instrumental.** Not felt except by a very few under especially favorable conditions detected mostly by seismography.
	II	**Feeble.** Felt only by a few persons at rest especially on upper floors of buildings.
3	III	**Slight.** Felt quite noticeably by persons indoors, especially on upper floors of buildings. Many people do not recognize it as an earthquake. Standing motor cars may rock slightly. Vibration similar to the passing of a truck.
	IV	**Moderate.** Felt indoors by many, outdoors by few during the day. At night, some awakening. Dishes, windows, doors disturbed; walls make cracking sound. Sensation like a heavy truck striking building. Standing motor cars rock noticeably.
4	V	**Rather strong.** Felt by nearly everyone; many awakened. Some dishes, windows broken. Unstable objects overturned. Pendulum clocks may stop.
5	VI	**Strong.** Felt by all, many frightened. Some heavy furniture moved; a few instances of fallen plaster. Damage slight.
	VII	**Very strong.** Damage negligible in buildings of good design and construction; slight to moderate in well-built ordinary structures; considerable damage in ordinary structures; considerable damage in poorly built or badly designed structures.

Likelihood of occurence

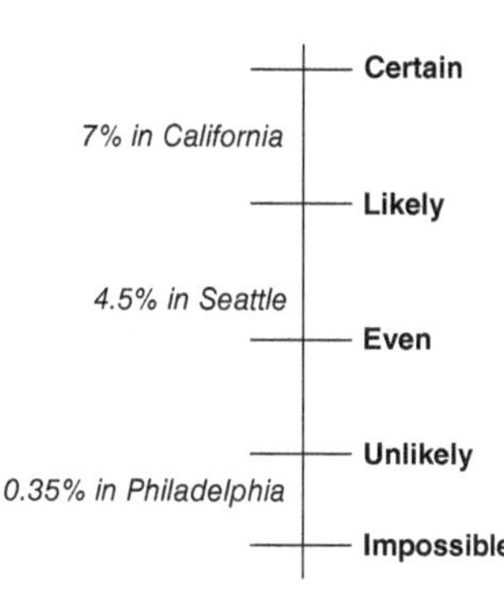

There are numerous other scales for severity based on the industry or sector. An example of an impact scale for medical devices from ISO 14971:2007 is shown in Table 26.1.

ISO 14971 is the risk management standard for medical devices, and their consequence scale focuses on the outcome of failure of a medical device. The standard mentions impact as "severity," which is literally more suitable as the qualitative classification here since the scale is based on the magnitude of impact on human health, which is better worded as the severity of impact of a device failure. This is similar to a popular scale of healthcare outcomes used in risk-benefit analysis known as the Clavien-Dindo

FIGURE 26.2 Severity scale for earthquakes.

	Modified Mercalli scale	Richter magnitude scale
I	Detected only by sensitive instruments	1.5
II	Felt by few persons at rest, especially on upper floors; delicately suspended objects may swing	2
III	Felt noticeably indoors, but not always recognized as earthquake; standing autos rock slightly, vibration like passing truck	2.5
IV	Felt indoors by many, outdoors by few, at night some may awaken; dishes, windows, doors disturbed; autos rock noticeably	3
V	Felt by most people; some breakage of dishes, windows, and plaster; disturbance of tall objects	3.5 4
VI	Felt by all, many frightened and run outdoors; falling plaster and chimneys, damage small	4.5
VII	Everybody runs outdoors; damage to buildings varies depending on quality of construction; noticed by drivers of autos	5
VIII	Panel walls thrown out of frames; fall of walls, monuments, chimneys; sand and mud ejected; drivers of autos disturbed	5.5
IX	Building shifted off foundations, cracked, thrown out of plumb; ground cracked; underground pipes broken	6
X	Most masonry and frame structures destroyed; ground cracked, rails bent, landslides	6.5 7
XI	Few structures remain standing; bridges destroyed, fissures in ground, pipes broken, landslides, rails bent	7.5
XII	Damage total; waves seen on ground surface, lines of sight and level distorted, object thrown up in air	8

Source: "The Relationship between Richter Magnitude and Modified Mercalli Intensity," Missouri Department of Natural Resources, accessed June 17, 2020, https://dnr.mo.gov/geology/geosrv/geores/richt_mercali_relation.htm.

classification. The Clavien-Dindo classification is a scheme of graded harm-based classifications of surgical complications which has been demonstrated to be of significant value in comparing surgical outcomes. The scale is shown in Table 26.2.

An example of a severity scale for seriousness of the effect of motor vehicle failures from the Automotive Industry Action Group (AIAG) and VDA *FMEA Handbook* is shown in Table 26.3.

FIGURE 26.3 Generic idea of an impact/consequence table.

Rating	Magnitude	Cost	Health	Machine	Environmental toxicity	Quality	Aviation	Stock market
Level 1	Minimum impact	$	Negligible injury	Minor start-up delay	Local reversible damage	Cosmetic defects	Slight vibration	Very bearish
Level 2								
Level 3				Increasing impact				
Level 4								
Level X	Maximum impact	$$$$$	Death	Machine out of order	Significant irreversible damage	Non-reworkable scrap material	Plane crash	Significantly bullish breakout

TABLE 26.1 Impact scale from ISO 14971.

Common terms	Possible description
Catastrophic	Results in patient death
Critical	Results in permanent impairment or life-threatening injury
Serious	Results in injury or impairment requiring professional medical intervention
Minor	Results in temporary injury or impairment not requiring professional medical intervention
Negligible	Inconvenience or temporary discomfort

Source: ©ISO. This material is reproduced from ISO 14971:2007, with permission of the American National Standards Institute (ANSI) on behalf of the International Organization for Standardization. All rights reserved.

MIL-STD-882E, the military standard from the Department of Defense, uses the impact scale shown in Table 26.4.

The risk management guidelines released by NASA as part of its independent verification and validation program show the following scales for consequences (Table 26.5). *Guidelines for Risk Management,* S3001, Revision G, suggests that a risk must be analyzed on all parameters listed to the left of the table, and the consequence score from the parameter that scores the highest must be taken into consideration for further risk management activities downstream.

The graded evaluation of consequence is the first major step of the risk analysis process. Depending on the organizational context, the specific parameters and scaling may differ, but the underlying foundation is the same, which is to place the consequence of each risk on a scale for comparison. The words "severity," "impact," "magnitude," "effect," and "consequence" are often used interchangeably by many texts. Literally speaking, the extent of every risk that has an effect of some consequence to the organization is measured on a predefined scale, and this measurement can be referred to as "impact" or "severity."

TABLE 26.2 Clavien-Dindo scale of surgical complications.

Grade	Definition
Grade I	Any deviation from the normal postoperative course without the need for pharmacological treatment or surgical, endoscopic, and radiological interventions Allowed therapeutic regimens are: drugs as antiemetics, antipyretics, analgetics, diuretics, electrolytes, and physiotherapy. This grade also includes wound infections opened at the bedside
Grade II	Requiring pharmacological treatment with drugs other than such allowed for grade I complications Blood transfusions and total parenteral nutrition are also included
Grade III	Requiring surgical, endoscopic or radiological intervention
Grade IIIa	Intervention not under general anesthesia
Grade IIIb	Intervention under general anesthesia
Grade IV	Life-threatening complication (including CNS complications)* requiring IC/ICU management
Grade IVa	Single organ dysfunction (including dialysis)
Grade IVb	Multiorgan dysfunction
Grade V	Death of a patient
Suffix "d"	If the patient suffers from a complication at the time of discharge (see examples in Table 2), the suffix "d" (for "disability") is added to the respective grade of complication. This label indicates the need for a follow-up to fully evaluate the complication.

*Brain hemorrhage, ischemic stroke, subarrachnoidal bleeding, but excluding transient ischemic attacks.
CNS, central nervous system; IC, intermediate care; ICU, intensive care unit.

Source: Table used with permission of Wolters Kluwer Health, from D. Dindo, N. Demartines, and P. A. Clavien, "Classification of Surgical Complications: A New Proposal with Evaluation in a Cohort of 6336 Patients and Results of a Survey," *Annals of Surgery* 240, no. 2 (2004): 206, https://doi.org/10.1097/01.sla.0000133083.54934.ae; permission conveyed through Copyright Clearance Center, Inc.

The second step is to assign a level of likelihood to the consequence. This determination of likelihood could be qualitative, semiquantitative, or quantitative. Regardless of the method, a likelihood scale is used to assign a score. Similar to the consequence scale, the choice of likelihood scale, its discrete levels, and descriptors depend on the context of the objectives. The scale must cover the practicable range of occurrences (positive or negative or both, as relevant) and should not be weighted or biased at one end, which could lead to excessive loading of one particular level. Weighting one end of the scale would defeat the purpose of the matrix, which is to compare the magnitude of risks with sufficient granularity. The lowest level on the probability scale must allow the risk with the highest impact to become acceptable so that the risk matrix can guide the users to manage high risks by graded mitigations before avoiding them rather than avoiding them straightaway.

Figure 26.4 shows the generic idea of a probability table or an occurrence scale. The probability is placed on a scale of varying discrete levels of increasing rate of occurrence.

TABLE 26.3 Severity scale from AIAG.

S	Effect	Severity criteria
10	Very High	Affects safe operation of the vehicle and/or other vehicles, the health of driver or passenger(s) or road users or pedestrians.
9		Noncompliance with regulations.
8	High	**Loss** of primary vehicle function necessary for normal driving during expected service life.
7		**Degradation** of primary vehicle function necessary for normal driving during expected service life.
6	Moderate	**Loss** of secondary vehicle function.
5		**Degradation** of secondary vehicle function.
4		Very objectionable appearance, sound, vibration, harshness, or haptics.
3	Low	Moderately objectionable appearance, sound, vibration, harshness, or haptics.
2		Slightly objectionable appearance, sound, vibration, harshness, or haptics.
1	Very low	No discernible Failure Effect.

Source: Reproduced by permission from *The FMEA Handbook: Failure Mode and Effects Analysis* (Southfield, MI: Automotive Industry Action Group, 2019), 185.

TABLE 26.4 Severity scale from MIL-STD-882E.

Severity categories		
Description	**Severity category**	**Mishap result criteria**
Catastrophic	1	Could result in one or more of the following: death, permanent total disability, irreversible significant environmental impact, or monetary loss equal to or exceeding $10M.
Critical	2	Could result in one or more of the following: permanent partial disability, injuries or occupational illness that may result in hospitalization of at least three personnel, reversible significant environmental impact, or monetary loss equal to or exceeding $1M but less than $10M.
Marginal	3	Could result in one or more of the following: injury or occupational illness resulting in one or more lost work day(s), reversible moderate environmental impact, or monetary loss equal to or exceeding $100K but less than $1M.
Negligible	4	Could result in one or more of the following: injury or occupational illness not resulting in a lost work day, minimal environmental impact, or monetary loss less than $100K.

Source: Department of Defense Standard Practice System Safety, MIL-STD-882E (U.S. Department of Defense, 2012), 11.

TABLE 26.5 Risk consequence criteria from NASA S3001 Rev G.

	Consequence				
	1	2	3	4	5
Performance	Minimal consequence to objectives/ goals	Minor consequence to objectives/ goals	Unable to achieve a particular objective/ goal, but remaining objective goals represent better than minimum success or outcome	Unable to achieve multiple objectives/ goals, but minimum success can still be achieved or claimed	Unable to achieve objectives/ goals such that minimum success cannot be achieved or claimed
Safety					
Human	Discomfort or nuisance	First-aid event per OSHA criteria	No lost time injury or illness per OSHA criteria	Lost-time injury or illness per OSHA criteria	Loss of life
Asset	Minimal consequence: asset has no sign of physical damage	Minor consequence: asset has cosmetic damage and is repairable	Minor consequence: asset is damaged but repairable	Major consequence asset is substantially damaged but repairable	Destroyed: asset is compromised and unrepairable: a total loss
Schedule	Minimal consequence	Critical path is not slipped; total slack of slipped tasks will not impact critical path in less than 10 days	Critical path is not slipped; total slack of slipped tasks is within 10 days of impacting the critical path	Critical path slips	Critical path slips and one or more critical milestones or events cannot be met
Cost	Minimal consequence	Minor cost consequence. Cost variance ≤5% of total approved FY baseline	Cost consequence	Cost consequence	Major cost consequence
			Cost variance >5% but ≤10% of total approved FY baseline	Cost variance >10% but ≤15% of total approved FY baseline	Cost variance >15% of total approved FY baseline

Source: IV&V Management System, Guidelines for Risk Management, S3001, rev. G, (Fairmont, WV: NASA, 2017), table 4-3. Retrieved from https://www.nasa.gov/sites/default/files/atoms/files/s3001_guidelines_for_risk_management_-_ver_g_-_10-25-2017.pdf.

FIGURE 26.4 Generic idea of a probability table or occurrence scale.

Rating	Descriptor of probability	Medical device risk	Car ignition failure	Aviation fatalities	Toxicity	Quality	Project risk	Stock market upswing
Level 1	Very unlikely	<0.001%	<0.01%	<1 in 100,000	<5 parts per billion	<3 DPMO	10% (P = 0.10)	90% (P = 0.90)
Level 2								
Level 3								
Level 4								
Level X	Extremely likely	>5%	>16%	>1 in 80	>1000 parts per million	> 66,800 DPMO	90% (P = 0.90)	5% (P = 0.05)

Increasing likelihood

TABLE 26.6 Probability scale from ISO 14971:2007.

Common terms	Examples of probability range
Frequent	$\geq 10^{-3}$
Probable	$< 10^{-3}$ and $\geq 10^{-4}$
Occasional	$< 10^{-4}$ and $\geq 10^{-5}$
Remote	$< 10^{-5}$ and $\geq 10^{-6}$
Improbable	$< 10^{-6}$

Source: ©ISO. This material is reproduced from ISO 14971:2007, with permission of the American National Standards Institute (ANSI) on behalf of the International Organization for Standardization. All rights reserved.

The ratings may be numbers or phrases and can thus be qualitative, semiquantitative, or quantitative. The probability can increase or decrease from top to bottom or vice versa.

Following are a few examples of scales used in various industries. Table 26.6 shows a scale for medical devices from ISO 14971:2007.

Table 26.7 shows a scale for the automotive industry from AIAG VDA.

Thus, using a probability scale, the likelihood of an event can be ordinally captured for consequent assessment.

Now let us move on to analysis of the risk by combining the consequence and probability. The logic used in this risk calculation is shown below:

$$\text{IF Probability is p AND impact is i, THEN risk is R.} \tag{26.1}$$

Risk R, in its most simple form, is:

$$\text{Risk (R)} = \text{Probability (p)} \times \text{Impact (i)} \tag{26.2}$$

The risk matrix is a basic tool that leverages the above calculation and can be used without much sophistication to create a neat visual representation of risks and assess their standing in comparison with other risks. In other words, the risk matrix combines the probability and impact to assign a risk level that visually shows the significance of risk

TABLE 26.7 Occurrence scale from AIAG.

O	Incidents per 1000 items/ vehicles	Occurrence criteria - DFMEA
10	≥ 100 per thousand >/=1 in 10	**First** application of new technology anywhere without operating experience and / or under uncontrolled operating conditions. No product verification and/or validation experience. Standards do not exist and best practices have not yet been determined. Prevention controls not able to predict field performance or do not exist.
9	50 per thousand, 1 in 20	**First** use of design with technical innovations or materials within the company. New application, or change in duty cycle / operating conditions. No product verification and/ or validation experience. Prevention controls not targeted to identify performance to specific requirements.
8	20 per thousand, 1 in 50	**First** use of design with technical innovations or materials on a new application. New application, or change in duty cycle / operating conditions. No product verification and/ or validation experience. Few existing standards and best practices, not directly applicable for this design. Prevention controls not a reliable indicator of field performance.
7	10 per thousand 1 in 100	New design based on similar technology and materials. New application, or change in duty cycle / operating conditions. No product verification and/or validation experience. Standards best practices, and design rules apply to the baseline design, but not the innovations. Prevention controls provide limited indication of performance.
6	2 per thousand 1 in 500	**Similar** to previous designs, using existing technology and materials. Similar application, with changes in duty cycle or operating conditions. Previous testing or field experience. Standards and design rules exist but are insufficient to ensure that the failure cause will not occur. Prevention controls provide some ability to prevent a failure cause.

Source: From the AIAG & VDA FMEA Handbook, 1st Edition, 2019. Reprinted with permission of AIAG (Automotive Industry Action Group). AIAG makes no representation or warranty as to the accuracy or usefulness of its materials when presented in contexts, with other materials, or for uses, other than as originally published by AIAG. For additional information, or to purchase the referenced AIAG publication, contact AIAG at (248) 358-3003 or www.aiag.org.

with respect to other risks. It consists of the likelihood (occurrence or probability) on one axis, and the other axis details the graded impact levels per the corresponding scales.

On a simple level, Figure 26.5 shows the four quadrants of a simple 2×2 risk matrix. It provides a visual location of the risk on the probability-impact heat map.

The matrix can be expanded from a simple 2×2 format, as shown in Table 26.8. Table 26.9 shows the commonly used 5×5 matrix.

FIGURE 26.5 A 2×2 risk matrix.

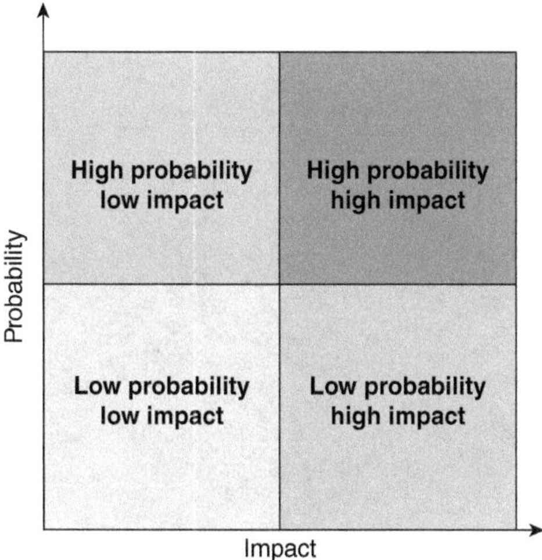

TABLE 26.8 "X by X" risk matrix.

		Impact levels				
		Level 1	Level 2	Level 3	Level 4	Level X
Probability levels	Level X	R5	R10	R15	R20	R25
	Level 4	R4	R9	R14	R19	R24
	Level 3	R3	R8	R13	R18	R23
	Level 2	R2	R7	R12	R17	R22
	Level 1	R1	R6	R11	R16	R21

TABLE 26.9 5×5 risk matrix.

		Impact levels				
		Level 1	Level 2	Level 3	Level 4	Level X
Probability levels	Level 5	M	M	H	H	H
	Level 4	L	M	H	H	H
	Level 3	L	M	M	H	H
	Level 2	L	L	M	M	M
	Level 1	L	L	L	L	L

From above, it can be seen that the combination of impact and probability, after these have been categorized per the relevant ordinal scales, falls into set places in the matrix identified as R1, R2, and so on. These are known as *risk levels*. With the increasing level of severity and occurrence, the risk level will be higher.

The risk level is assigned as follows:

1. Rate the risk with respect to the likelihood of occurrence or probability (of the risk consequence)

FIGURE 26.6 Three-dimensional representation of a 5 × 5 risk matrix.

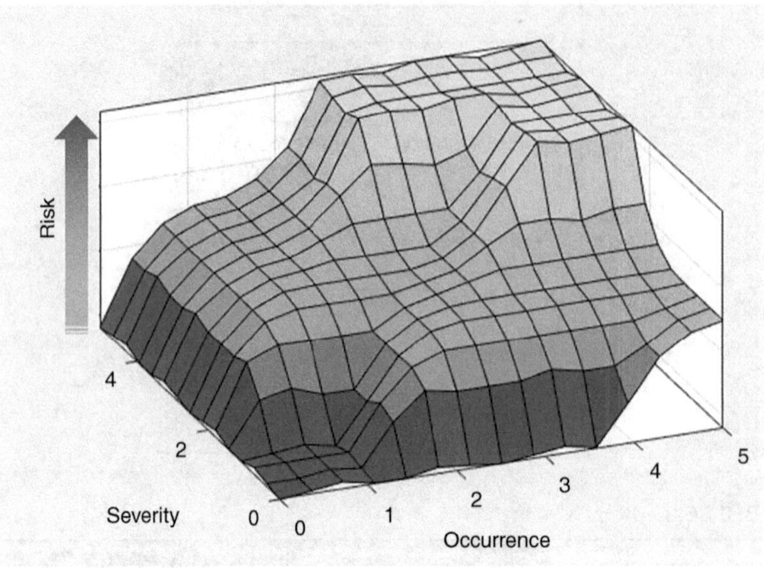

FIGURE 26.7 Steps of risk level assignation.

Common terms	Examples of probability range
Frequent	$\geq 10^{-3}$
Probable	$<10^{-3}$ and $\geq 10^{-4}$
Occasional	$<10^{-4}$ and $\geq 10^{-5}$
Remote	$<10^{-5}$ and $\geq 10^{-6}$
Improbable	$<10^{-6}$

		Impact levels				
		Level 1	Level 2	Level 3	Level 4	Level 5
Probability levels	Level X	M	M	H	H	H
	Level 4	L	M	H	H	H
	Level 3	L	M	M	H	H
	Level 2	L	L	M	M	M
	Level 1	L	L	L	L	L

Common terms	Possible description
Catastrophic	Results in patient death
Critical	Results in permanent impairment or life-threatening injury
Serious	Results in injury or impairment requiring professional medical intervention
Minor	Results in temporary injury or impairment not requiring professional medical intervention
Negligible	Inconvenience or temporary discomfort

2. Rate the risk with respect to the magnitude of the consequence (impact) of the risk being realized
3. Locate the convergence of occurrence and impact on the matrix
4. Note the level within which the located risk falls

This can be shown three-dimensionally, as in Figure 26.6.

Figure 26.7 shows the three steps of risk level assignation.

These risk levels are also known as risk ratings and are the basis of prioritization, which occurs during the evaluation phase.

CHAPTER 27

Risk Evaluation

THE PROCESS OF RISK EVALUATION IS PERFORMED BY COMPARING the estimated risk against the baseline criteria initially set to determine the risk acceptability. It is the exercise of assessing action for estimated risks based on their respective significance to the objectives in terms of concerned product, service, process, or business.

ISO 31000:2018 mentions the following:

> *Risk evaluation involves comparing the results of the risk analysis with the established risk criteria to determine where additional action is required. This can lead to a decision to:*
>
> *—do nothing further;*
> *—consider risk treatment options;*
> *—undertake further analysis to better understand the risk;*
> *—maintain existing controls;*
> *—reconsider objectives.*[1]

As discussed in the earlier chapters, the risk is estimated by identifying the severity of the consequence of the event and the probability of occurrence of the consequence. The most critical aspect of risk evaluation is the risk acceptability criteria. In Chapter 26 we discussed the requirement to have the risk acceptability criteria before starting the risk management process. The criteria that are used to determine whether the risk is acceptable have to be defined based on the organizational willingness to accept the level of risk. This is informed by the risk tolerance and risk appetite.

There are different methods followed in determining the acceptability criteria based on the organizational context, nature of risks, external environment, and known stakeholder concerns. The willingness to accept the risk for a thermometer is very different from that for a life-sustaining device. We won't accept the risk of death or injury for the use of a thermometer, but we may accept a risk of injury or burn from a life-sustaining

1. ©ISO. This material is reproduced from ISO 31000:2018, with permission of the American National Standards Institute (ANSI) on behalf of the International Organization for Standardization. All rights reserved.

device if it makes a difference between life and death. Regulations or standards also could determine the level of acceptability for each product type. It is a good practice to document the rationale for the selection of a particular acceptance criteria. The manufacturer either could choose single acceptance criteria for all products or could have different criteria for different products based on the unique context and environment of operation.

After each risk is determined (i.e., the occurrence/probability) and the consequence is estimated, the level of the risk is charted on the risk matrix, as seen in the last chapter. This level is now compared with the earlier set value of the acceptability criteria and checked for acceptability based on RPN, risk levels, or other methods. If the risk is not acceptable, risk reduction is in order by applying appropriate risk control or mitigation measures.

In the risk matrix, the color changes correspond to a heat map, which usually shows the varying risk levels. The examples in the last chapter correspond to the risk matrix shown in Table 27.1, where three levels of risk (low, medium, high) are shown. The number of impact levels, number of probability levels, demarcation between risk levels, and the number of risk levels are the prerogative of the organization and are dependent on the context within which the organization operates, risk appetite, and available resources for risk management activities.

The levels of risk can be seen as levels of tolerance or in terms of acceptability or nonacceptability. These risk levels are sometimes known as risk criticality levels. Commonly, three levels of low, medium, and high are used, but five-level criticality scales of very low, low, medium, high, and very high and similar classifications are also acceptable. The important thing to remember is that the criticality levels must provide the right balance between grading of the risks according to their magnitude and separating them out in terms of acceptability. Thus, decision rules must be defined for each risk level.

Decision rules decide which levels of risk are acceptable and which levels are not. This is where the key to the heat map is decided. In the matrix shown in Table 27.1, the rules in Table 27.2 may apply.

The decision rules may also choose to use a risk probability number (RPN) to decide on the level of criticality. The RPN is a risk index compiled using a scoring approach with the logic shown below:

$$\text{Risk probability number (RPN)} = \text{Probability level} \times \text{Impact level} \qquad (27.1)$$

TABLE 27.1 A 5×5 risk matrix.

		Impact levels				
		Level 1	Level 2	Level 3	Level 4	Level X
Probability levels	Level 5	M	M	H	H	H
	Level 4	L	M	H	H	H
	Level 3	L	M	M	H	H
	Level 2	L	L	M	M	M
	Level 1	L	L	L	L	L

TABLE 27.2 Risk levels and decision rules.

Risk criticality level	Decision rule
High	Generally unacceptable—needs concurrence of top management
Medium	Reduce as low as reasonably practicable
Low	Acceptable risk—monitor and trend

TABLE 27.3 Risk matrix populated using RPN (Probability × Impact).

		Severity level				
		Grade I (1)	Grade II (2)	Grade III (3)	Grade IV (4)	Grade V (5)
Probability level	Frequent (5)	5	10	15	20	25
	Probable (4)	4	8	12	16	20
	Occasional (3)	3	6	9	12	15
	Remote (2)	2	4	6	8	10
	Improbable (1)	1	2	3	4	5

TABLE 27.4 Risk criticality levels and RPN.

Risk criticality level	RPN	Decision rule
High	>10	Unacceptable risk (intolerable)—needs concurrence of top management
Medium	From 5 to 10	Tolerable risk but reduce/mitigate as low as reasonably practicable (ALARP)
Low	Less than 5	Acceptable risk (tolerable)—monitor and trend

The levels of probability and severity of impact are graded on a linear or weighted ordinal scale. In either case, an increasing number can be used to denote increasing magnitude. In Table 27.3 we multiply the ordinal probability level by the impact level to get an RPN.

Now, based on the RPN, the decision in Table 27.4 may be chosen to apply.

This gives us the risk matrix shown in Table 27.5.

The type of risk matrix and the decision rules to be used should be defined in the risk management plan. ISO 31010:2019 provides us with the following caveat:

If the highest consequence is deemed to be tolerable at some low likelihood then the lowest step on the likelihood scale should represent an acceptable likelihood for the highest defined consequence (otherwise all activities with the highest consequence are defined as intolerable and cannot be made tolerable).[2]

This means that one must not shun high-risk pathways but instead aim to reduce the risk as much as possible to an acceptable level. The lowest probability level must correspond to the acceptability level for the highest consequence.

Common approaches to risk matrices are discussed below. ISO 14971 specifies a qualitative approach whereby both probability and occurrence are qualitatively determined from Tables 27.6–27.9.

Since there are three levels of both, a 3×3 matrix as shown in Table 27.8 can be used for risk analysis (where R1–R6 are sample charted risks).

The standard also details a semiquantitative approach where the actual probability is estimated in numerical terms from Table 27.9.

This scale of likelihood is combined with a 5-point scale of severities to give the 5×5 matrix shown in Table 27.10. Individual risks, based on the severity and probability levels, can now be assigned risk levels; here, either unacceptable (shaded) or acceptable (unshaded).

ISO 31010:2019 mentions a 5×5 matrix with five risk levels or priority ratings (Table 27.11). This standard recognizes the value of the risk matrix as a screening tool to prioritize risks of highest magnitude for deeper analysis and to categorize risk according to acceptability or nonacceptability according to their location in the matrix, which acts as a heat map.

The 5×4 risk matrix in Table 27.12 is provided in MIL-STD-882E.

TABLE 27.5 Risk matrix coded for risk levels by acceptability decisions.

		Severity level				
		Grade I (1)	Grade II (2)	Grade III (3)	Grade IV (4)	Grade V (5)
Probability level	Frequent (5)	ALARP	ALARP	Unacceptable	Unacceptable	Unacceptable
	Probable (4)	Acceptable	ALARP	Unacceptable	Unacceptable	Unacceptable
	Occasional (3)	Acceptable	ALARP	ALARP	Unacceptable	Unacceptable
	Remote (2)	Acceptable	Acceptable	ALARP	ALARP	ALARP
	Improbable (1)	Acceptable	Acceptable	Acceptable	Acceptable	Acceptable

2. ©ISO. This material is reproduced from ISO 14971:2007, with permission of the American National Standards Institute (ANSI) on behalf of the International Organization for Standardization. All rights reserved.

TABLE 27.6 Severity scale from ISO 14971:2007.

Common terms	Possible description
Significant	Death or loss of function or structure
Moderate	Reversible or minor injury
Negligible	Will not cause injury or will injure slightly

Source: ©ISO. This material is reproduced from ISO 14971:2007, with permission of the American National Standards Institute (ANSI) on behalf of the International Organization for Standardization.

TABLE 27.7 Occurrence scale from ISO 14971:2007.

Common terms	Possible description
High	Likely to happen, often, frequent
Medium	Can happen, but not frequently
Low	Unlikely to happen, rare, remote

Source: ©ISO. This material is reproduced from ISO 14971:2007, with permission of the American National Standards Institute (ANSI) on behalf of the International Organization for Standardization.

TABLE 27.8 3×3 risk matrix from ISO 14971:2007.

		Qualitative severity levels		
		Negligible	**Moderate**	**Significant**
	High	R_1	R_2	
Qualitative probability levels	**Medium**		R_4	R_5, R_6
	Low		R_3	

Source: ©ISO. This material is reproduced from ISO 14971:2007, with permission of the American National Standards Institute (ANSI) on behalf of the International Organization for Standardization.

TABLE 27.9 Probability scale from ISO 14971:2007.

Common terms	Examples of probability range
Frequent	$\geq 10^{-3}$
Probable	$< 10^{-3}$ and $\geq 10^{-4}$
Occasional	$< 10^{-4}$ and $\geq 10^{-5}$
Remote	$< 10^{-5}$ and $\geq 10^{-6}$
Improbable	$< 10^{-6}$

Source: ©ISO. This material is reproduced from ISO 14971:2007, with permission of the American National Standards Institute (ANSI) on behalf of the International Organization for Standardization.

TABLE 27.10 Risk matrix shaded with acceptable and unacceptable risk levels.

		Qualitative severity levels				
		Negligible	Minor	Serious	Critical	Catastrophic
Semi quantitative probability levels	Frequent					
	Probable	R_1	R_2			
	Occasional		R_4		R_5	R_6
	Remote					
	Improbable			R_3		

Key

unacceptable risk (shaded)

acceptable risk (unshaded)

Source: ©ISO. This material is reproduced from ISO 14971:2007, with permission of the American National Standards Institute (ANSI) on behalf of the International Organization for Standardization.

TABLE 27.11 5 × 5 risk matrix from ISO 31010:2019.

Consequence rating ⟶					
a	III	III	II	I	I
b	IV	III	III	II	I
c	V	IV	III	II	I
d	V	V	IV	III	II
e	V	V	IV	III	II
	1	2	3	4	5
	Likelihood rating ⟶				

Source: ©ISO. This material is reproduced from ISO 31010:2019, with permission of the American National Standards Institute (ANSI) on behalf of the International Organization for Standardization.

ANSI Z590.3-2011 takes a fully qualitative approach, as shown in Table 27.13.

The choice of risk matrix must be governed by its purpose, which is assessment of a risk by assignation of a risk criticality level or rating to all identified risks to check the level of acceptability. We are trying to "bucket" risks of a similar nature for prioritization.

In the unlikely event that an organization has identified a very low number of risks and has ample resources, it may not need a matrix since all risks may get the same level of attention. If it has a high number of risks and needs to prioritize them for resource distribution, then a 3 × 3 matrix as shown in Table 27.14 can suffice.

If there are still a high number of risks, then the organization must choose the number of risk levels with respect to functional ease of the risk management process.

A commonly used 5 × 5 matrix with five levels is shown in Table 27.15.

The goals of using a risk matrix are the following:

TABLE 27.12 5×4 risk matrix from MIL-STD-882E.

Risk assessment matrix				
Severity / Probability	Catastrophic (1)	Critical (2)	Marginal (3)	Negligible (4)
Frequent (A)	High	High	Serious	Medium
Probable (B)	High	High	Serious	Medium
Occasional (C)	High	Serious	Medium	Low
Remote (D)	Serious	Medium	Medium	Low
Improbable (E)	Medium	Medium	Medium	Low
Eliminated (F)	Eliminated			

Source: Department of Defense Standard Practice System Safety, MIL-STD-882E (U.S. Department of Defense, 2012), p. 12.

TABLE 27.13 5×4 risk matrix from ANSI Z590.3-2011.

Likelihood of occurrence or exposure for selected Unit of Time or Activity	Severity of Injury or Illness Consequence and Remedial Action			
	Catastrophic Death or permanent total disability	**Critical** Disability in excess of 3 months	**Marginal** Minor injury, lost workday accident	**Negligible** First Aid or Minor Medical Treatment
Frequent Likely to Occur Repeatedly	**High** Operation not permissible	**High** Operation not permissible	**Serious** High Priority Remedial action	**Medium** Take Remedial action at appropriate time
Probable Likely to occur several times	**High** Operation not permissible	**High** Operation not permissible	**Serious** High Priority Remedial action	**Medium** Take Remedial action at appropriate time
Occasional Likely to occur sometime	**Serious** High Priority Remedial action	**Serious** High Priority Remedial action	**Medium** Take Remedial action at appropriate time	**Low** Risk Acceptable: Remedial Action Discretionary
Remote Not likely to occur	**Medium** Take Remedial action at appropriate time	**Medium** Take Remedial action at appropriate time	**Medium** Take Remedial action at appropriate time	**Low** Risk Acceptable: Remedial Action Discretionary
Improbable Very unlikely—unrealistically perceivable	**Low** Risk Acceptable: Remedial Action Discretionary	**Low** Risk Acceptable: Remedial Action Discretionary	**Low** Risk Acceptable: Remedial Action Discretionary	**Low** Risk Acceptable: Remedial Action Discretionary

Source: Reproduced by permission from *Prevention through Design: Guidelines for Addressing Occupational Hazards and Risks in Design and Redesign Processes*, ANSI/ASSE Z590.3-2011 (New York: American National Standards Institute, 2011), p. 36.

TABLE 27.14 3×3 risk matrix.

		Impact level		
		Level 1	Level 2	Level 3
Probability level	Level 3	L	M	M
	Level 2	L	L	M
	Level 1	L	L	L

TABLE 27.15 5×5 risk matrix.

		Impact level				
		Level 1	Level 2	Level 3	Level 4	Level 5
Probability level	Level 5	M	M	H	H	H
	Level 4	L	M	H	H	H
	Level 3	L	M	M	H	H
	Level 2	L	L	M	M	M
	Level 1	L	L	L	L	L

FIGURE 27.1 Outcomes of the risk evaluation process.

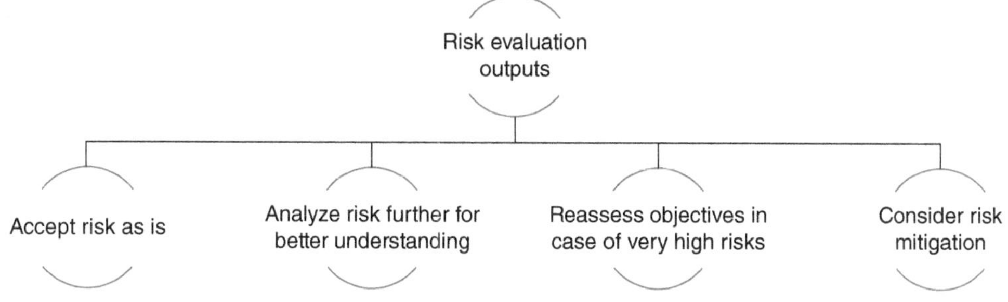

1. To have a consistent analysis method for risks
2. To have a method that assigns risk levels based on the same characteristics of probability and consequence for all risks
3. To be a visual tool for risk criticality estimation
4. To be a comparative tool to rank risks that have the most and least influence on objectives
5. To be a tool to assess changes in risk levels or ratings as the consequence or probability of a risk changes through the life cycle
6. To aid in risk prioritization

The decision for risk acceptability is always the organization's prerogative. Some guidance in the right direction can be obtained by reviewing historically similar risks; acceptable risk in the state of art, yardstick, or generally accepted gold standard product, process, or service; international standards; regulatory guidance; scientific evidence; industry benchmarking; and best practices. Stakeholder communication is the key to defining risk acceptability criteria as stakeholder risk appetites majorly feed into the organizational risk appetite, which largely dictates the level of acceptability along with the points listed earlier. There are four major outcomes of the risk evaluation process, as shown in Figure 27.1 and discussed below.

1. *Risk acceptance* for low risks or for risks for which the organization has a high tolerance.
2. *Further analysis* for medium-, high-, or medium-high-level risks that need greater analytical understanding before their magnitude and resulting impact can be evaluated.
3. *Risk mitigation* is the most common operation performed on all risks that are not acceptable in this stage. Here begins the assessment of risk treatments.
4. In case of certain high or very high risks in which it is amply clear without any detailed analysis that the risk control or mitigation will be fruitless or too straining, the organization must *reassess the need for the objective that is the cause of the risk.* These are the cases where cost-benefit to risk-benefit analysis may show a negative outlook. Top management is usually involved in the decision to reconsider already set objectives.

Now that the risk has been evaluated against baseline criteria and candidates for risk review have been prioritized, these risks undergo a risk treatment, which is detailed in the next chapter.

CHAPTER 28

Risk Treatment/Modification Selection

THE AIM OF RISK TREATMENT OR RISK MODIFICATION is to determine a set of actions to be applied to the evaluated and prioritized risks to ensure that the organizational objectives are successfully achieved by attempting to change the existing risk profile or exposure. Since we have already broken down the risk in terms of impact and probability, the risk treatment can be considered to involve the following for classical negative risks, commonly known as threats:

1. Reduction in the probability of occurrence
2. Reduction in the magnitude of impact
3. A decrease in the liability from risk realization
4. Elimination of probability of occurrence

The first two measures are risk *mitigation* measures, whereby response planning is conducted to ensure a decrease in risk exposure. *Risk mitigation* is defined as a reduction in the risk level to an acceptable limit. It involves taking certain actions that result in system change that allows the reduction of impact or occurrence.

The third measure falls under the category of risk *transfer*. *Risk transfer* means taking steps to transfer all or part of the impact of the risk outside the organization such that when the risk is realized, the fallout or at least a part of it (commercial, financial, etc.) is absorbed by another party.

The fourth measure falls under the category of risk *avoidance*. *Risk avoidance* means taking steps to ensure that the probability of occurrence of the risk is zero. This usually involves a major foundational change and either significantly more resources for realization of the objective or abandonment of a specific objective. Avoidance is recommended when either the risk exposure is too large for the organization to sustain and an impact will likely cripple the organization or the risk attitude is too averse.

If we choose to do none of the above, then we accept the risk as is without any reduction. This is often the case with low-level risks. Risks can be accepted in two ways:

1. **Passive acceptance:** a reactive approach with no contingency planning. As the risk materializes, the response is decided ad hoc.

2. **Active acceptance:** a proactive approach where risk control measures are thought out as part of the treatment and control plan. It involves anticipating the risk and preparing for the contingency to minimize negative risk impact.

In case the mitigative efforts for a high-level risk are too resource-consuming, a decision may still be made to accept the risk. In such cases, the acceptance should always be supported by a strong contingency plan. In many cases, this decision rests with the leadership since the impact and exposure of a high-priority risk are usually significant.

Figure 28.1 shows the potential risk responses to the risk of getting into an accident while driving in the snow to pick up groceries.

For positive risks or opportunities, the following avenues are available for risk treatment:

1. Increasing the probability of occurrence
2. Increasing the magnitude of impact
3. Eliminating the probability of nonoccurrence
4. Sharing ownership of risk to ensure realization of maximum benefit

The first two measures fall under risk *enhancement*. The organization is using a dedicated strategy to ensure that the possibility of a positive impact is as high as possible. In doing so, the exposure to risk is increased in an attempt to effect the realization of the positive event.

For example, in 2018 Ford announced that it would stop producing most sedans in the United States to focus on trucks, SUVs, and crossover vehicles. The risk here is revenue stream change due to the change in vehicle segment offerings. Since Ford made a cost-benefit decision to remove less profitable offerings due to a change in the preferences

FIGURE 28.1 Four options for risk treatment or modification.

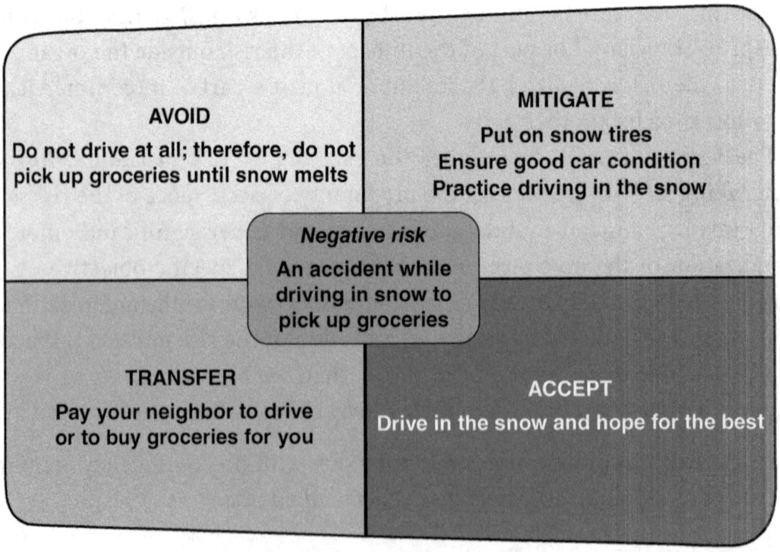

of American consumers, it had an opportunity to capitalize on its more profitable offerings by devoting all energies of commercial and marketing teams to popular and higher-revenue-generating vehicles. Thus, while withdrawing from the small car segment is very much a risk, it is also an opportunity to leverage strengths. Enhancing those strengths will increase the probability of success of this decision, and targeted emphasis on customer requirements (like the introduction of electric crossovers and trucks) may induce more customers to buy larger Ford vehicles, thereby increasing the magnitude of positive impact. This decision may also have negative risk associated with it. If customer preferences change or a competitive threat emerges, the decision may not prove profitable at all. Thus, sometimes, focusing on positive risk may also require paying attention to reduction of circumstances that can turn the positive risk negative.

The third measure talks about risk *exploitation*. This means that each and every measure is taken to ensure that the positive risk is realized. Risk exploitation is the opposite of risk avoidance and means that the organizational strategy is set such that the risk is realized 100%. There are two kinds of risk exploitation:

1. Direct exploitation creates the system structure specifically to ensure realization of opportunity. This may include specific design and process changes in the manufacturing sector or inclusion of specific objectives in scope in project management or inclusion of specific investment portfolios in the financial sector.
2. Indirect exploitation means steering the system to ensure realization of positive risk without a major change in initial objectives and functional structure built to support those objectives. This is a bottom-up approach to risk exploitation as opposed to the direct top-down approach.

For example, Tesla understood that a consumer demand for sporty and powerful electric vehicles was unmet and chose to take a risk to sell such vehicles in an unexplored and unproven market. The vehicles became very popular, and thus by initially becoming the sole company to do so, Tesla exploited the market condition by selling vehicles for a premium. At the time of the writing of this book, Tesla briefly surpassed Toyota with a market capitalization of $180 billion to become the world's most valuable automaker.

The fourth point is risk *sharing*. At times, one organization is unable to ensure an effective positive risk realization strategy despite devoting significant resources. Due to the global and variegated nature of businesses, it becomes incumbent at times to seek a partnership with another organization for mutual benefit. In risk sharing, an organization sacrifices some ownership of the risk (and the return) to another organization to ensure higher chances of occurrence of positive impact. For example, multinational companies often form joint ventures with local companies when entering into a new market. This way, they leverage the local know-how of culture, regulations, and the economy in general, which complements the technical knowledge of the venturing company to ensure successful and profitable market entry.

The risk responses to negative and positive risks are summarized in Figure 28.2.

FIGURE 28.2 Risk responses to positive and negative risks.

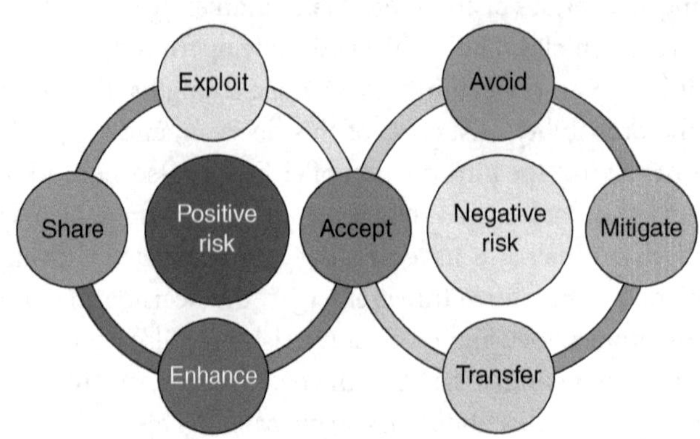

POSITIVE RISK REALIZATION BY DESIGN

It is sometimes difficult to imagine positive risk realization in terms of specific products, processes, or service. In automotive, healthcare, food manufacturing, or medical devices, the negative risks are so common and easy to imagine that it becomes difficult to extract oneself out of the negative connotation of the word "risk." The truth is that while the narrative on positive risks in these sectors is scarce, by default, good decision makers do consider them most of the time. Unfortunately, the process of positive risk consideration is not structured, and hence good opportunities are sometimes missed in the myriad of threats.

One must begin by ensuring that all negative risks have been evaluated, and have a response plan that at the very least includes documentation on acceptance of the risk. Once this is done, a creativity session should be held with relevant stakeholders to brainstorm any other avenues of increasing customer outcomes or satisfaction. The practical success of this stage is dependent on the maturity and integration of risk management practices with the design and development process. If the system is mature and risks are being assessed holistically early on in the process, then major changes can be effected. If the system is not mature and risks are assessed after completion and freeze of the design parameters, then minor changes or delta improvements can be effected. Regardless, this process should reveal a multitude of ideas since no product, process, or service is 100% efficient and robust.

Once the best ideas for improvement are prioritized from the brainstorming session, they can be rewritten in terms of the risk metalanguage, as follows:

Due to <cause>, <outcome> can occur, which will lead to <effect>

This allows us to assign a probability and impact rating that in turn allows for classification of these ideas in a risk matrix, such as the one shown in Table 28.1.

A change with high probability of impact and a high impact is a desirable change, while one with low probability of least positive impact is unlikely to add any value to an existing system. Once the additional features have a risk rating, they must be

TABLE 28.1 Risk matrix for design improvement reliability.

		Positive impact level				
		Customers or end users do not notice difference	"Nice to have" for customers or end users	Customer or end user prefers the system with this rather than without it	Customer or end user is highly appreciative	Customer or end user considers this premium and is delighted
Probability level	Will work every time	M	M	H	H	H
	Highly likely to work	L	M	H	H	H
	Will work 50% of the time	L	M	M	H	H
	Will work often	L	L	M	M	M
	Unlikely to work	L	L	L	L	L

L = Low, M = Medium, H = High

TABLE 28.2 Risk matrix for risk-based resource considerations.

		Resource requirement		
		High	Medium	Low
Risk level	High	Consider	Implement	Implement
	Medium	Consider	Consider	Implement
	Low	Ignore	Ignore	Consider

further compared in terms of resource requirements, which include human, quality, financial, compliance, and regulatory requirements, among others. The matrix shown in Table 28.2 may further help in this process.

Finally, the new addition must be assessed to see if any new negative risks are effected by its introduction. If so, the new risks must be assessed again. If not, then the choice must be made regarding exploitation or enhancements. A flowchart for assessing opportunities based on risk is shown in Figure 28.3.

Example 1

A credit card call center was focused on reducing wait times. It eventually did so but suffered a loss in customer satisfaction rating since the call center employees were rushed, which led to the customer perception of being brushed off. The organization did a risk analysis and decided to increase the workforce. It also focused on training the employees toward modulating their delivery and not rushing to get to the next

FIGURE 28.3 Flowchart to assess risk-based opportunities.

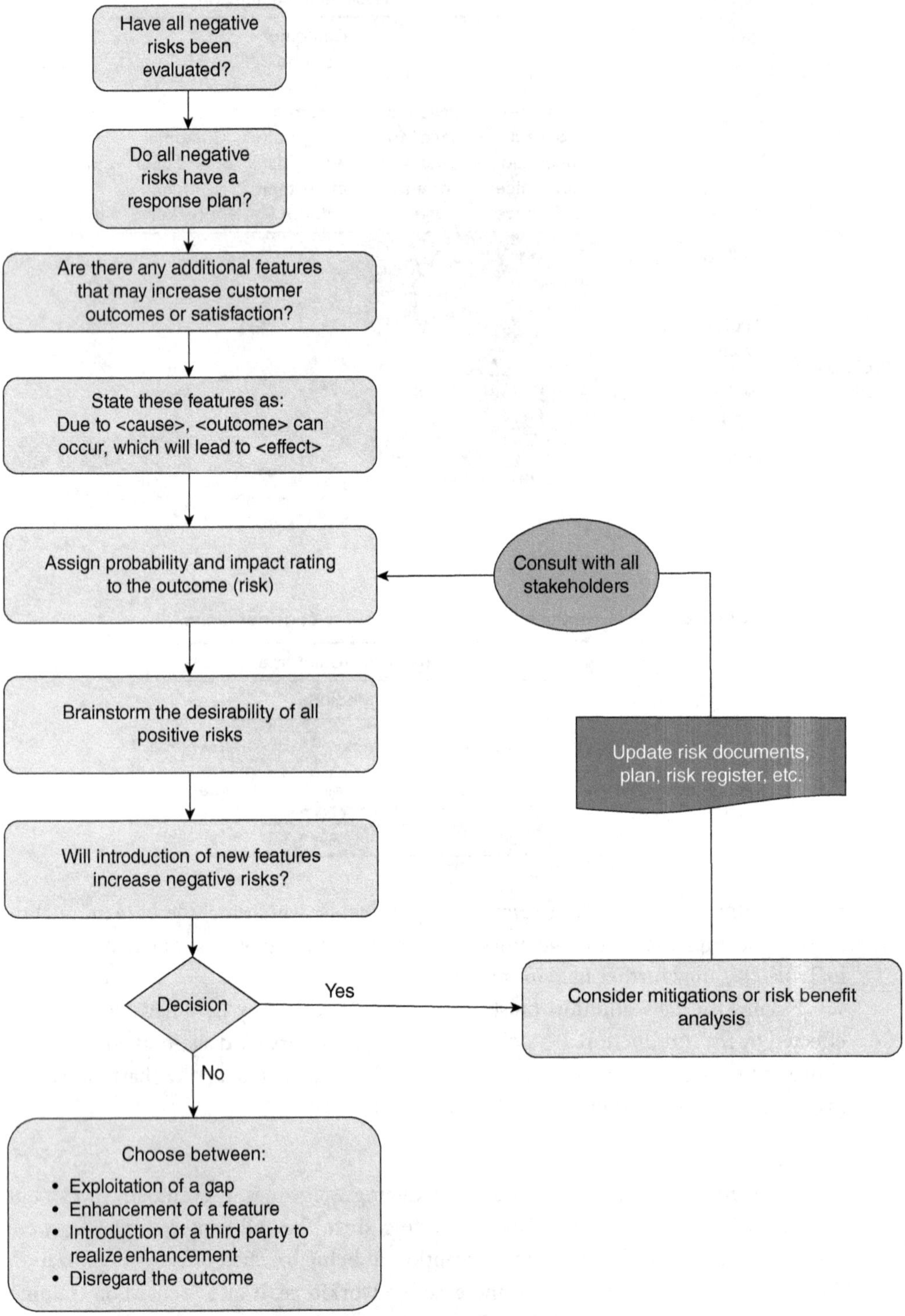

FIGURE 28.4 Use of flowchart to assess and act on opportunities based on risk.

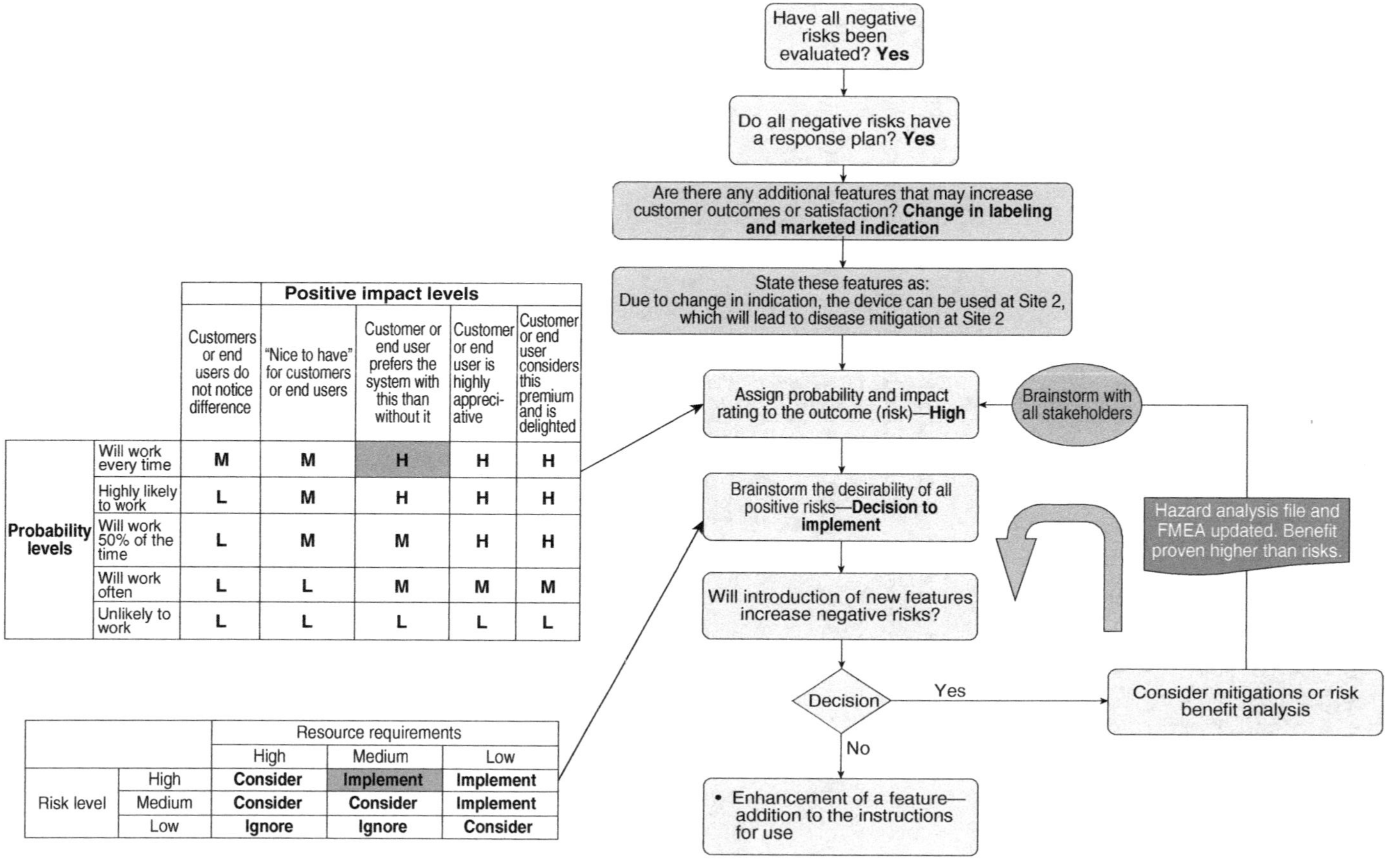

		Positive impact levels				
		Customers or end users do not notice difference	"Nice to have" for customers or end users	Customer or end user prefers the system with this than without it	Customer or end user is highly appreci-ative	Customer or end user considers this premium and is delighted
Probability levels	Will work every time	**M**	**M**	**H**	**H**	**H**
	Highly likely to work	**L**	**M**	**H**	**H**	**H**
	Will work 50% of the time	**L**	**M**	**M**	**H**	**H**
	Will work often	**L**	**L**	**M**	**M**	**M**
	Unlikely to work	**L**	**L**	**L**	**L**	**L**

		Resource requirements		
		High	Medium	Low
Risk level	High	**Consider**	**Implement**	**Implement**
	Medium	**Consider**	**Consider**	**Implement**
	Low	**Ignore**	**Ignore**	**Consider**

Have all negative risks been evaluated? **Yes**

Do all negative risks have a response plan? **Yes**

Are there any additional features that may increase customer outcomes or satisfaction? **Change in labeling and marketed indication**

State these features as:
Due to change in indication, the device can be used at Site 2, which will lead to disease mitigation at Site 2

Assign probability and impact rating to the outcome (risk)—**High**

Brainstorm with all stakeholders

Brainstorm the desirability of all positive risks—**Decision to implement**

Will introduction of new features increase negative risks?

Decision

Yes

Consider mitigations or risk benefit analysis

Hazard analysis file and FMEA updated. Benefit proven higher than risks.

No

- Enhancement of a feature—addition to the instructions for use call. While these measures decreased customer complaints significantly, they did not increase the satisfaction rating. A positive risk analysis was done, and the following risk was identified:

Due to a follow-up outreach, confirmation of issue resolution or nonresolution can occur, which can lead to closure of the issue or further escalation.

A decision was made to add an additional step of a follow-up email asking whether the customer's problem was resolved, and if not, calling the customer to try again. The customers whose issues were resolved did not usually reply, but the ones who were still having issues would promptly respond to the organization with the problem in detail. Thus, the organization enhanced its outreach efforts, which eventually led to an increase in customer satisfaction.

Example 2

A medical device was being used off-label in a location for which it was not intended at high rates. The manufacturer decided to conduct a risk analysis:

Due to the device being used at Site 2 instead of intended Site 1, therapy can occur at Site 2 leading to disease mitigation.

The company followed the flowchart from Figure 28.3, as shown in Figure 28.4.

CHAPTER 29

Risk Response Planning

THE GOAL OF RISK RESPONSE PLANNING is to choose and implement risk treatment options to address the evaluated and prioritized risks. In previous chapters we went over the available risk treatments in detail and saw that the decision to avoid, mitigate, transfer, accept, exploit, enhance, or share risk is a critical risk treatment step. We learned that, when choosing an option, the risk attitudes of the stakeholders, risk tolerance of the organization, organizational obligations, competitor performance, market perceptions, and regulatory, legal, or compliance commitments must be taken into consideration.

Once the decision for how to treat risk has been made, practical options must be considered for realizing this decision. The viability of treatment must be assessed before it is implemented to ensure its effectiveness and to ensure that new unacceptable risks are not introduced as a part of the treatment plan. Figure 29.1 summarizes the risk response planning process with its inputs and outputs. Let us discuss this in a little more detail.

The response planning starts by assessing the available treatment options for the prioritized risks based on communication and consultation. The rationale for the selection of the treatment must be documented. The expected actions and outcomes of the selected treatment must be assessed and documented as well; this is the expected change in the risk as a result of the applied treatment.

The actual treatment itself may require resources and an action plan for deployment. Thus, relevant process owners and responsible persons must be identified to actuate the treatment effectively and in a timely manner. Finally, the risk should be monitored continually after application of the treatment. For effective monitoring, performance measures must be defined such that verification of effectiveness of treatment can be carried out.

A risk response plan at a minimum must consist of the following:

1. Identification of the type of treatment and justification
2. Identification of the treatment actions and a plan for implementation
3. Expected outcome/benefit of the treatment
4. Measures to monitor the effectiveness of the treatment
5. Risk reassessment after treatment

FIGURE 29.1 Risk response planning process.

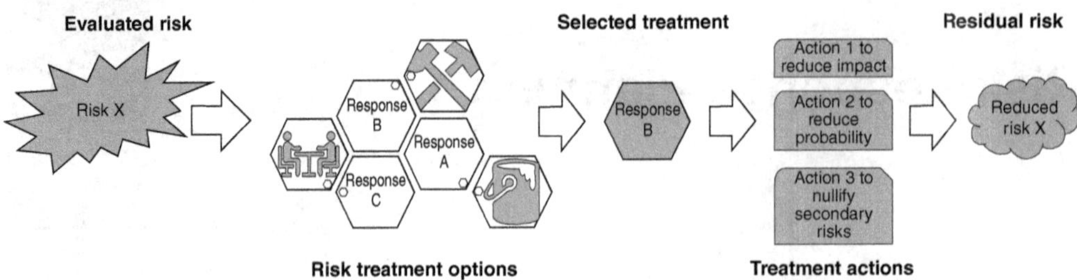

A detailed risk response plan should ideally consist of the following:

1. List of all available risk treatments for every prioritized risk
2. Justification for selection of one treatment over another
3. Testing the chosen treatment for effectiveness
4. Checking the treatment as a source of secondary negative risks
5. Conducting a stakeholder review of the treatment
6. Documenting the scope of the treatment
7. Documenting assumptions and constraints of the treatment
8. Documenting the resource requirements of the treatments
9. Plan of action for treatment implementation, including schedule and timing (one time or staggered)
10. Risk reassessment after treatment is over
11. Documented level of residual risk acceptability
12. Performance monitoring
13. Plan actions in case of treatment failure

THE CONCEPT OF SECONDARY RISK

The risk treatments must be analyzed for their outcomes and effects in terms of additional risks that may be generated when they are implemented. It is very common for a response to a risk to either result in some change in other risks or result in new risks. The risks that are engendered by risk responses to already assessed or unassessed risks are known as *secondary risks*. If such risks arise, one must either choose another risk response or assess the secondary risk to check its acceptability and to understand its drivers and mitigators.

THE CONCEPT OF RESIDUAL RISK

Residual risk is the risk that remains after a satisfactory application of risk treatment. Analysis of the residual risk is the key to understand the current and realistic risk profile. This analysis must be continual to ensure that the risk profile is maintained.

FIGURE 29.2 From original risk to residual risk.

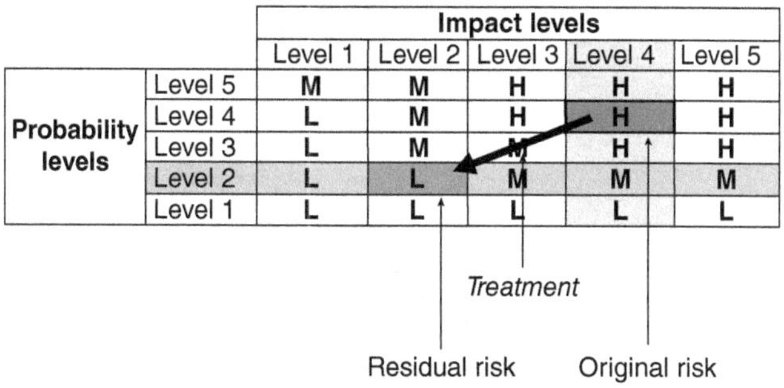

		Impact levels				
		Level 1	Level 2	Level 3	Level 4	Level 5
Probability levels	Level 5	M	M	H	H	H
	Level 4	L	M	H	H	H
	Level 3	L	M	M	H	H
	Level 2	L	L	M	M	M
	Level 1	L	L	L	L	L

Treatment

Residual risk Original risk

For example, consumer behaviors may change over time, which would falsify certain assumptions that were valid a few years ago.

As another example, a medical device could be repurposed for a procedure it was not intended for. Initially, the manufacturer acknowledged the risk and due to its low occurrence decided that a warning on a label was a sufficient mitigation. With changing surgical techniques, doctors found it more and more useful to repurpose the device, thereby increasing the occurrence rate. Thus, a new and stronger risk response would now be needed from the manufacturer.

The level of acceptability of the residual risk must be assessed with the same techniques used to assess the level of original risk. The risk matrix again proves useful here since the levels of risks are already charted on a matrix and the change in impact and probability levels after the treatment can be objectively assessed in terms of risk levels or ratings as shown in Figure 29.2.

THE CONCEPT OF INHERENT RISK

The natural level of raw, untreated risk associated with any activity is known as *inherent risk*. After a risk undergoes treatment, the remaining risk is residual risk. The word "residual" originates from the reduction of negative risk; thus, in the case of negative risks, the diagram shown in Figure 29.3 is applicable.

Most times, it is not possible to mitigate all risk, and some level of residual risk always remains. It is valuable to discuss these cases to understand the level of mitigation afforded by risk treatments. The source of risks is often a hazard, and to totally remove a risk would be to remove the hazard that causes the risk. Since this is not always possible, there is always a component of inherent risk that remains. This is the untreatable inherent risk shown in Figure 29.4.

For example, however powerful the grip of a tire can be made for traction, if a car is driven on ice or through tracts of accumulating snow, there is always a risk of slipping. This is because the snow or ice is the hazard and leads to the hazardous situation of low friction when a rubber tire is driven on it. There are numerous ways to reduce

FIGURE 29.3 Residual risk and inherent risk.

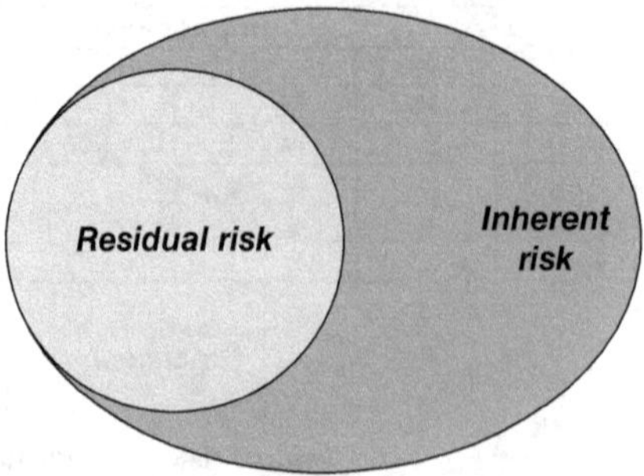

FIGURE 29.4 Inherent risk, residual risk, and untreatable risk.

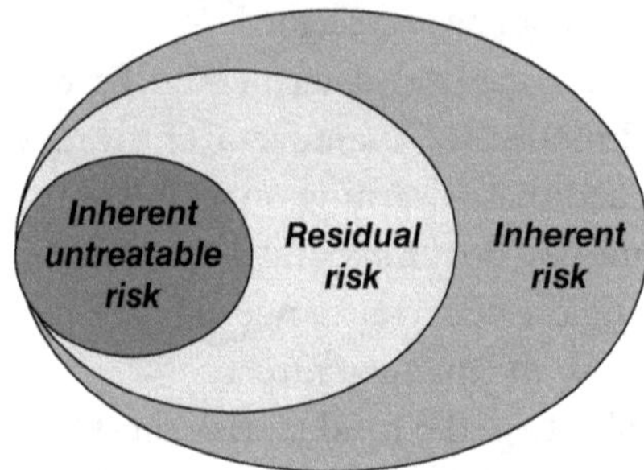

slippage, but there will always be a small inherent untreatable risk present unless one decides to avoid risk and just not drive the car in snow at all.

Similarly, every medical procedure has inherent risks. If a surgery is performed, there is risk of infection since a 100% sterile environment is hard to guarantee. This is a hazard, but we operate despite the hazard and attempt to reduce the initial inherent risks by taking multiple precautions.

This understanding helps us modulate our risk treatment efforts. Recognizing the untreatable risks prevents us from excessively spending resources in the wrong place. Consensus from stakeholders must always be gained before a portion of risk is deemed untreatable.

CONTINGENCY PLANNING

When there is no treatment of the risk planned and the risks are accepted as is, the organization must proactively prepare a strategy to deal with those risks as they manifest themselves. This active acceptance of risk and planning actions for foreseen risks when they present themselves is known as *contingency planning.* A contingency plan should mitigate the negative effects of the risk and should clarify the type and level of action along with responsibilities for execution. Sometimes an amount of money known as the

FIGURE 29.5 Flowchart for risk response planning process.

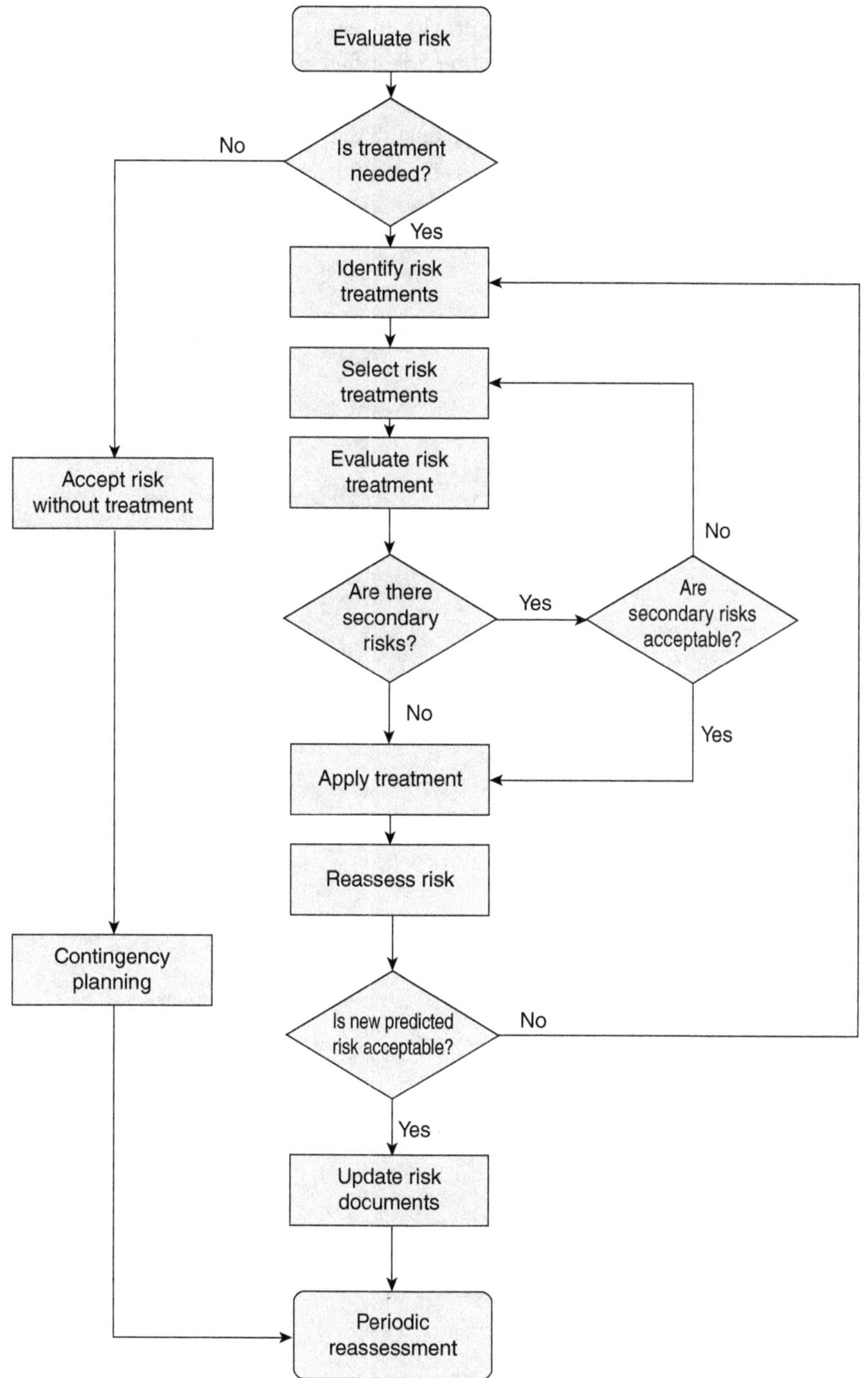

contingency reserve is kept aside for these untreated risks that have been identified and evaluated but not mitigated. There may be unforeseen risks that arise during the system life cycle, and these must also be dealt with to ensure sustained achievement of goals. Since these emergent risks were neither identified nor evaluated, their response will be reactive in nature. It means that the organization must be sufficiently agile to triage resources at the first sign of these risks to ensure that they do not have an adverse impact.

The risk response planning process is summarized in Figure 29.5.

CHAPTER 30

Monitoring and Reviewing Risk

THE RISKS THAT HAVE BEEN IDENTIFIED, analyzed, evaluated, and treated fall in the following categories:

1. Mitigated or enhanced
2. Avoided or exploited
3. Transferred or shared
4. Accepted

These are the possible outputs of the risk response plans for the evaluated risks. It does not mean that these risks have been 100% treated. A response plan for risk mitigation may be anticipated to reduce risk by 80%, but will it really do so? How accurate are our predictions about risk and our response to it? Since there is a subjective and predictive aspect to risk assessment and treatment, we need to put systems in place to monitor and verify the assessment and treatment as more real-world data and evidence become available to ensure that the risks stay stable at predefined levels.

The monitoring phase of risk management is where real-world data are used to track the risks and/or their constituents to ensure that the risks are behaving in the manner anticipated during risk treatment and response planning. Risk monitoring can be accomplished in two ways:

1. Reassessment of risks after treatment and continually throughout the life cycle
2. Tracking by using key risk indicators

All risks need not be reassessed continually. An organization must prioritize which risks are to be reassessed and set schedules or conditions for their reassessment throughout the life cycle. Precipitating events like complaints, defects, losses, warranty claims, and service requests can be used as checkpoints to reassess risks at discrete times to ensure acceptable risk profiles.

There arises a need for indicators that inform us about the status of the risk without us having to conduct full risk reassessments every time. The trending status of these indicators can act as a flag for investigations, which may result in complete risk reassessments.

A risk indicator is simply a metric that *indicates* the state of the level of risk. It is important to note that not all indicators show the exact level of risk exposure; most indicators usually provide just a trend of the drivers, causes, or intermediary effects of risk.

Not all risks are the same. The most important risks are categorized as key risks and the indicators for these key risks are known as key risk indicators (KRIs). These are defined as:

> *A metric that provides a leading or lagging indication of the current state of risk exposure on key objectives. KRIs can be used to continually assess current and predict potential future risk exposure.*

The KRIs should have a strong relationship with the key performance indicators (KPIs) of the organization's goals. The KPIs are metrics that are quantifiable measurements to assess performance of a specific process, product, system, or function.

ISO 31000:2018 says that:

> *The results of monitoring and review should be incorporated throughout the organization's performance management, measurement and reporting activities.*[1]

KPIs are metrics that help gauge performance of the organization in terms of achievement of objectives. If an objective has a KPI, then it is highly likely that a KRI can be defined for that objective. If a risk has assigned controls as a result of risk treatment, then the risk indicator can become a metric to assess the effectiveness of the treatment.

Leading indicators are measurements of an element that influences the risk performance, while lagging indicators are actual measurements of the major components of the risk performance itself.

Leading indicators have predictive value, while lagging indicators are outputs of events that have already occurred, which help set future strategy. Some metrics can act as leading or lagging indicators based on the measured parameter, which may be an input to one process and an output of another.

The KRIs must be able to qualitatively or quantitatively present the risk exposure by having a strong relationship with the risk, its intermediate output, or its drivers.

In Figure 30.1, there are two choices for risk monitoring:

1. Reassess risk for every manufacturing issue, supply chain issue, inspection issue, and complaint issue as these events occur
2. Define performance of each risk in terms of its main driver and assign a KRI to track the risk

For point 2, let us consider the operational goal of "production of defect-free product." Let us assume the KPI for this is 99.5% final yield. The risks related to this goal are the following:

---

1. ©ISO. This material is reproduced from ISO 31000:2018, with permission of the American National Standards Institute (ANSI) on behalf of the International Organization for Standardization.

FIGURE 30.1 Risk monitoring example with KRIs.

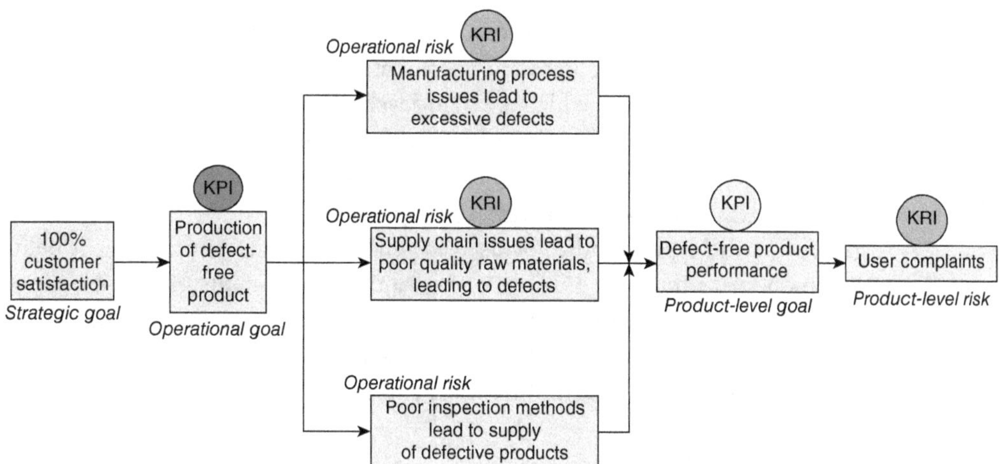

Risk One: Due to manufacturing process issues, process steps A, C, and D are inefficient, which has led to an increase in nonconformances during sampling

Risk Two: Due to supply chain issues, raw materials X and Y are being sourced from new suppliers who are barely able to meet tolerance levels, leading to a high in-process scrap rate

Risk Three: Due to loose and nonstandard inspection methods, the product is sometimes not inspected for all features, leading to an increase in defective products being shipped out

Now, there should have been probabilities and impacts assigned for these risks from an operational standpoint, and these risks should have had mitigations in place. If this original risk were to be reassessed, one may notice an increase in probability and impact and realize that the risk exposure has increased and the mitigation has failed, or one may see a minor change that does not increase the risk level.

Another method to monitor these risks is to use KRIs. The indicator that would most closely state the health of the process would be the following:

For Risk One: nonconformance rate

For Risk Two: incoming inspection reject rate and raw material scrap rate

For Risk Three: product complaint rate

A rise in nonconformance and scrap rate is both a leading indicator for user complaints and a lagging indicator for a poor production process. User complaints are a lagging indicator for poor product performance.

The KRIs could vary in their specificity. They might be very focused on one aspect, or they may be an amalgamation of various sub-indicators. For example, an organization with very high sensitivity to consumer complaints may choose to have that as a specific

KRI against a performance indicator of customer satisfaction. Another organization may choose to create a balanced scorecard for quality and include consumer complaints as a line item along with manufacturing defects, supplier issues, delivery timeliness, service satisfaction, and so on and assign an overall score that becomes an amalgamated KRI.

Indicators can be top down, which are high-level composite indicators constituted of multiple sub-indicators to show the health of a greater operational or strategic goal. They can also be bottom up, where increased specificity can be afforded to monitor the exposure on a functional product, process, or service level.

Regardless of the type of indicator used, it must always be ensured that it helps to identify, monitor as much as possible, and quantify the elements of the risk exposure. It must be noted that some KRIs will be more accurate in their representation of the actual risk than others. Some KRIs may represent the frequency of events, which informs the probability assignation of the risk, and some may use elements from the impact assignation.

The benefits of KRIs are the following:

1. They can be easily converted to charts and trends
2. They are easily associated with objectives through KPIs
3. They can be shown on visual dashboards or converted to scorecards
4. Trending of KRIs can help predict future risk breaches
5. They allow risk monitoring without reassessing the risk every single time
6. They test the effectiveness of the risk treatment
7. They act as a bellwether for risk breaches
8. They can be hierarchically defined

CHAPTER 31

Monitoring and Reviewing Risk 2

MONITORING AND REVIEWING RISK ENTAILS KEEPING a pulse on the risk to outputs and objectives using suitable, efficient, and accurate methods. Since for every event full risk reassessments become time-consuming and impractical, risk indicators are often used to gauge the course of identified risk in terms of drifts in risk profile. This may not be an easy task. Many times the risk professionals fail to identify the correct indicators and thus track the risk incorrectly. It is best to view the process hierarchically and confirm risk indications and risk profile changes using more than one measurement.

Keeping these things in mind, a holistic and hierarchical process for risk monitoring can be defined using the following features:

1. Discrete level measurement
2. Trending
3. Benchmark comparison
4. Aggregation
5. Emergent risk monitoring

The level of the risk after treatment must be monitored at discrete intervals to ensure the actual value of risk has not changed significantly—that is, the risk level is acceptable and the risk exposure is contained. This step involves risk reassessment using the same technique with which the risk was originally assessed so that a change in risk, if any, may become apparent. Usually this means recalculating the impact and probability to recalculate the risk level. Risk monitoring using risk reassessments provides the actual current exposure levels for comparison with the previously evaluated baseline. While it is ideal to reassess risk at every signal of changed uncertainty, the process can be resource-consuming. Usually, the following events trigger a full reassessment:

1. Occurrence of a major change
2. Extemporaneous events
3. End of a life-cycle stage
4. Scope changes
5. Periodic reviews

The trending of risk is usually realized by assigning KRIs to the risk and charting their trends. In some cases, it may be possible to trend the events themselves, like for complaint events, or it may be possible to trend the mean time between events using control charts. In other cases, the frequency of occurrence of constituent subevents that feed into the risk can be trended.

Commonly, the trending is based on a time series that shows the change of the variable through the passage of time as opposed to a snapshot in time. This allows the organization to visualize, anticipate, and extrapolate the increase or decrease in risk exposure and the likelihood of impact. In case a risk response treatment has been applied due to an excursion, the trends will allow the organization to track the improvement in the risk profile.

KRI trending of leading indicators allows us to anticipate risky events with some specificity of scope; these may be pointers leading to already identified risks or even emergent risks. KRI trending of lagging indicators allows us to monitor the exposure of antecedent risk events that have either materialized or could occur again. This allows for better preparedness for impact and gives us time to add additional controls as needed.

Benchmark comparison means that the level and trends of organizational risks must be investigated and verified in an external context. If a competitor is making similar products or provides similar services, it will be of value to check its performance parameters (e.g., stock prices, defect rates, complaint rates) to benchmark the internal performance. This may be done using public databases or media reports, or it can be accomplished by partnerships or industry events and conferences. As much as possible, the performance should be compared with that of industry leaders and purveyors of state-of-the-art products and services in the organization's sector.

Aggregation means that the risk must be assessed in aggregate at the operational, strategic, or enterprise level based on the specific risk information from individual levels and trends. Similar risks trended individually may not look threatening, but if clustered together they may show a different picture. There must be some level of aggregation strategy to connect all risk indicators and performances.

Finally, new risks, which were not anticipated, may emerge through the life cycle. These must be first addressed reactively to contain them and then assessed and treated. A strategy must be defined with contingency planning to account for monitoring and response for such risks.

WHAT ARE TRIGGER CONDITIONS AND WHY SHOULD THEY BE MONITORED?

Trigger conditions occur when a set threshold or boundary for a risk level is breached, leading to greater than expected risk exposure. The main aim of risk monitoring and tracking is to assess the risk and its indicators for trigger conditions.

The most common and obvious trigger conditions are preestablished occurrence rates and impact level and corresponding risk levels. As discussed earlier, it is not always possible to reassess each and every risk periodically. In such cases, the KRIs themselves must have set trigger conditions as well.

If the KRI is a chart of discrete events on a time series, then a two-sigma, three-sigma, or four-sigma standard deviation from the historical mean may be an example of a threshold. If the indicator breaches the set sigma limit, the KRI can be said to be triggered, which may warrant an investigation into the cause and a full risk reassessment.

In addition, the level of attention a KRI generates can be divided per the level of the breach of the trigger condition. For example, a two-sigma breach can be a local functional threshold, a three-sigma breach can be the site management threshold, and a four-sigma breach can be a top management threshold. These levels can help decide urgency or action and direct proper resources toward the future actions for change in risk exposure.

Monitoring of the trigger condition not only means establishment of a threshold but also goes hand in hand with detailing the risk response after its breach. This should be synchronous with the risk response plan, which should specify the action owners and the action itself.

The risk monitoring process is summarized in Figure 31.1.

FIGURE 31.1 A holistic risk monitoring process.

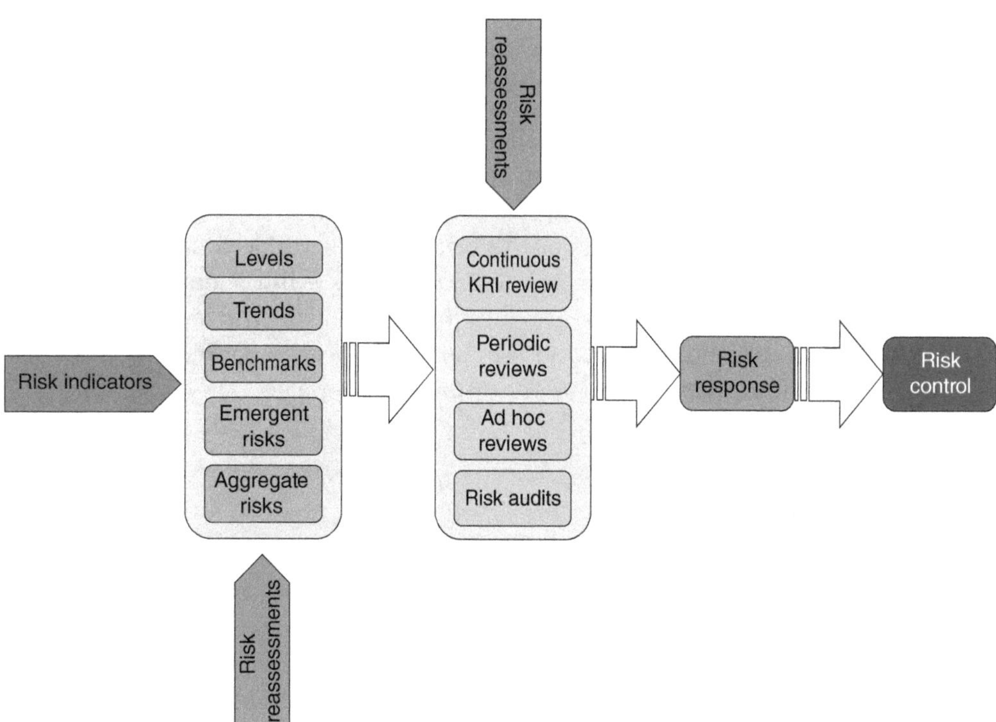

RISK AWARENESS

The generating and tracking of KRIs and reassessments may be done by specific risk owners or stakeholders, but formal outputs of these activities in the form of reports should be shared at periodic meetings with all relevant stakeholders and interested parties. Depending on the specificity of the review, some reports may be suitable for functional managers, while some will be suitable for the top management. In some form or another, the risk monitoring information should percolate through all relevant levels of the organization to ensure risk and risk exposure awareness. Regular risk status meetings must be scheduled, or they can be a part of an agenda on a common calendar cycle of meetings like management review, quality review, or project status meetings. If some indicators show sudden movements or new emergent risks are identified, ad hoc meetings must be scheduled with stakeholders and team members to first communicate the issue and then work on a response plan. These meetings may include the following on the agenda:

1. Status check of highest-rated risks
2. Trigger conditions and risks breached for the review period
3. Status of the risk responses
4. Risk and risk response ownership clarification
5. Challenges in implementing risk response plans
6. Emergent risks identified in the review period and reactive actions to those risks
7. KRI trends
8. Risk levels, if risks are reassessed

In addition to meetings, the chain of communication and ownership must be defined, such as emergence of risk can be immediately communicated to the relevant risk owner, who can begin on preestablished risk responses without waiting to convene a meeting. Sometimes, indicators or risk reassessments will need to be verified and approved. The owners of this activity must be defined as well. The urgency and spread of risk communication and awareness must be guided by the risk level. For example, a risk manager at a hospital may not be notified of every minor bleeding event but should be alerted as soon as possible for a patient death event.

RISK AUDITS

Risk audits attempt to verify and validate specific aspects of risk management, which can include risk identification, risk assessment, risk treatment, risk response planning, and risk monitoring and reporting. The scope of the risk audits either can be one of these areas or can encompass all of them. Usually, audit trails will lead to review of a specific risk through its life cycle from identification to monitoring.

Many times, risk auditing is focused on verification of effectiveness of risk responses, which is a good place to start since it acts as a gauge for success or failure of the risk management process as a whole. The effectiveness of risk response refers to the extent to which the planned risk responses and outcomes achieve their intent by delivering expected outcomes.

A generic risk audit may take the following path:

1. Setting audit scope to cover specific risks or processes
2. Defining data gathering methods
3. Reviewing available risk documentation
4. Reviewing KRIs and risk reassessments
5. Reviewing risk responses or rationales for no responses
6. Ensuring that risk management process and procedures were followed
7. Interviewing stakeholders and interested parties for all of the above

CHAPTER 32

Graphical Tools for Monitoring and Reviewing Risk

GRAPHICAL TOOLS CAN BE USED for monitoring and reviewing risks to visually or numerically show the risk levels, trends, and, where appropriate, aggregate risks. The tools can track any of the following features:

1. Occurrence or probability levels
2. Impact levels
3. Risk levels or their constituents
4. Drivers of any of the above

Following are descriptions of common tools for monitoring risk.

PARETO CHARTS

A *Pareto chart* is a special histogram that ranks the most commonly occurring risk events or risk indicators by their frequency of occurrence. This is useful for lower-level repetitive risks. It does not chart the change in impact level but is useful for assessing the most frequent risks for prioritization and further analysis.

As seen in Figure 32.1, the issues are arranged from left to right, from the highest frequency to the lowest. The bars may represent variables other than frequency, like quantity, time, cost, and so on. The red curve is the cumulative percentage arc, which gives an indication of the percentage contribution of each issue to the total. Figure 32.2 shows a Pareto chart for time instead of frequency of event occurrence.

While the Pareto chart cannot cumulatively measure impact, the Pareto principle states that the most impactful problems are the top 20%, which cause 80% of the fallout. This tool can be used for focusing response planning toward the most commonly occurring risks: the top 20%, which are likely to have a higher cumulative impact than the other 80%.

SCATTER PLOTS

A *scatter plot* shows the strength of the relationship between two variables using a regression line. This is useful in showing a change in risk impact if it is dependent

FIGURE 32.1 Pareto chart example: production risks.

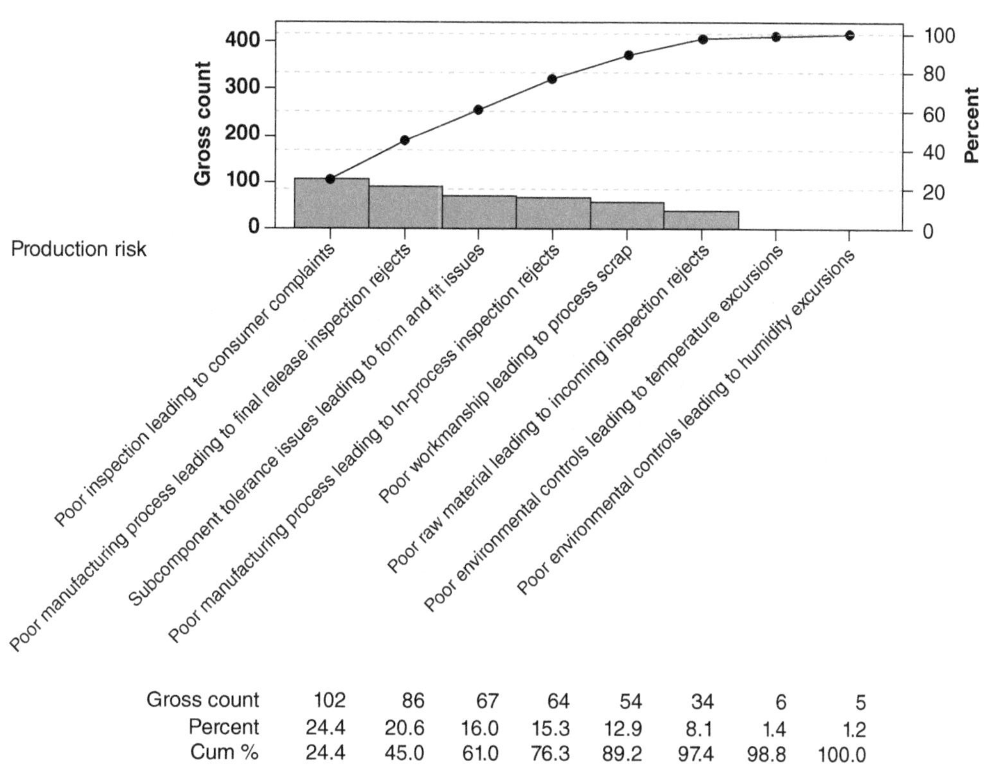

Gross count	102	86	67	64	54	34	6	5
Percent	24.4	20.6	16.0	15.3	12.9	8.1	1.4	1.2
Cum %	24.4	45.0	61.0	76.3	89.2	97.4	98.8	100.0

on one specific variable or a combination of variables that can be represented by one variable.

The scatter plot in Figure 32.3 shows a relationship between the S&P 500 and three-year returns of a particularly well-managed fund. In this case the regression equation could be given by:

$$\begin{aligned} Regression\ Fit\ (Return,\ y) &= 9.016 + 0.8559\,(Stock\ Volatility) \\ R - Sq &= 92.3\% \end{aligned} \tag{32.1}$$

This example demonstrates a quantitative measurement of impact (returns) due to a risk (stock market volatility). In this case, higher volatility leads to higher returns since the risk was managed very well. This analysis is one sided since it does not incorporate the probability aspect of the risk. The main limitation of the scatter plot is that while it can provide us with a quantitative relationship between a dependent variable and a response variable, which could be very helpful in assessing the drivers of change in consequence, it is difficult to place both probability and consequence on the same plot.

Figure 32.4 shows the correlation between process sigma levels and generated non-conforming parts.

While the distribution of points is a little disparate, the regression line does make it clear that there is a relationship between process sigma and nonconformances. The

FIGURE 32.2 Pareto chart example: time in days for new product design.

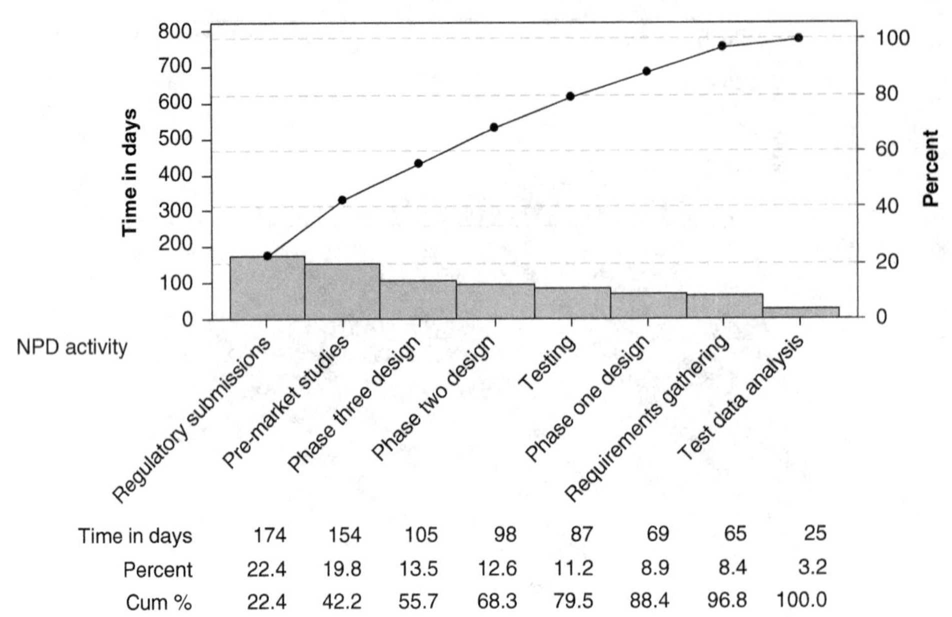

Time in days	174	154	105	98	87	69	65	25
Percent	22.4	19.8	13.5	12.6	11.2	8.9	8.4	3.2
Cum %	22.4	42.2	55.7	68.3	79.5	88.4	96.8	100.0

FIGURE 32.3 Scatter plot example: stock return and volatility.

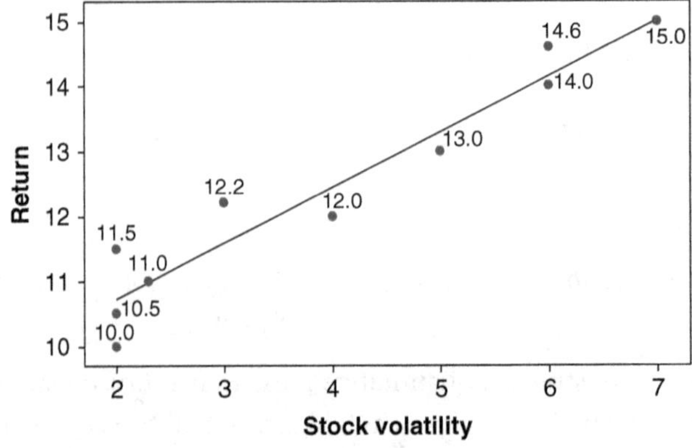

risk impact here could be the number of nonconforming parts or the actual dollar value of those parts. A subset of scatter plots is the bubble chart, which can achieve an added layer of analysis by not only plotting the correlation between two values but also showing a third parameter by using the size of the "bubble." Figure 32.5 shows the same data as above but quantifies the cost impact of the nonconformances in dollar terms, thereby giving us another unit of risk impact.

FIGURE 32.4 Scatter plot example: nonconformances and process sigma.

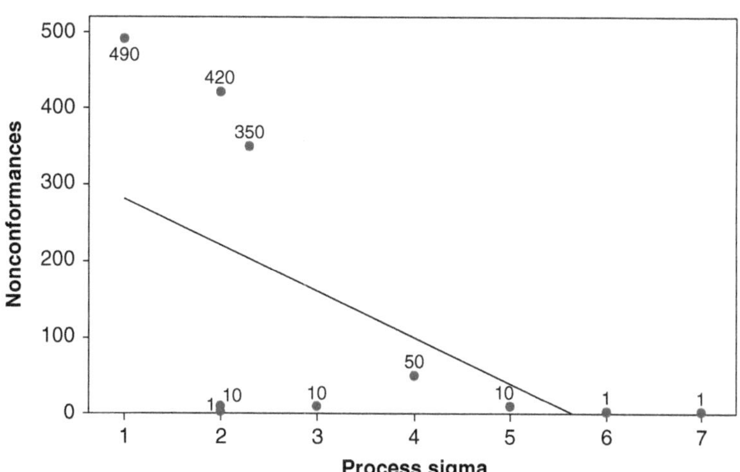

FIGURE 32.5 Scatter plot with impact chart: nonconformances and process sigma.

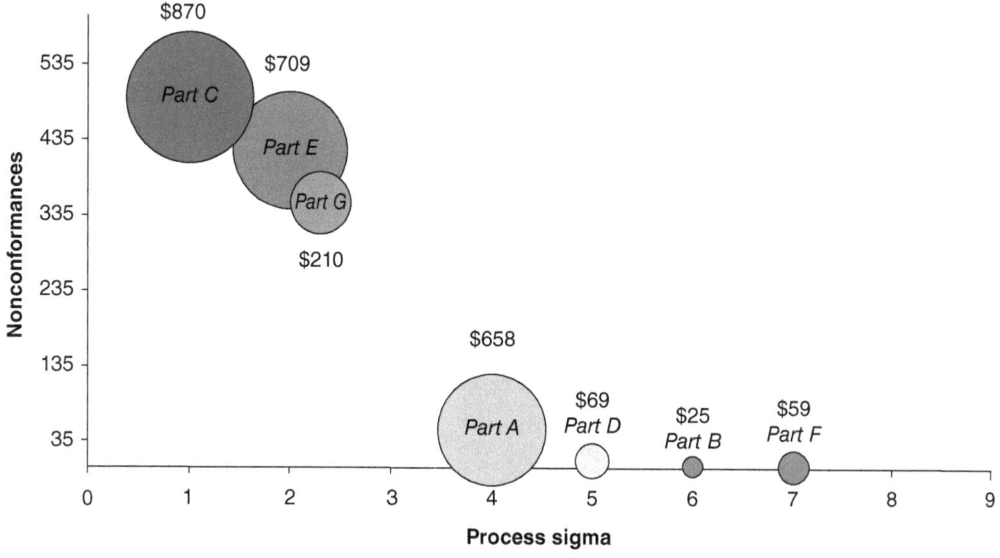

BAR GRAPHS AND HISTOGRAMS

A *bar graph* simply shows numerical data as rectangular bars with their height being the quantified numerical value. Figure 32.6 is a bar chart of the production risks that were shown in a Pareto chart in Figure 32.1. Unlike a Pareto chart, there is no ordering of the bars.

Similar to Pareto charts, bar charts can be used to track occurrences. Due to their simple construction, easy adaptability to any data, and visual appeal, these charts are often present in some form in many risk dashboards.

FIGURE 32.6 Bar chart example.

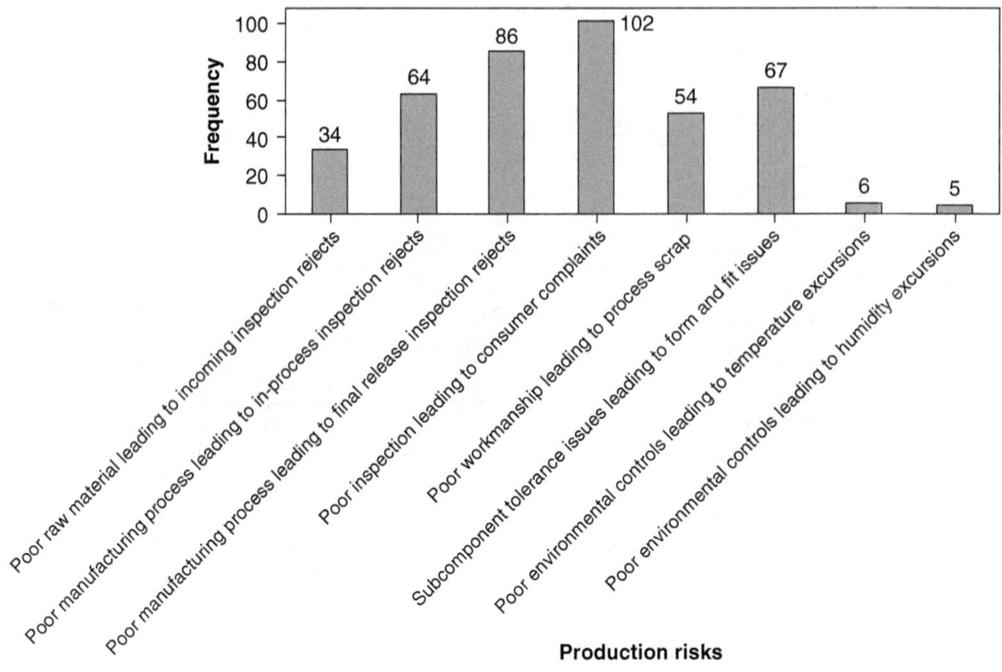

FIGURE 32.7 Histogram example: quality defects.

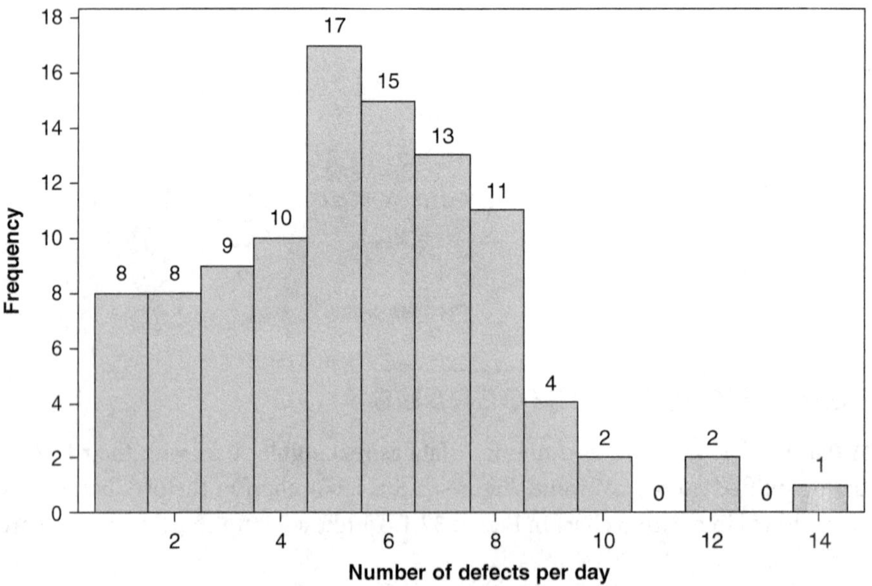

A *histogram* is a special type of bar chart that shows frequency distribution of values. The height of the bars, similar to that of the bar charts, represents the frequency of occurrence, which makes these charts useful for tracking very high-occurrence values. For a higher number of values, as the shape of the data distribution is revealed, useful statistical inferences can be drawn from these charts. ASQ recommends at least 50 data points for histogram construction. The histogram in Figure 32.7 shows the frequency distribution of quality defects per day by count. This graph is useful for visually assessing values such as the mean and standard deviations, which can feed into risk probability or occurrence level calculations. It can also be used to show the occurrence of repetitive risks or impacts. For example, in a hospital, the histogram can show the number of bleeding events per day and provide us with a visual graphic for the occurrence rate of a particular consequence.

LINE AND TIME SERIES CHARTS

A *line chart* is a simple plot of points on a Cartesian plane and their connection by a line. It is usually used to portray a trend in a series of data points.

Indicators, including many KRIs, can be plotted to show occurrence levels over time. A line chart that has a time duration plotted on the x-axis is known as a *time series* chart. An example is shown in Figure 32.8, where the quality defect counts are plotted over successive months. Several streams of time-based trends can be overlaid in one graph to show multiple occurrence trends over the same period of time, as shown in Figure 32.9. When plotting a time series plot it is important to note the following:

FIGURE 32.8 Time series plot example: defect counts.

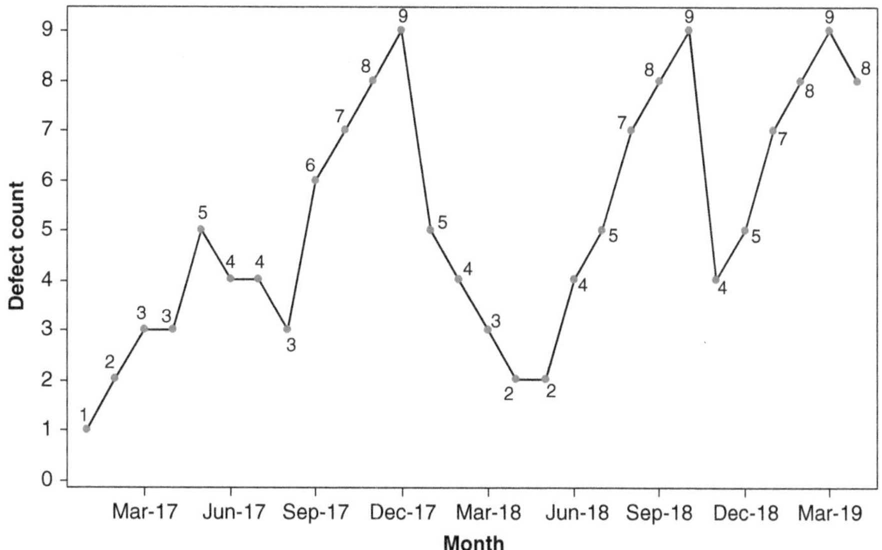

FIGURE 32.9 Time series plot (two variables) example: defect count of Machines A and B.

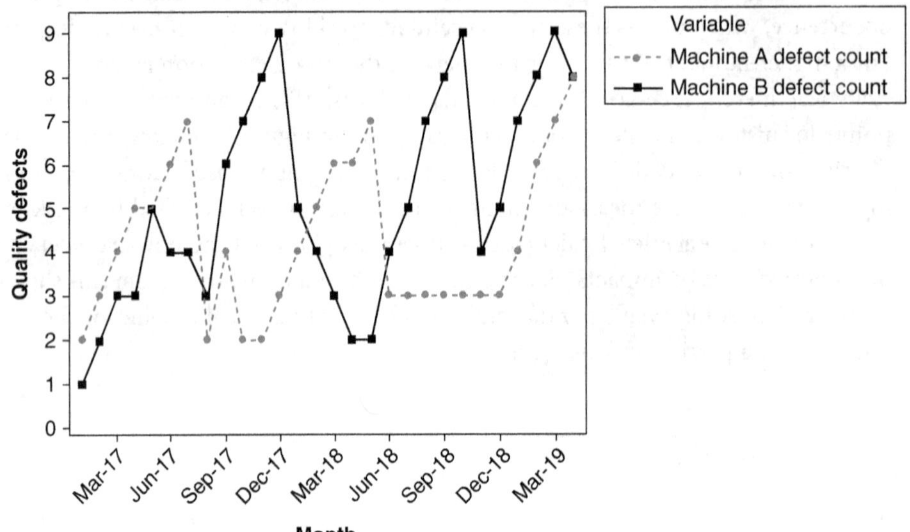

1. The frequency of data collection is uniform (e.g., every day, every hour, every month)
2. The data are ordered chronologically

RUN CHARTS

A subset of line charts, *run charts* show a trend of the collected data in a sequential order. While the order is often dictated by time, it may not always be time dependent like the time series chart. The sequence of observations in a run chart is geared toward plotting a characteristic and its sequential change. Thus, run charts are used to plot univariate data, which have only one variable. The primary goal of a run chart is to look for patterns in the data like upswing or downswing trends, clustering, oscillations, and other nonrandom behavior. The horizontal line shows a measure of central tendency, which could be the mean or median as applicable to the data.

It is a good tool to check for indicator trends. An example of a run chart is shown in Figure 32.10. A long series or "runs" of cyclic consecutive increases show a trend that may be worth investigating for risk reassessment and risk profile verification.

CONTROL CHARTS

A *control chart* is used to trend time-ordered changes. It is a time series chart with limits based on statistical rationales (usually certain sigma levels from the mean) that provide tolerance thresholds for variability.

FIGURE 32.10 Run chart example: defect count.

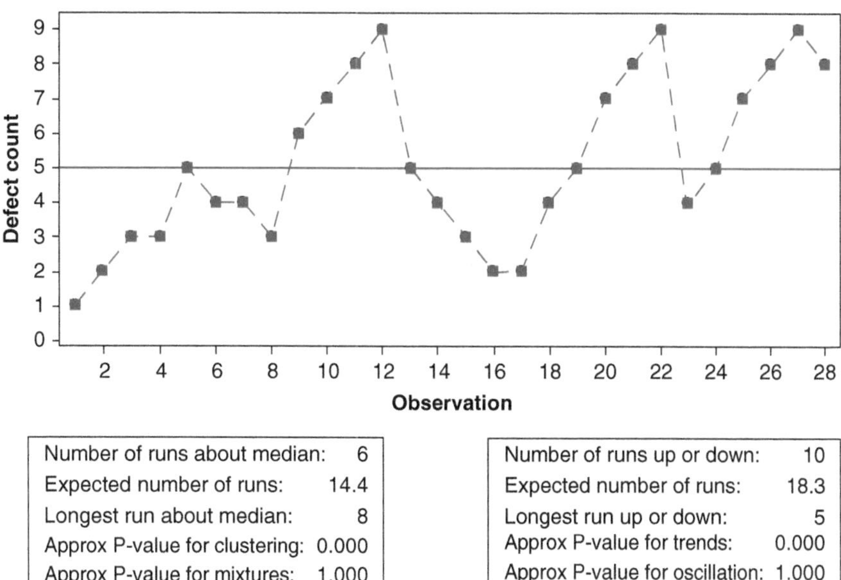

Defect count
Observation
Number of runs about median: 6
Expected number of runs: 14.4
Longest run about median: 8
Approx P-value for clustering: 0.000
Approx P-value for mixtures: 1.000
Number of runs up or down: 10
Expected number of runs: 18.3
Longest run up or down: 5
Approx P-value for trends: 0.000
Approx P-value for oscillation: 1.000

The three main elements of a control chart, as shown in Figure 32.11, are the following:

1. A time series graph
2. A central line (C) is added as a visual reference for detecting shifts or trends
3. An upper control limit (UCL) and lower control limit (LCL) are computed from available data and placed equidistant from the central line

For attribute control charts (for noncontinuous data), control limits are calculated by:

1. Estimating the standard deviation of the sample data
2. Multiplying that number by three
3. Adding for the UCL and subtracting for the LCL

Control rules take advantage of the normal curve, in which 68.26% of all data are within plus or minus one standard deviation from the average, 95.44% of all data are within plus or minus two standard deviations from the average, and 99.73% of all data are within plus or minus three standard deviations from the average.

Thus, for events occurring with a stable frequency, 99.73% of data are expected within a three-sigma range on both ends. Any point that falls outside this six-sigma range should become apparent as an uncommon occurrence.

Control charts can be used to trend KRIs such as complaints, defects, and performance indices. The benefit of using control charts is that they provide an automatic statistical threshold that can be useful for determining trends. ASQ recommends the following signals for an out-of-control trend:

FIGURE 32.11 C chart example: quality defects.

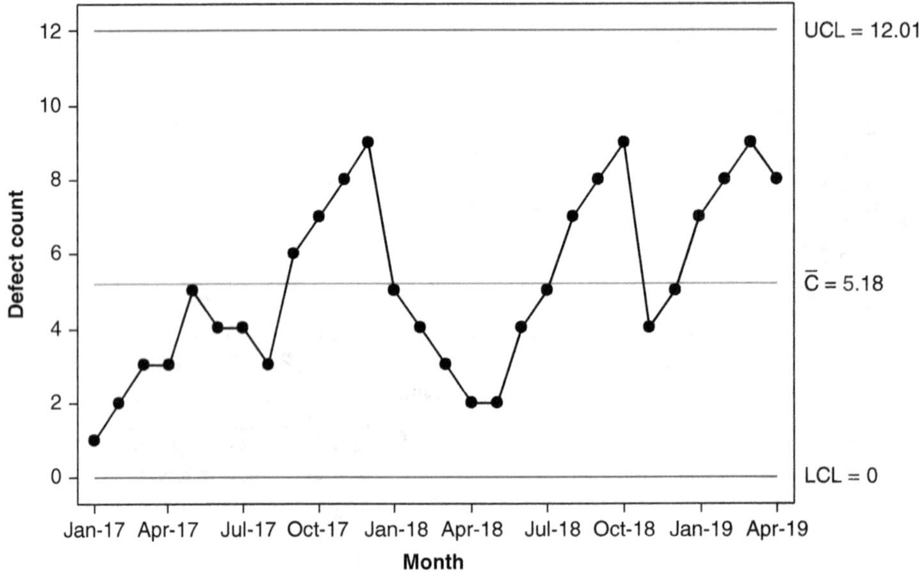

- A single point outside the control limits
- Two out of three successive points are on the same side of the centerline and farther than 2 sigma from it
- Four out of five successive points are on the same side of the centerline and farther than 1 sigma from it
- A run of eight points in a row are on the same side of the centerline

While these charts were primarily designed for manufacturing process control, they are very much applicable to all data trending as long as the underlying statistical rules are satisfied. Further elaboration on control charts is given in Chapter 33.

PIE CHARTS

A *pie chart* is a straightforward visual tool to compare proportions. The parts of the chart are displayed as slices of different colors, designs, or patterns within a whole to show the relative percentage or fraction represented by each part. The biggest strength of the chart is its simplicity of creation and understanding. An example is shown in Figure 32.12.

It provides a quick visual to compare the operational costs of the plants and draw conclusions on these costs. These charts can show both occurrence and impact when used to calculate *levels* at a particular time. They cannot be used for trending as there is no time or duration component.

FIGURE 32.12 Pie chart example: operational costs.

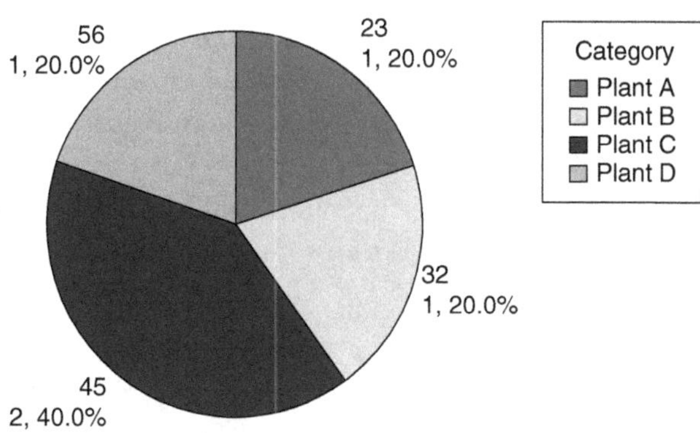

FIGURE 32.13 Dotplot example: quality defects.

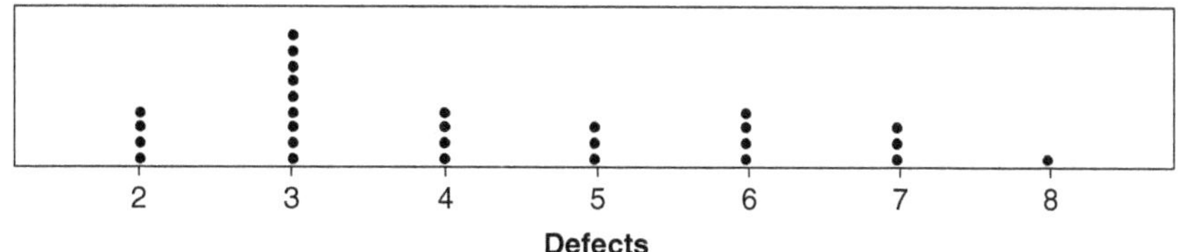

FIGURE 32.14 Dotplot (two variables) example: defect count for Machines A and B.

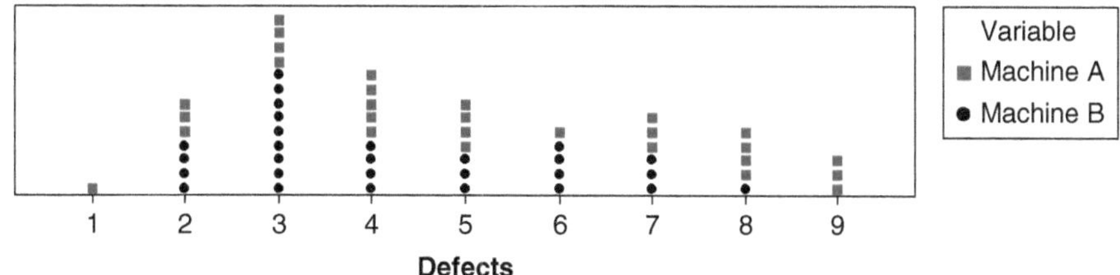

DOTPLOTS

A *dotplot* is a frequency representation using dots plotted on a scale shown by the x-axis. This tool plots the number of times an event or observation occurs per the x-axis scale. In the dotplot shown in Figure 32.13, the quality defects by number are plotted. It clusters the defect count by number and, in the example below, shows that it is most common to have three quality defects and least common to have eight.

A dotplot can also be used for comparing two sets of data, as shown in Figure 32.14. It is useful to show the distribution of the defect frequency between two data sets and better visualize data distributions.

INDIVIDUAL VALUE PLOTS

An *individual value plot* shows the point plots of the individual values that make up a data set. When used as a risk tracker, this chart can show the occurrence distribution of particular indicators and events. In the example in Figure 32.15, calls attended by three operators in a call center per day over nine days are compared using this tool. All nine data points are shown for three operators. Thus, this plot gives a macro view of the distribution of a data set and allows for spotting of outliers.

RADAR CHARTS

A *radar chart* is a two-dimensional tool for displaying and comparing multivariate data. Each spoke of the chart represents a variable, and the levels, which make up the scope, show a categorical sequence of progression. In Figure 32.16, three variables of claim, return, and replacement costs are shown for three production plants. Three triangles are formed by connecting the value of each plant for each of the variables. Similarly, more than three variables can exist as well, as represented by polygons as shown in Figures 32.17 and 32.18. These charts are good for comparing risk indicator levels between different locations or across products or services where more than more variable is involved in the comparison. Radar charts readily show any outliers and contrast them with commonalities across the parameters being compared for categorical variables.

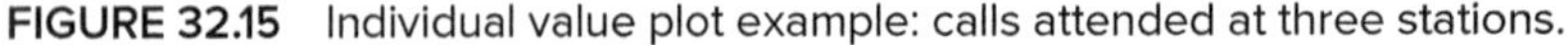
FIGURE 32.15 Individual value plot example: calls attended at three stations.

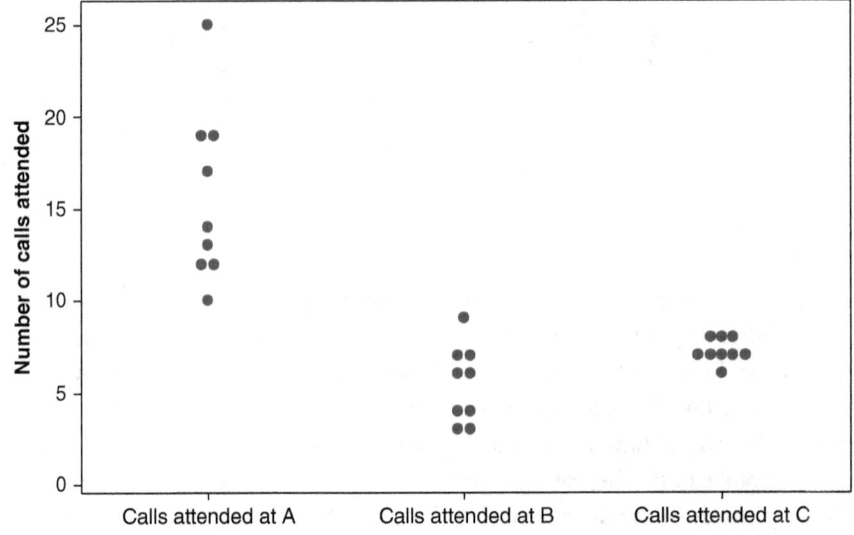

FIGURE 32.16 Radar chart: external failure costs.

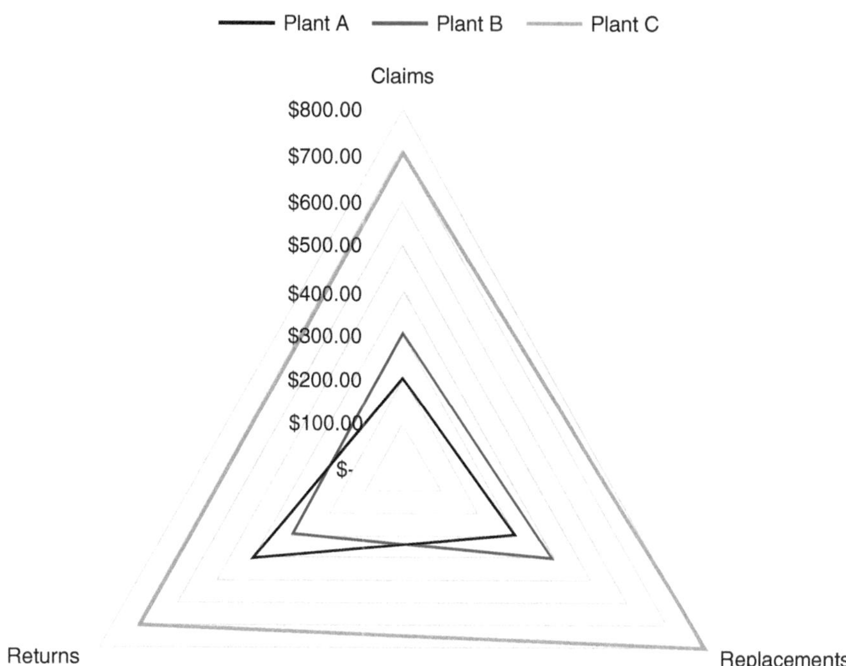

AREA CHARTS

The *area chart* is used to assess trends in multiple stacked time series charts and visually show each charted variable's contribution to the sum. The area chart allows us to assess proportion and change in proportion over time. This chart can be used to check both levels and trends for risk indicators. Figure 32.19 shows the sum of the monthly defect counts for two plants. The chart is divided into two shaded areas to distinguish each plant's proportion of defects.

J CHARTS

The *J chart* attempts to represent the failure mode, along with severity and occurrence, in a graphical way with statistically significant control limits available for comparison. It adds a visual layer of analysis to the U control chart (discussed in detail in Chapter 34) in terms of rate of occurrence of actual harms related to the failure mode.

The UCL for a J chart is defined by the same formula for UCL for a U chart (discussed in Chapter 34). The normalization of every type of harm is done by dividing the number of harm events by the normalizing factor (e.g., number of sales) for the applicable time period such that they can be trended complementarily to the failure mode. All normalized harms together mathematically make up the failure mode trend line. In

FIGURE 32.17 Radar chart: failure costs by plant.

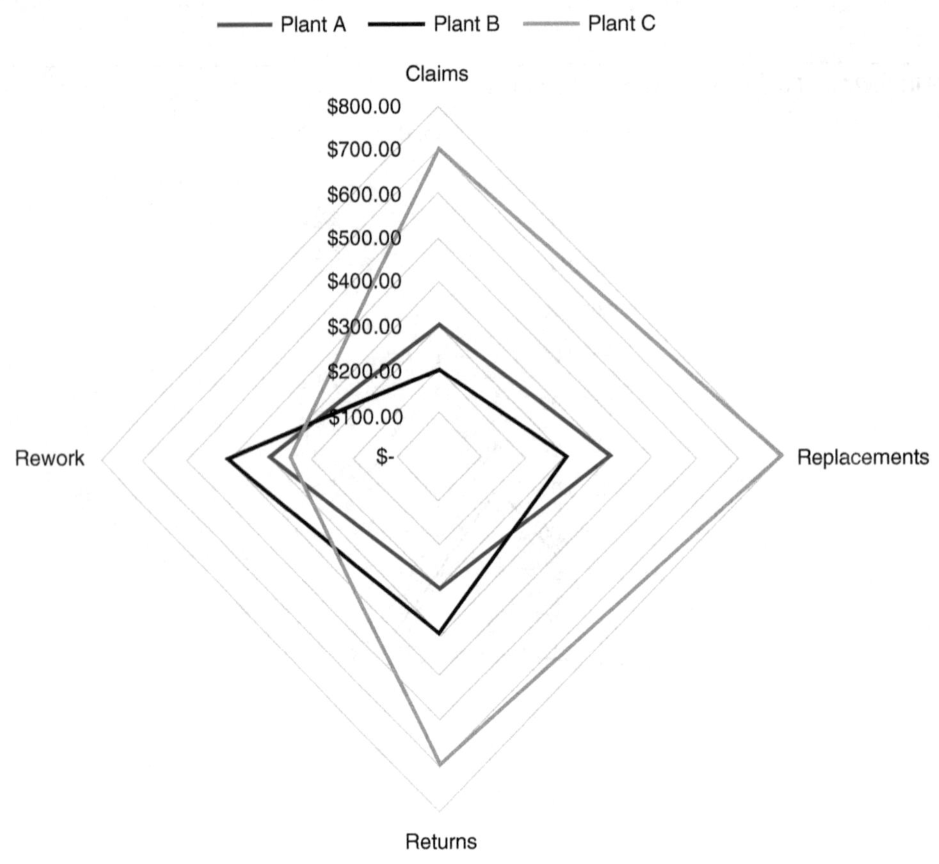

FIGURE 32.18 Radar chart: external and internal failure costs by plant.

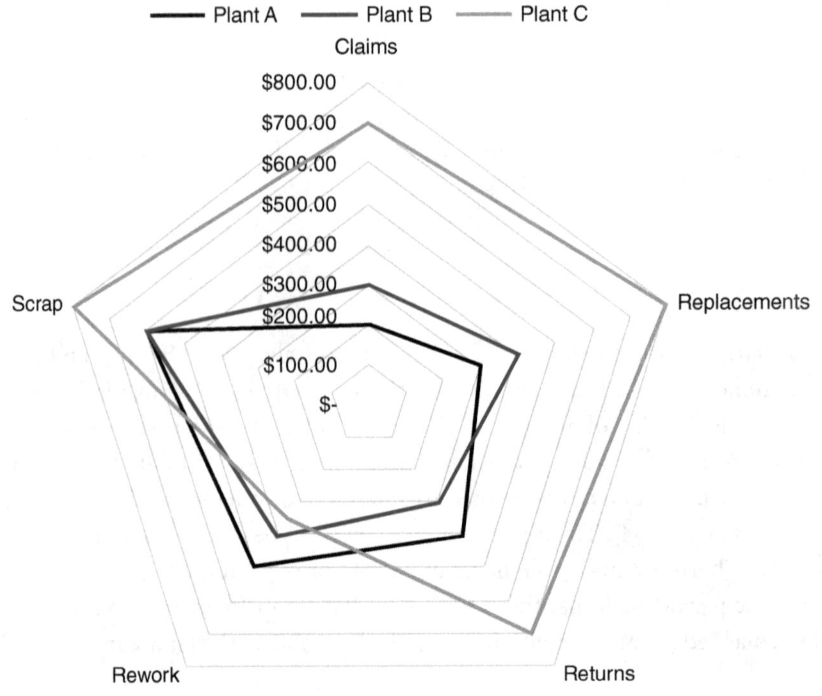

FIGURE 32.19 Area chart example: defect count by plant.

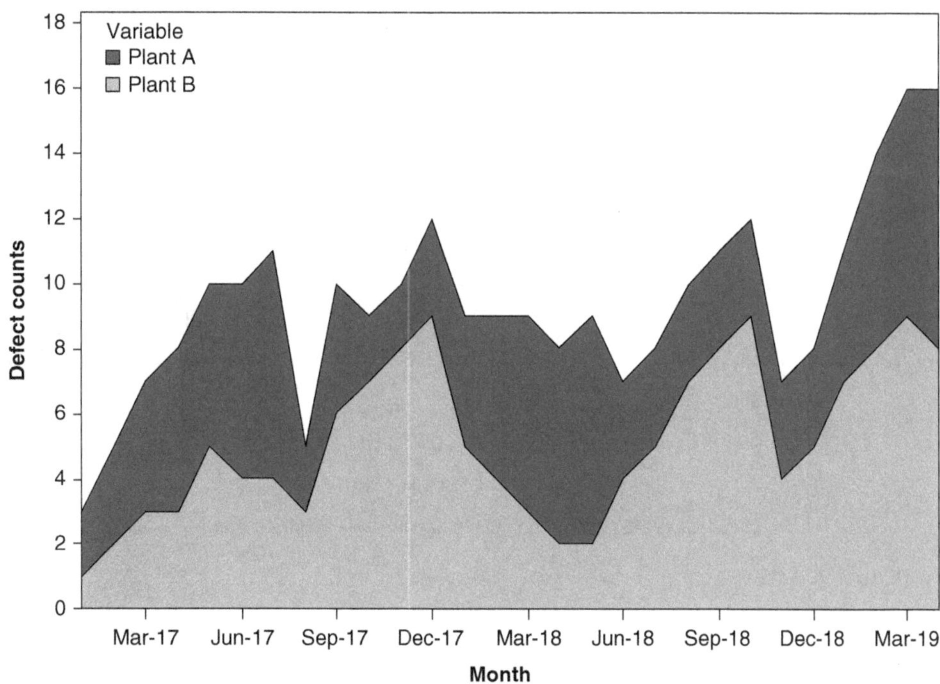

FIGURE 32.20 J chart example: hypothetical failure mode leading to bleeding, hematoma, and infections.

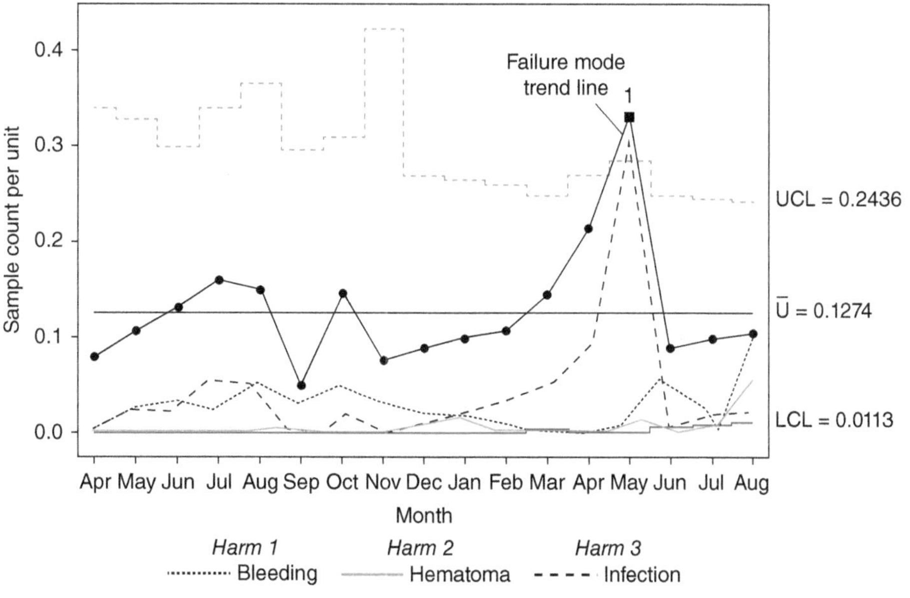

Source: Adapted from J. Moon, "Theory and Application of J Charts for Holistic Risk Based Statistical Adverse Event Trending," *International Journal of Health and Economic Development* 4, no. 1 (2018): 26.

FIGURE 32.21 J chart variation.

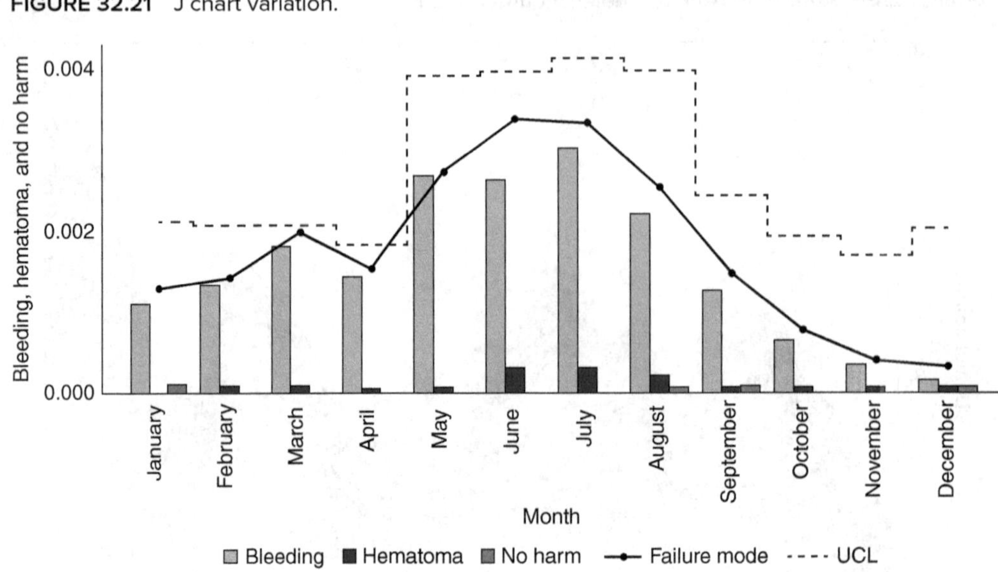

Figure 32.20, bleeding, hematoma, and infection together add up to the overall failure events, which are noted by the failure mode trend line.

The excursive event in the J chart is exactly similar to an excursive event in the U chart. The former gives more detail regarding the nature of the failure mode in terms of harm and the severity of the harm such that a direct graphical, trend-able comparison can be made against the line item in the FMEA or the failure modes and effect criticality analysis (FMECA).

In this case, all resultant harms can be seen for the failure mode under study. For example, for the month of May, when the excursion occurs, it can be plainly seen what harms are tailing the failure mode. Thus, quick action can be taken if the profile of the trend of any of the harms is different from the predetermined severity and occurrence combination in the FMEA.

Likewise, instead of using line charts to trend the constituent harms resulting from the failure mode, bar charts can be used, as shown in Figure 32.21.

CHAPTER 33

Visual Risk Exposure Tracker

A METHOD OF RISK MONITORING that complements the risk matrix for easy visualization of risk exposure and continuous risk tracking is an impact-occurrence bubble chart. In these charts, one axis is the qualitative impact (consequence) ordinal rating, and the other axis is the qualitative or quantitative rating for frequency of occurrence.

In Figure 33.1, the x-axis is the quantitative level of occurrence, and the y-axis contains the qualitatively rated impact levels. Table 33.1 shows the corresponding risk parameters.

For consistency, both axes can be made qualitative. While this will lead to some loss of specificity due to probabilities or occurrence rates being "basketed" together, the chart is still a very useful prioritization tool. In the next example, we have assigned an occurrence level (using a key of 1 [low] to 5 [high]) as shown in the third column of Table 33.2, and in Figure 33.2 we have charted the rating levels. The RPN, here composed of occurrence and impact levels, is the exposure represented by the area of the circle.

We can summarize the process of making the risk exposure bubble charts as follows:

1. Convert the probability and impact scales to x- and y-axes
2. Locate the risk for an impact-probability pair on the x-y grid (similar to the risk matrix)
3. Enlarge the circle such that its area corresponds to a numerical value of risk, which commonly is impact multiplied by probability

The advantage of bubble charts over risk matrices is that the risk exposure not only is visually evident in a handy graph but also can be tracked over time or after risk treatment. Figure 33.3 uses data from the previous examples and tracks the change in risk after treatment. Here, Risk 3 is the original risk, and Risk 3′ is the mitigated risk with lower impact and occurrence, therefore lesser risk exposure.

FIGURE 33.1 Impact-probability chart.

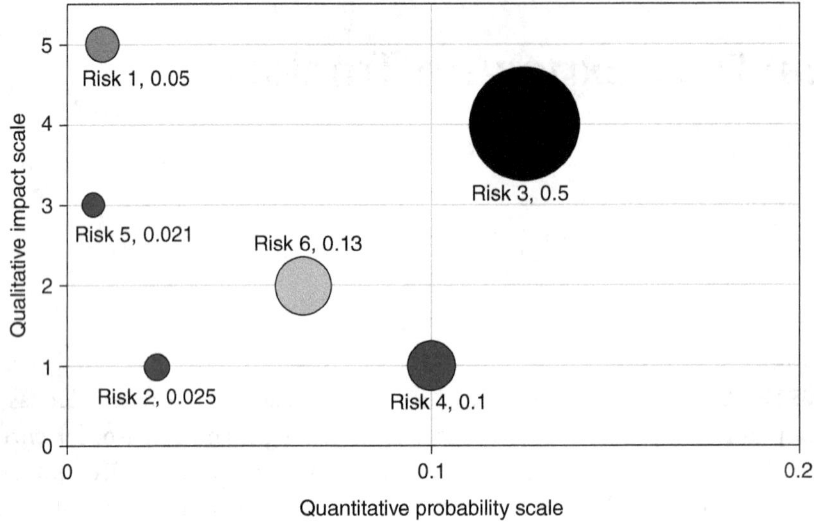

TABLE 33.1 Risk parameters for Figure 33.1.

Risk	Occurrence rate (quantitative)	Impact level (qualitative low [1] to high [5])	Exposure (P × I)
Risk 1	0.01	5	0.05
Risk 2	0.025	1	0.025
Risk 3	0.125	4	0.5
Risk 4	0.1	1	0.1
Risk 5	0.007	3	0.021
Risk 6	0.065	2	0.13

TABLE 33.2 Risk parameters for Figure 33.2.

Risk	Probability	Probability level	Impact level	Exposure	RPN
Risk 1	0.01	1	5	0.05	5
Risk 2	0.025	3	1	0.025	3
Risk 3	0.125	5	4	0.5	20
Risk 4	0.1	5	1	0.1	5
Risk 5	0.007	1	3	0.021	3
Risk 6	0.065	4	2	0.13	8

FIGURE 33.2 Impact-probability chart with qualitative x- and y-axes.

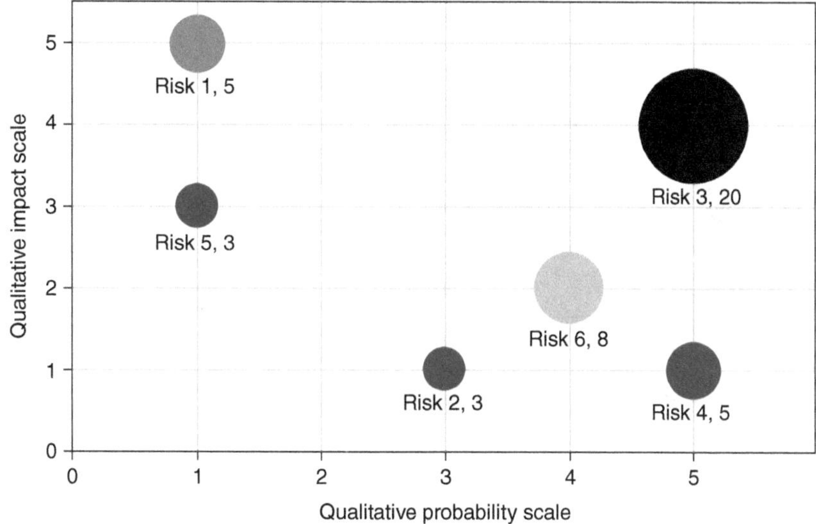

FIGURE 33.3 Use of impact-probability chart to show decrease in risk post-treatment.

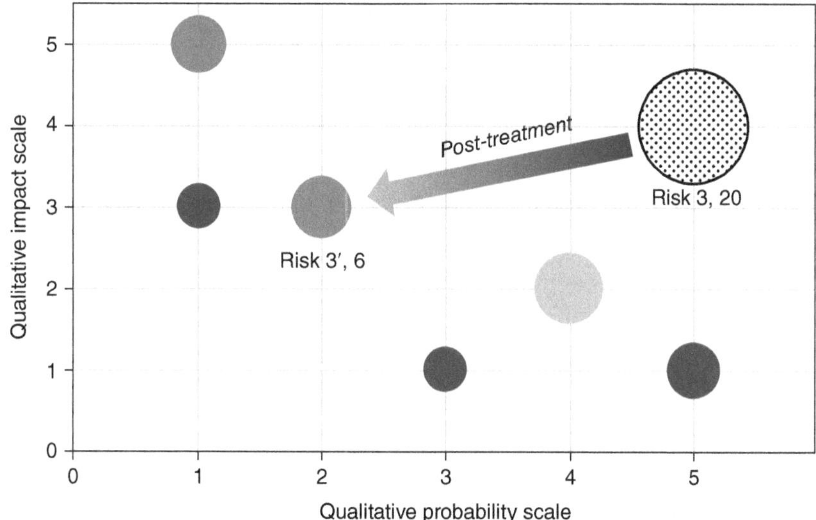

CHAPTER 34

A DMAIC Approach for Structured Risk-Based Trending

TRENDING OF KRIs GIVES A QUANTIFIED time-based measure of risk constituents that can be used for visual tracking, early problem detection, and prioritization. As shown in Figure 34.1, trending is based on and driven by integral source data. The trends should be looked at from a risk perspective and parsed out or stratified accordingly to drive action commensurate to the risk.

To ensure effectiveness of any trending process, its inputs and outputs must be clearly defined. Trending of KRIs may be done in two ways:

1. Occurrence based (gross count of occurrence of events per week or per month or per quarter)
2. Impact/severity based (count of occurrences by assignation of a cost, harm, loss, etc.)

An efficient and effective interface of the trending system with the risk response system is mandatory to ensure risk assurance and to maintain the risk profile. A simple and straightforward method of ensuring the efficacy and productivity of this interface is by using statistically sound methods of trending such as control charts.

APPLICABILITY OF CONTROL CHARTS FOR TRENDING

Statistical quality control was founded as a discipline by W. E. Deming and W. A. Shewhart, who advocated use of quality tools such as run charts, Pareto charts, control charts, and histograms to achieve the goal of quality assurance and continuous improvement.

Control charts have been demonstrated to be of growing value in the industry for trending of signal detection and continuous improvement. Many studies have confirmed their analytic capabilities as they relate to service quality, complaints, hospital infection surveillance, infection control, and adverse healthcare events. Usage of control charts as a method of statistical process trending and control for comparing performance with historical patterns while assessing variation and stability is well established especially in manufacturing quality engineering, but less widespread is the use in trending for risk review purposes.

FIGURE 34.1 Risk-based trending.

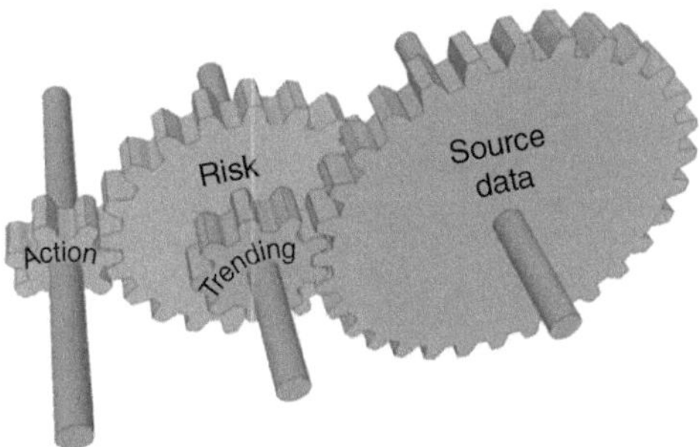

Government regulations and guidances like the Code of Federal Regulations Title 21 Part 820 Subpart O Section 820.250 and ICH Q9 mandate manufacturers of medical devices and pharmaceuticals, respectively, to establish statistical techniques to control and verify product characteristics. Though such legal enforcements are not found in all industries, these charts can qualify as a great tool for proactive problem detection, continual improvement, and targeted problem solving.

WHAT IS RISK-BASED TRENDING?

Risk-based trending means trending parameters that constitute a risk such that the trends become an indicator of risk realization. The trends over time can provide a direction to the developing risks and can act as a bellwether.

A five-step approach for the application of risk-based trending is as follows:

1. Define the tool
2. Define its usage and baselines
3. Define what is acceptable and unacceptable quantitatively
4. Use predefined trends to check the acceptability or unacceptability of the impact/severity and occurrence rates over time
5. Ensure that the trends trigger a pathway to mitigate or reduce risk

THE FIVE-STEP DMAIC PROCESS

A statistically sound events trending approach can follow the five-step process shown in Figure 34.2 and described in detail below.

The first step is to define raw data, the trending methodology, and the concomitant tools. Figure 34.3 illustrates major activities of the Define phase.

A trending tool is made meaningful only if it provides accurate results and identifies true problems without false alarms. Improper usage of charts, especially control charts, is very common. Inaccurate application of a complicated tool without understanding its

FIGURE 34.2 Five-step process for risk-based complaints trending.

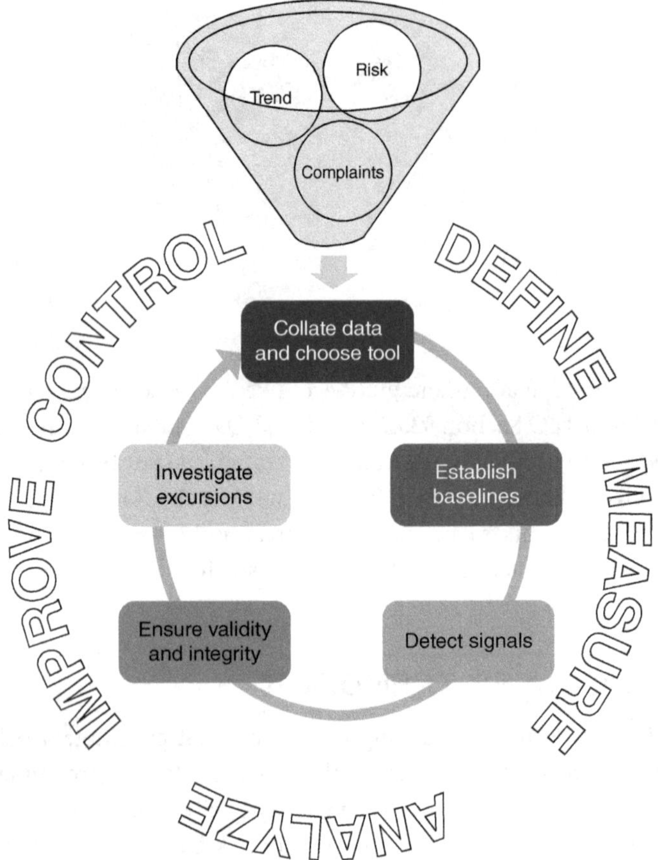

arithmetic may result in the tool being overly sensitive or undersensitive, thereby defeating its purpose.

To ensure proactive trending and reduce false alarms, the following points must be kept in mind:

1. How is the trigger (for escalation) defined? Is it a sigma rate based on history, or is it a predefined rate from risk analysis documents?
2. Do the data follow "rational subgrouping"? What subgroup sizes do we have, and how many subgroups have we chosen? For example, charting complaints daily would give a lot of data points that would vary a lot, giving us a random trend as opposed to charting complaints monthly, which would provide a much more stable trend line. Rational subgrouping is done on a case-by-case basis. A set of parameters that is rational for one system may be completely irrational for another.
3. If using control charts, what run rules (or Westinghouse rules) fit the data? Do they even fit at all, or should new rules be defined?

FIGURE 34.3 The Define phase.

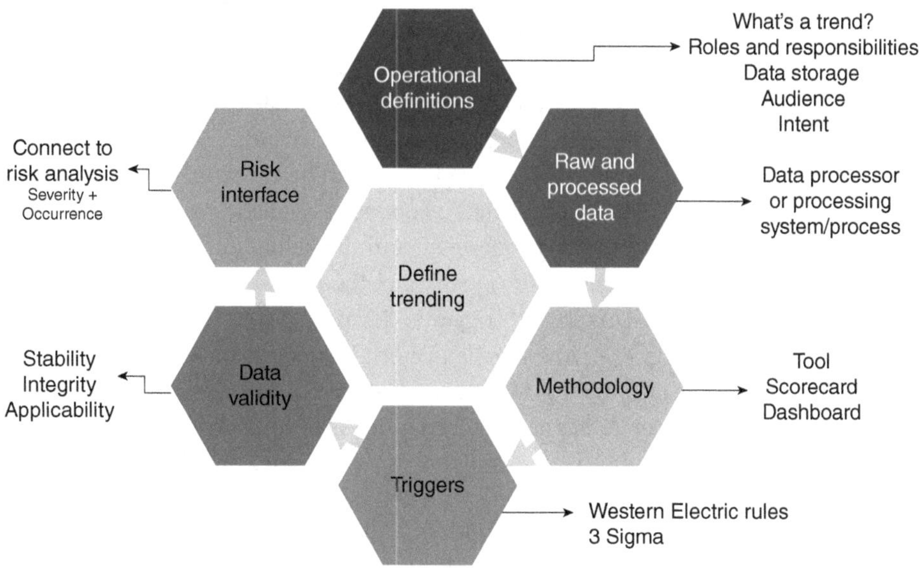

The next phase is Measure, where the chosen tool is used to track and trend the occurrences or impacts (physical or monetary). This can be a simple trend line using Excel or a control chart with three or two sigma limits. Regardless of the tool, it is important to ensure the validity and integrity of the data as detailed in the earlier step. This may mean checking things like normality or probability distribution, making sure the sample sizes are correct and consistent, or ensuring proper application of trigger criteria.

Once the quantity of interest is plotted for a period of time and a minimum number of data points have been gathered, we can define *baselines*. It is common to have baselines based on historical rates as a trigger criterion. A breach of three sigma limits is a simple and commonly used trigger in statistical process control (SPC). Other, more sensitive triggers can be employed per the Western Electric rules as follows:

- One point beyond three standard errors
- Nine consecutive points on the same side of the centerline within one standard error of the centerline
- Six consecutive points increasing or decreasing
- Fourteen consecutive points alternating, increasing and decreasing
- Two of three consecutive points between two and three standard errors on either side of the centerline
- Four of five consecutive points on either side of the centerline beyond one standard error from the centerline
- Fifteen consecutive points within one standard error of the centerline
- Eight consecutive points on either or both sides of the centerline—with none within one standard error of the centerline

The predefined rates for such triggers from the risk register, hazard log, and risk analysis documents created during design, such as FMEA, HAZOP, PHA, etc., can also be used for this purpose. This constitutes part one of the Analyze phase.

Once the signal has been detected, the data must be double-checked to ensure that it is not a false alarm. This may mean something as simple as going through the raw data to ensure all valid incidences are charted and no "voids" are included, or it may mean that the calculations for three sigma limits must be checked. If there is suspicion, the data integrity and validity checks may be repeated, including tests for probability distribution. Once this activity is completed and the validity of the signal is ensured, we have a bona fide excursion. This means that the process has shifted from historically determined limits. This should trigger an investigation.

In the Improve phase, an investigative determination is made regarding the event. In this phase, greater insight into the data may be needed based on the excursive event. A deeper dive into the issue can be done using stratification, which may mean increasing the resolution of the data by focusing on a specific trend or failure.

Stratification is defined as the act of sorting data into distinct groups or layers. It is a technique used in combination with other data analysis tools. When data from a variety of sources or categories have been lumped together, the meaning of the data can be difficult to see. This data collection and analysis technique (which is considered one of the seven basic quality tools) separates the data so that patterns can be seen.

Once the exact issue is established, risk reassessment should be performed and the root cause analysis and risk response activities should be performed commensurate to this risk.

After the desired deep dive into the issue is achieved, a targeted root cause analysis activity should uncover the primary cause and drive the risk response that will result in mitigation of the issue. If it is discovered that, due to some reason, an escalated rate is to be expected and will be the "new normal," then the trending tool and its limits must be redefined. Figure 34.4 shows the aforementioned steps being used sequentially for targeted problem solving.

In the Control phase, after the excursion has been resolved, the limits are either redefined based on the investigative analysis or kept the same. In either case, a decision may be made to selectively trend certain KRIs separately such that a greater level of sensitivity is afforded. The decision must be made on the confidence of the mitigative actions taken for the excursion.

WHICH CONTROL CHARTS SHOULD WE USE?

The choice of control charts depends on the nature of the raw data, which are primarily composed of two components:

1. The trended quantity
2. The sample size

FIGURE 34.4 An example of targeted problem solving using control charts, risk assessment, and quality tools.

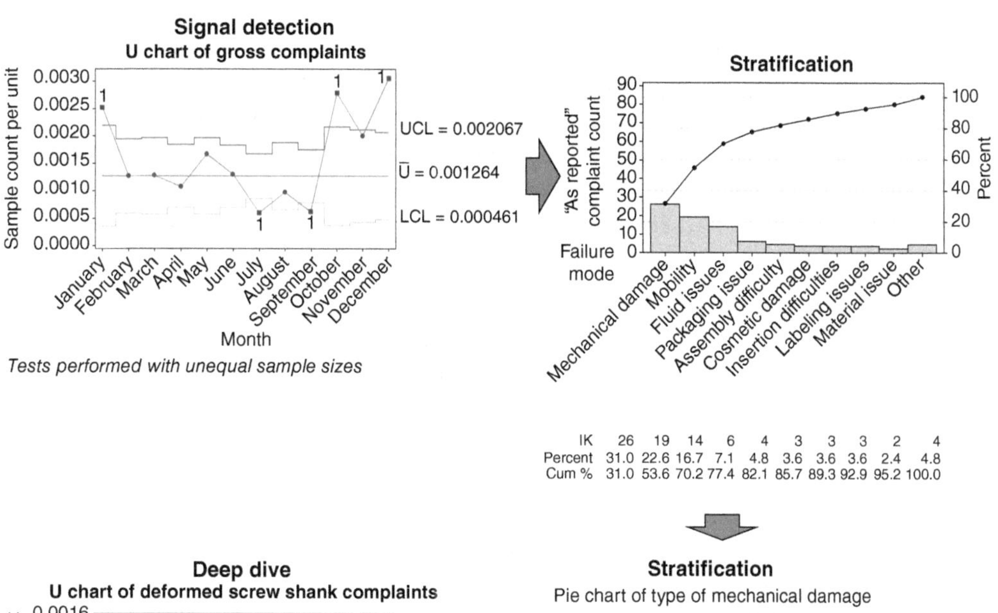

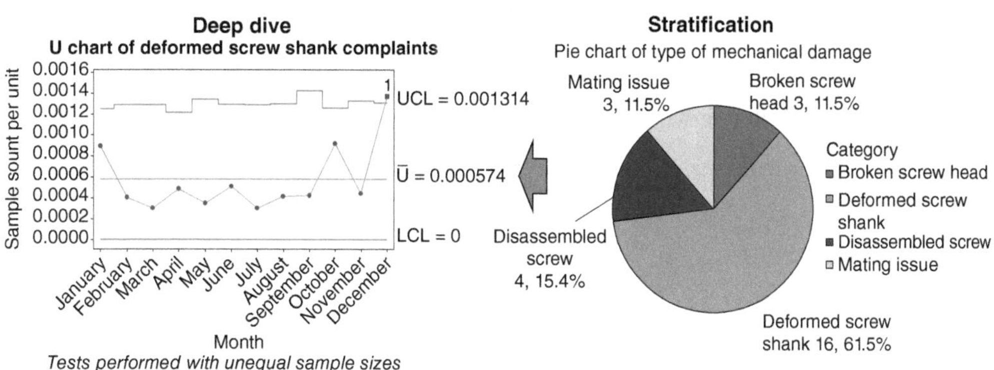

Risk assessment

12 month rolling rate % (P1)	0.057%
FMEA occurrence rate (component stuck × bleeding) (P1 × P2)	0.01% (or 1 in 10,000)
P1 × P2 from the chart (component stuck × bleeding)	0.025%
Risk level change [hard trigger]	R4 to R3

CAPA and RCA

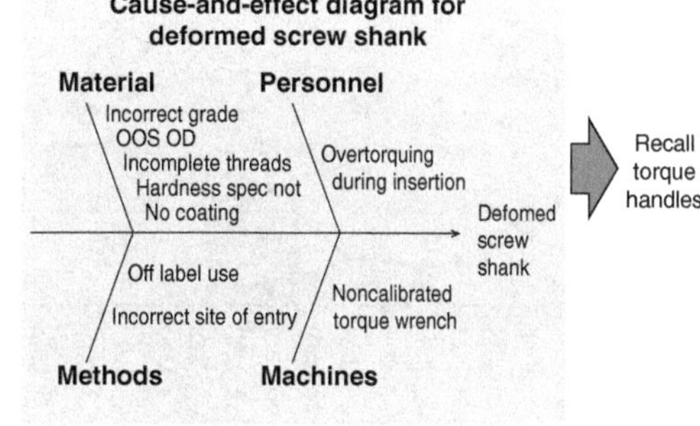

Recall torque handles

If the trended quantity can be classified as yes/no or pass/fail (i.e., it is a discrete quantity), then a P chart or NP chart should be used since these types of data follow a binomial distribution.

If the trended quantity is expected to be composed of numerous subevents within a greater event, then a C or U chart should be used—for example, if we are counting the number of failures for each surgical event for a month, or the number of drug side effects for sales each week, or the number of unique failures of the single product per unique event. In such cases, a product was expected to fail in more than one way during use, or a drug may have more than one side effect after consumption. Such types of data fit the Poisson distribution, which lends itself to control charting via C and U charts.

ATTRIBUTE CHART ASSUMPTIONS

The following must be true for the above-mentioned charts to be valid and to minimize false excursions:

1. The data must have Poisson (for U chart) or binomial (for C chart) distribution
2. The number of opportunities for failure must be large compared with the number of failures
3. The probability of failure at each sample should be small
4. Criteria to adjudge failure are the same for each sample and are consistent

The three main elements of a control chart, as shown in Figures 34.5 and 34.6, are as follows:

FIGURE 34.5 Example anatomy of a control chart of post-launch consumer complaint events.

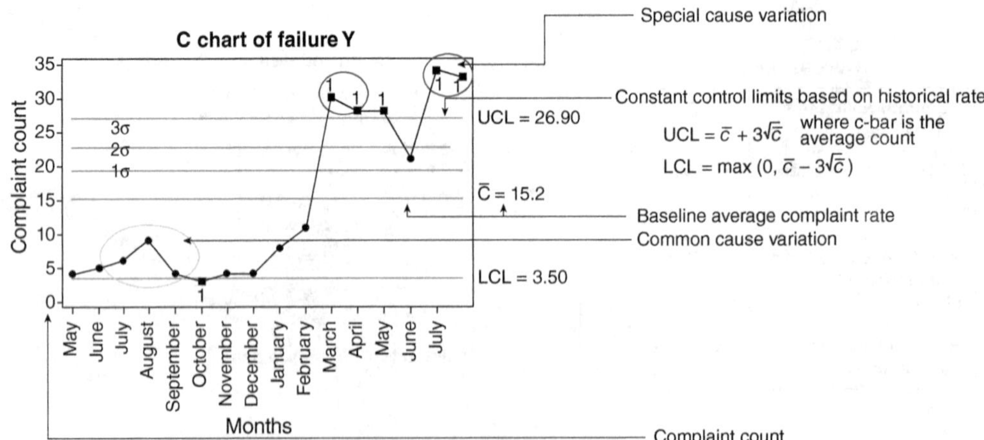

A special cause is present in the process if any points fall above the upper control limit. Action should be taken to find the special cause and permanently remove it from the process.

FIGURE 34.6 Anatomy of a U chart.

U cthart: shows complaint rate normalized by sales such that increased sales do not give a false trigger.

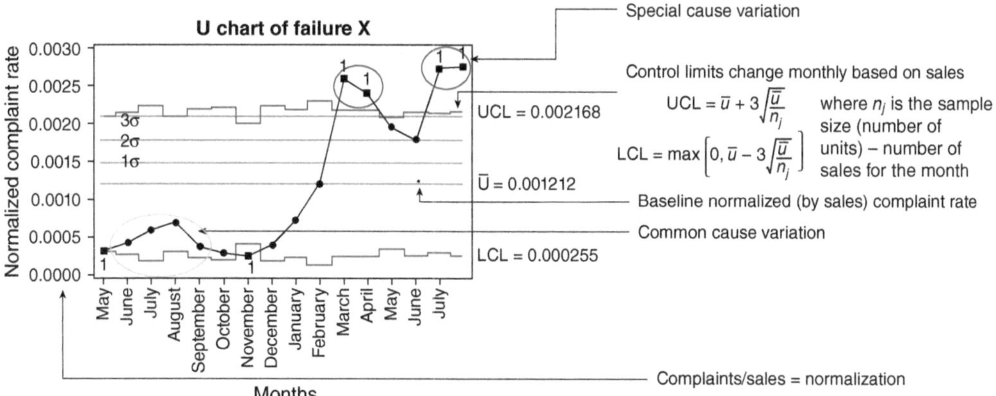

Tests performed with unequal sample sizes

1. A time series graph (black line connected by black dots)
2. A central line (in green) is added as a visual reference for detecting shifts or trends
3. Upper and lower control limits (UCL and LCL) are computed from available data and placed equidistant from the central line

The control limits are calculated by:

1. Estimating the standard deviation of the sample data
2. Multiplying that number by three
3. Adding for the UCL and subtracting for the LCL

Many statistical software packages, such as Minitab, Datalyzer, and JMP, automatically calculate these limits.

REAL-WORLD APPLICATION

In May and June 2011, a leading medical device manufacturer recalled all lots of an intra-arterial device. Portions of these devices were breaking during and after insertion into the vasculature and could potentially lead to embolism, thrombotic events, infarction, or death. Let us take a look at the adverse event reports stemming from complaints submitted by the manufacturer to the Food and Drug Administration. The data from June 2009 to June 2011 are as shown in Table 34.1.

We will attempt to draw a control chart to trend the rate of failures, verify timeliness of the recall action, and verify the effectiveness of corrective action.

The application of concepts introduced early in this chapter leads us to verify the following parameters:

TABLE 34.1 Adverse event reports by month.

Data point	Month	# Adverse event reports	Data point	Month	# Adverse event reports
1	Jun-09	3	13	Jun-10	0
2	Jul-09	0	14	Jul-10	1
3	Aug-09	0	15	Aug-10	3
4	Sep-09	1	16	Sep-10	2
5	Oct-09	1	17	Oct-10	0
6	Nov-09	1	18	Nov-10	0
7	Dec-09	4	19	Dec-10	1
8	Jan-10	2	20	Jan-11	1
9	Feb-10	0	21	Feb-11	1
10	Mar-10	0	22	Mar-11	4
11	Apr-10	1	23	Apr-11	5
12	May-10	2	24	May-11	3
			25	Jun-11	7

1. Trended quantity = defects (device breakage during surgery)
2. Sample size = constant (since we are not privy to monthly sales of the company)
3. Probability distribution = binomial (since device breakage is a binary event, it either breaks or stays; pass or fail)
4. Number of subgroups = 25

Based on the key in Figure 34.5, and based on our constraints and the nature of the data, the C chart best suits our needs.

A first warning could be seen in March and April (see Figure 34.7) as the adverse events trended upward and finally breached the trigger limit in June 2011. The company's action to conduct a recall was very timely since if no action had been taken at the time of the three-sigma breach, the rate of failures would have risen uncontrollably and probably caused serious injuries or deaths.

In this particular case, the company was able to identify a root cause and implement corrections. The manufacturer changed its production practices and was able to see a drastically reduced rate after the recall, as shown in Figure 34.8.

A manufacturer will be aware of the number of sales of the device or the lot size. The number of complaints can be divided by the sales or lot size to get a rate of occurrence of failure. This rate can be continually updated as more complaints come in. The failure of the device can be compared with either the rate in the risk analysis conducted before the launch or the rates of similar devices to get an idea of occurrence with regard to a baseline.

We must also remember that occurrence is only one dimension of risk (tracked in the control chart); there is also the dimension of severity. Trending driven by risk puts

FIGURE 34.7 C chart of device failures from June 2009 to June 2011.

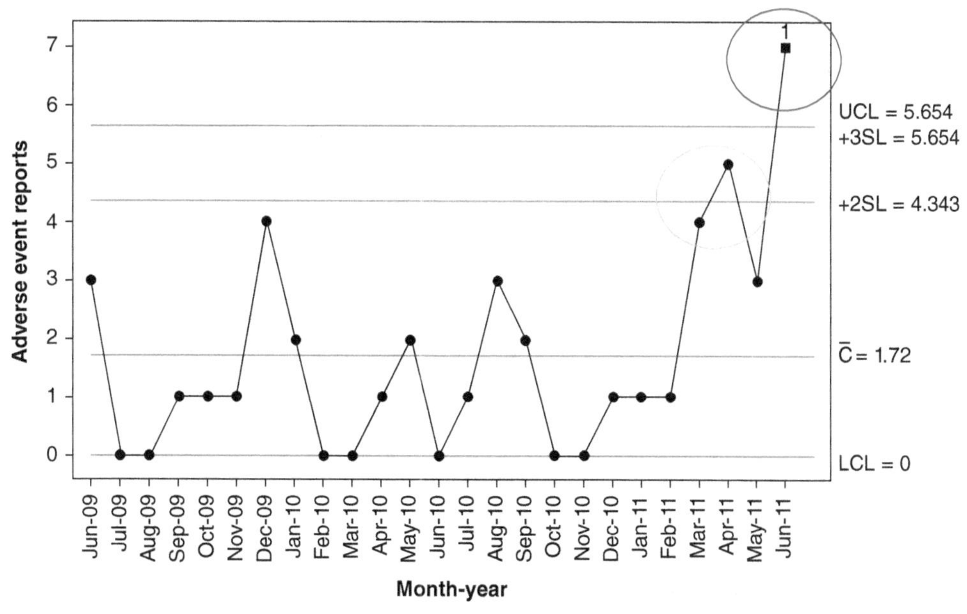

FIGURE 34.8 C chart of pre- and post-recall catheter failure.

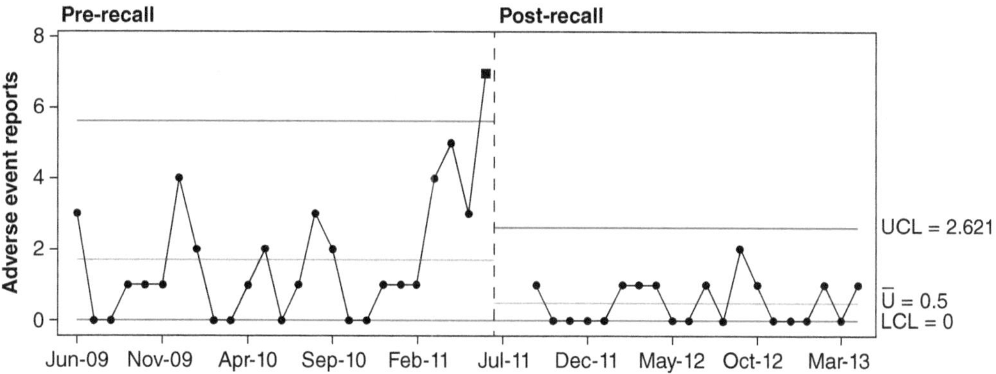

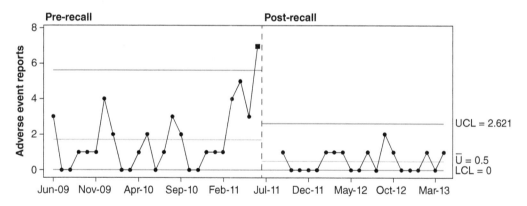

the severity foremost in prioritizing issues. Every time there is a complaint event, the risk level must be tested by calculating both occurrence and severity. With a risk level, trends can be established, but if there is even one complaint of a very high severity, an investigation must result, regardless of the trend of occurrence.

In the example above, let us consider that before 2010 the rate of failures was "remote" ($< 10^{-5}$ and $> 10^{-6}$) and outcomes were only "minor" injuries. The risk level can be charted as shown in Figure 34.9 using concepts learned in Chapter 26. Based on the "remote" failure rate and "minor" severity, the risk level is low.

FIGURE 34.9 Risk level correlation with KRI—pre-trending issue risk level is low.

Common terms	Examples of probability range
Frequent	$\geq 10^{-3}$
Probable	$< 10^{-3}$ and $\geq 10^{-4}$
Occasional	$< 10^{-4}$ and $\geq 10^{-5}$
Remote	$< 10^{-5}$ and $\geq 10^{-6}$
Improbable	$< 10^{-6}$

		Impact level				
		Level 1	Level 2	Level 3	Level 4	Level 5
Probability level	Level 5	M	M	H	H	H
	Level 4	L	M	H	H	H
	Level 3	L	M	M	H	H
	Level 2	L	L	M	M	M
	Level 1	L	L	L	L	L

Common terms	Possible description
Catastrophic	Results in patient death
Critical	Results in permanent impairment or life-threatening injury
Serious	Results in injury or impairment requiring professional medical intervention
Minor	Results in temporary injury or impairment not requiring professional medical intervention
Negligible	Inconvenience or temporary discomfort

FIGURE 34.10 Risk level correlation with KRI—increase in level due to uptick in complaints picked up by KRI.

Common terms	Examples of probability range
Frequent	$\geq 10^{-3}$
Probable	$< 10^{-3}$ and $\geq 10^{-4}$
Occasional	$< 10^{-4}$ and $\geq 10^{-5}$
Remote	$< 10^{-5}$ and $\geq 10^{-6}$
Improbable	$< 10^{-6}$

		Impact level				
		Level 1	Level 2	Level 3	Level 4	Level 5
Probability level	Level 5	M	M	H	H	H
	Level 4	L	M	H	H	H
	Level 3	L	M	M	H	H
	Level 2	L	L	M	M	M
	Level 1	L	L	L	L	L

Common terms	Possible description
Catastrophic	Results in patient death
Critical	Results in permanent impairment or life-threatening injury
Serious	Results in injury or impairment requiring professional medical intervention
Minor	Results in temporary injury or impairment not requiring professional medical intervention
Negligible	Inconvenience or temporary discomfort

Continual monitoring of the occurrence rate can give a signal when the rate changes from "remote" to "occasional" as shown in Figure 34.10. At the same level of frequency, the risk level has now changed to medium instead of low.

Finally, a change in both occurrence and severity can lead to an unacceptable risk level as shown in Figure 34.11, which would demand a drastic mitigative action such as a recall.

FIGURE 34.11 High occurrence rate and high severity—drastic increase in risk level.

Common terms	Examples of probability range
Frequent	≥ 10^{-3}
Probable	< 10^{-3} and ≥ 10^{-4}
Occasional	< 10^{-4} and ≥ 10^{-5}
Remote	< 10^{-5} and ≥ 10^{-6}
Improbable	< 10^{-6}

		Impact level				
		Level 1	Level 2	Level 3	Level 4	Level 5
Probability level	Level 5	M	M	H	H	H
	Level 4	L	M	H	H	H
	Level 3	L	M	M	H	H
	Level 2	L	L	M	M	M
	Level 1	L	L	L	L	L

Common terms	Possible description
Catastrophic	Results in patient death
Critical	Results in permanent impairment or life-threatening injury
Serious	Results in injury or impairment requiring professional medical intervention
Minor	Results in temporary injury or impairment not requiring professional medical intervention
Negligible	Inconvenience or temporary discomfort

Through this example we saw the power of the control charts not only in trending complaint activity but also in serving as a proactive signal detector, a warning tool, and a powerful quantitative method to verify effectiveness of corrective actions. When control charts are paired with risk analysis, risk-based trending can be effected, which allows for risk monitoring and timely discovery of issues (and timely application of mitigative actions) for preemptive risk management.

CHAPTER 35

Risk-Based Auditing

THE MAJOR CHANGE IN ISO 19011:2018 over the 2011 version is the addition of the risk-based approach to auditing (see Figure 35.1). The standard mentions:

> *The risk-based approach should substantively influence the planning, conducting and reporting of audits in order to ensure that audits are focused on matters that are significant for the audit client, and for achieving the audit programme objectives.*[1]

A risk-based approach to auditing comprises the following:

1. Identifying the risks of the audit program itself and setting a course in cognizance of them
2. Evaluating the auditee's processes based on risk
3. Setting audit objectives and criteria based on risk
4. Using the audit program to identify negative risks and opportunities

The effectiveness of the audit program itself should be assessed using a risk management framework to ensure that all threats to the success of the program are identified and all opportunities are leveraged. Risks that can affect the audit program should be proactively addressed by response planning. This can be done on the following three levels:

1. Determining the extent of the program based on risk
2. Determining the audit leadership based on competency to manage associated audit risks
3. Taking a risk-based approach to planning audits

The audit program must be relevant to the context of the organizational mission and objectives, and the best method to ensure this is to commensurately focus on areas of threats to and opportunities for the organizational goals. For specific audits, risk-based prioritization of objectives can result in targeted inquiry and extraction of

1. ©ISO. This material is reproduced from ISO 19011:2018, with permission of the American National Standards Institute (ANSI) on behalf of the International Organization for Standardization. All rights reserved.

FIGURE 35.1 Elements of a risk-based approach to auditing.

maximum value out of the audit program. The objectives may include evaluation of organizational or departmental capability to address threats and opportunities in a changing internal and external organizational context.

The chosen audit leaders must exhibit risk competencies to manage the risks arising in the audits and to understand the risk framework of the system to be audited. The auditor must have competency to manage risks at the operational level of the audit and communicate risks as needed to the management or auditees. The leader must anticipate the information needed for identifying and evaluating the risks and prepare accordingly to effectively achieve audit objectives with sufficient risk awareness.

A risk-based approach to planning audits considers the risks of the audit to the auditee's process and aims to use preventive thinking to minimize any disruptions based on preparation, setting expectations, and mutual understanding. The allocation of resources to the audits must also be based on risk profiles of the objectives. If a remote audit is being conducted, the risks to the effectiveness of the audit and the risks to achievement of the objectives must be considered.

The audit should look for evidence of risk assessments and methods of risk responses of the auditee along with their effectiveness. The process approach directs the auditor to holistically review the effectiveness of the system as a whole to address threats and opportunities. In some cases, the audit itself can be used as a tool for risk identification by making risk identification the audit objective.

AUDIT OUTCOMES

The goal of an audit is to scrutinize the system to measure the conformity of the constituting subparts and processes to the preset criteria, which may overlap with various risk management aspects. ISO 19011:2018 mentions the following in this regard:

> *Audit conclusions should address issues such as . . . the extent of conformity with the audit criteria and robustness of the management system, including the effectiveness of the management system in meeting the intended outcomes, the identification of risks and effectiveness of actions taken by the auditee to address risks.*[2]

2. ©ISO. This material is reproduced from ISO 19011:2018, with permission of the American National Standards Institute (ANSI) on behalf of the International Organization for Standardization. All rights reserved.

TABLE 35.1 Risk matrix for classifying nonconformities during audits.

		Occurrence levels			
		First occurrence of nonconformity		Second occurrence of nonconformity	
	Finding	Low likelihood of current process to reduce impact	High likelihood of current process to reduce impact	Low likelihood of current process to reduce impact	High likelihood of current process to reduce impact
Nonconformance severity levels	Grade I (contained local impact)	1	1	3	1
	Grade II (uncontained local impact)	4	2	4	4
	Grade III (impact spreading from local to global)	5	5	7	5
	Grade IV (minor global impact)	8	6	8	8
	Grade V (major systemwide impact)	9	9	9	9

When there are gaps in conformity, a need to issue a finding may arise. An objective graded scale for findings makes it easy to classify the level and extent of loss of conformity. By incorporating a risk-based approach, this graded method can help engender urgency of response by classifying the nonconformity in terms of its impact on the management system.

An example of a nonconformity grading matrix is shown in Table 35.1. While rules of escalation can be set based on the organizational context, an example rule would be to mandate a reaudit and assign a major nonconformance for all nonconformity scores greater than 4.

AUDITING RISKS: THREATS AND OPPORTUNITIES

The call for auditors to incorporate risk auditing through the process approach is explicit in many sections of ISO 19011:2018. To realize this, an auditor must look for evidence of the following:

1. Risk identification process
2. Risk analysis and evaluation
3. Risk treatment or response planning and its effectiveness
4. Risk monitoring and review
5. Risk communication

It is not necessary for the organization or department to have a detailed and intricate method for all the above. The auditor's focus should be on the maturity shown by the

FIGURE 35.2 Major inputs of risk audits.

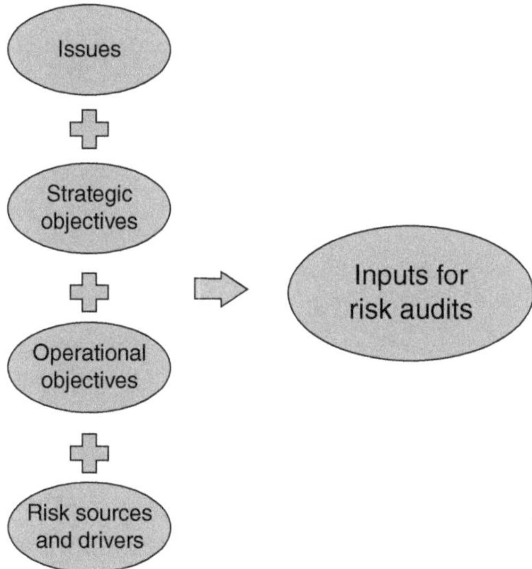

organization in instituting and practicing a risk-based approach. The auditor must be cognizant that some organizations may not have detailed steps or phases for doing so but may accomplish this effectively based on a pervasive preventive-thinking culture.

The major inputs of risk audits are shown in Figure 35.2.

Issues are the threats or opportunities that have been realized. The organization's response to these issues will speak volumes regarding risk response planning. Issues usually are associated with corrective actions or projects. The auditor must look for a risk-based approach to problem detection and solution determination.

The strategic and operational objectives of an organization can provide a road map for an audit trail. By following the key performance indicators (KPIs), one can review the organization's response to increasing or decreasing performance. Changes in strategic direction often mean changes in the risk landscape.

Finally, the auditor should evaluate various sources of risks to validate the organization's risk identification process. This may include an assessment of the hazards, or it could have a broader scope of the review of enterprise and strategic risk drivers. Regardless of the level of scrutiny, on a fundamental level, the auditor should look for evidence of risk-based decision making.

CHAPTER 36

Risk-Benefit Analysis

THERE IS AN OBVIOUS RELATIONSHIP between risks and rewards. General intuition leads us to believe that the greater the risk, the higher the reward. A gambler betting $5000 at a blackjack table will earn more than one betting $5.

Wrong. The truth is that the gambler betting $5000 will earn more only if she or he *wins*.

Risk assessment, treatment, and monitoring help us understand this risk-return relationship and help us make informed risk-based decisions. Sometimes, due to the negative connotation of the word "risk" and its focus on loss and failures, one needs to apply special focus on the rewards, returns, or benefits to be realized upon venturing to take a risk. An analysis that puts the benefits front and center is known as *risk-benefit analysis.*

Going back to the classical definition of risk, there are two components of risk that are evaluated during risk analysis and evaluation:

1. Occurrence or probability (likelihood) of a consequence
2. Magnitude of the consequence

In addition, integrative risk assessments involve more than a qualitative or quantitative line-item-based risk assessment of occurrence and severity. The overall risk must be compared with the overall benefit such that an aggregate metric is generated that can be compared with a baseline metric, thus allowing one risky pathway to be holistically compared with another.

Traditionally, to calculate risk, these two inputs are combined (usually by multiplication), and the output is often perceived to be a quantified value of risk. "Negative risk" and its adverse consequences are just one dimension. The classical definition of risk must be expanded to create an aggregate measurement that takes into special consideration the positive impact of risk despite the presence of negative risks. To holistically gauge the impact, the "benefit" must be taken into consideration. The definition of risk, as described in this book, is suited to both risk and benefit calculation, and it explicitly includes parameters for adjudging the seriousness of an event and its incidence rate.

Two industries where similar analyses are common are the financial sector and pharmaceuticals. In the financial sector, a common form of risk-benefit analysis is the Sharpe ratio, which tries to mathematically quantify the volatility and uncertainty of the market using the standard deviation of an asset expected to provide returns. It views the benefit as the monetary accretion over a nonrisky asset and is defined as follows:

A measure that indicates the average return minus the risk-free return divided by the standard deviation of return on an investment.

Mathematically, it can be written as:

$$S = \frac{Return}{Risk} = \frac{E(r - r_f)}{\sigma(r - r_f)} \tag{36.1}$$

where

r = Return of the invested portfolio

r_f = Return on a risk-free portfolio

$E(r - r_f)$ is the excess return of our portfolio over that of a risk-free portfolio

$\sigma(r - r_f)$ is a standard deviation of our portfolio over a risk-free portfolio

For example, I have a stock portfolio that has returns of 4.2% over the standard deviation of 16.21. My Sharpe ratio is 0.25. Berkshire Hathaway had a Sharpe ratio of 0.46 over 15 years preceding 2015. This means that Berkshire Hathaway made better risk bets than I did, which is evident by greater returns from its portfolio.

Due to the inherent volatility of the market, the higher the risk, the higher the returns. The Sharpe ratio does not have a predictive value but is a good comparative tool to gauge performance of several portfolios.

Another way to quantify the volatility is to look at risk from the standpoint of losses. Maximum drawdown (MDD) is one such parameter, which is defined as:

The maximum observed loss from a peak to a trough of a portfolio, before a new peak is attained.

This can be seen in Figure 36.1.

This metric focuses on the size of the most impactful loss, which in the chart above is \$13k.

$$MDD = \frac{23 - 10}{23}\% = 56.5\% \tag{36.2}$$

The MDD portrays the risk in terms of the most impactful volatility. Now the benefit is the actual return from the asset at a set date, which here is 29.4% since the asset increased in value from \$12k to \$17k despite volatility. Now that we have quantified the risk and return, a risk reward ratio can be calculated as:

$$Risk\ reward\ ratio = \frac{Return}{Risk} = \frac{Return\%}{MDD\%} = 0.52 \tag{36.3}$$

Hence, multiple assets can be compared using this ratio, which incorporates the aggregate risk as volatility.

FIGURE 36.1 Time series chart of asset value showing volatility in value over time.

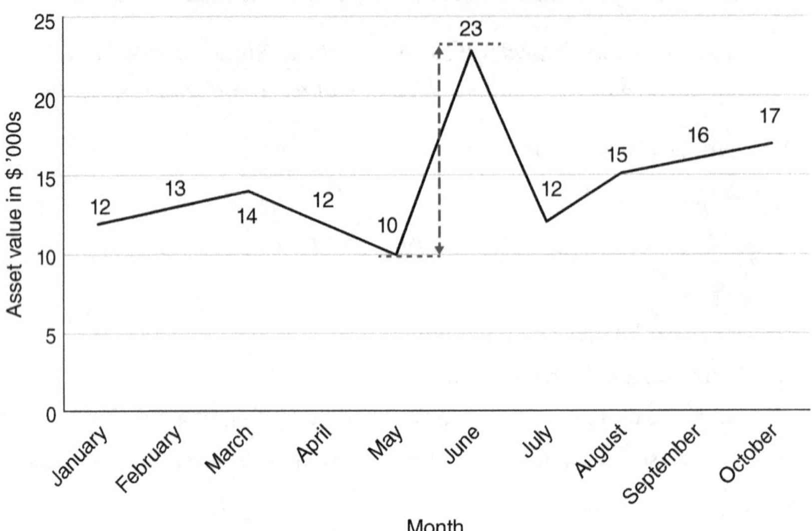

In both of the risk reward ratios shown above, the risk of loss was compared with the benefit or gain to provide a metric for further comparison. This can also be seen as a comparison between two pathways in terms of opportunity and threats. In financial sectors, the word "risk" is associated with a loss and considered as a risk of threat. The return, on the other hand, becomes the benefit realized by the risk of opportunity. It can be written as:

$$\textit{Risk-benefit ratio} = \frac{\textit{Risk of opportunity}}{\textit{Risk of threat}} \tag{36.4}$$

On a general level, to calculate risk-benefit ratios for all industries, any of the following definitions can be used:

1. Gain (benefit) over baseline over uncertainty of the gain (benefit)
2. Gain (benefit) over baseline over maximum loss
3. Loss of gain (benefit) over uncertainty over gain (benefit)
4. Benefit afforded by opportunity over loss incurred by the threat
5. Benefit afforded by opportunity over loss incurred by mitigating threat
6. Benefit afforded by opportunity over loss incurred to realize the opportunity

Wilson and Crouch, in their book *Risk-Benefit Analysis*, consider the net worth of a coal mining operation.[1] They define net worth as:

$$W(t) = B(t) - C(t) - R(t) \tag{36.5}$$

1. E. A. Crouch and R. Wilson, *Risk-Benefit Analysis* (Cambridge, MA: Harvard Center for Risk Analysis, 2001).

where the benefits of a mining operation are quantified per $B(t)$ and costs and negative risks per $C(t)$ and $R(t)$, respectively. They also introduce further parameters that help convert all variables on the same scale to ensure proper units as below:

$$W(t) = \alpha(B, t)B(t) - \beta(C, t)C(t) - \gamma(R, t)R(t) \tag{36.6}$$

When considering risk-based decision making, the time of decision is also crucial. Wilson and Crouch thus decided to introduce a new risk factor of decision-making duration.

It is best to add this net worth valuation over different times to obtain total effect; thus, a time factor $D(t)$ is introduced to obtain a net present value:

$$NPV = \int_{t=0}^{T} D(t)\,W(t)dt \tag{36.7}$$

where,

$$D(t) = \frac{1}{(1+r)^t}$$

r is a discount rate, which is based on how patient the decision maker is and shows the rate of return of investment. The slower the expected return, the lower the rate.

If NPV > 1, the decision should be accepted.

In this example of risk-benefit analysis, the following methodology was used:

1. Construct the risk-benefit model using parameters of interest
2. Ensure that the units are balanced to allow for arithmetic or logical operations
3. Correct for additional parameters if needed (here, time factor)
4. Define acceptability

In pharmacology and drug safety, the principle of threes postulated by Edwards, Wiholm, and Martinez is a common tool for risk-benefit analysis.[2] It asks the practitioner to first rate the three main aspects of negative risk as follows:

1. Seriousness and severity of the reaction
2. Duration of adverse event
3. Frequency with which the adverse event occurs

The next step is to rate the benefits of the drug as follows:

1. How serious is the disease being treated versus the extent of improvement?
2. What is the time course of disease versus reduction in time by the treatment?
3. What is the incidence of disease versus the incidence of improvement due to treatment?

This information can be used to rate the benefits and risks based on the scale given in Table 36.1.

2. I. R. Edwards, B. E. Wiholm, and C. Martinez, "Concepts in Risk-Benefit Assessment," *Drug Safety* 15, no. 1 (1996): 1–7.

TABLE 36.1 Grading of main aspects of negative risks.

Gradation	High = 3	Medium = 2	Low = 1
Seriousness	Fatal	Disabling	Inconvenient
Duration	Permanent	Persistent	Temporary
Incidence	Common	Frequent	Rare

Thus, two treatments can be scored and compared in a semiquantitative manner.

Similarly, a global risk-benefit score is introduced by Chuang-Stein, Mohberg, and Sinkula,[3] which looks at the benefit through the double negative spectrum of adverse events. It assigns scores and weights to the following parameters:

1. Benefit with no adverse drug reaction (π_1)
2. Benefit with adverse drug reaction (π_2)
3. No benefit with no adverse drug reaction (π_3)
4. No benefit with adverse drug reaction (π_4)
5. Adverse drug reaction leading to serious complications and study withdrawal (π_1)

Based on these values, the risk-benefit score can be calculated as:

$$r = \frac{(w_1\pi_1 + w_2\pi_2)^e}{w_3\pi_3 + w_4\pi_4 + w_5\pi_5} \tag{36.8}$$

where $e > 0$ is a weighing factor for the benefits along with the w_x, which are also multiplicative weights per the risk professional's choice.

As already described, both risks and benefits have similar foundational parameters of occurrence and impact, which a risk professional can attempt to quantify.

The Transparent Uniform Risk Benefit Overview (TURBO) model attempts to provide a single metric representing favorability or unfavorability (along with its degree) of a treatment that can be charted on a graph. The method starts with definition of the following:

$$\text{R-factor} = R_o + R_c \tag{36.9}$$

$$\text{B-factor} = B_o + B_c \tag{36.10}$$

where R_o is the risk associated with the medically most serious adverse effect, R_c represents an additional risk (e.g., the next most serious adverse reaction or the most frequent), B_o represents a primary benefit, and B_c represents an ancillary benefit or benefits. The scores for B_o and R_o range on a scale from 1 to 5, and R_C and B_C range from 0 to 2. R_o is calculated using the matrix in Table 36.2.

Severity = impact on health status and socioprofessional capabilities

3. C. Chuang-Stein, N. R. Mohberg, and M. S. Sinkula, "Three Measures for Simultaneously Evaluating Benefits and Risks Using Categorical Data from Clinical Trials," *Statistics in Medicine* 10, no. 9 (1991): 1349–1359.

TABLE 36.2 R score associated with adverse effects.

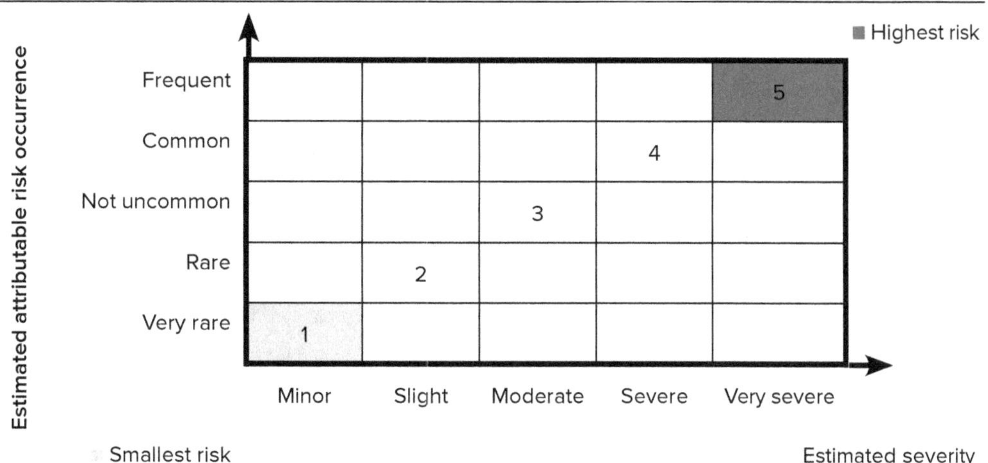

Source: Reproduced by permission from Council for International Organizations of Medical Sciences (CIOMS) Working Group IV, *Benefit-Risk Balance for Marketed Drugs: Evaluating Safety Signals* (Geneva, Switzerland: Council for International Organizations of Medical Sciences, 1998), 152, https://cioms.ch/wp-content/uploads/2017/01/benefit-risk.pdf.

Definition for risk severity:[4]

1 = some hindrance, but not really incapacitating
2 = temporarily/intermittently incapacitating
3 = incapacitating, but not life-threatening/-shortening
4 = life-shortening, but not life-threatening
5 = life-threatening

Take the next severe adverse effect or, if there is no other severe adverse effect, the most frequent one and estimate "R" score for this adverse effect = R' using the following:

$$\text{"R"-factor} = \text{Ro} + \text{correction factor Rc} \tag{36.11}$$

$$\begin{aligned} &\text{Correction factor Rc} = \\ &+2 \text{ if } R' = 5 \\ &+1 \text{ if } R' = 4 \\ &+0 \text{ if } R' = 3 \end{aligned} \tag{36.12}$$

Similarly, the benefit B factor is calculated using the risk matrix shown in Table 36.3 and the key that follows.

4. Key and definitions reproduced by permission from Council for International Organizations of Medical Sciences (CIOMS) Working Group IV, *Benefit-Risk Balance for Marketed Drugs: Evaluating Safety Signals* (Geneva, Switzerland: Council for International Organizations of Medical Sciences, 1998), 151–154, https://cioms.ch/wp-content/uploads/2017/01/benefit-risk.pdf.

TABLE 36.3 B score associated with benefit.

■ Largest benefit

Probability of benefit	Minor	Slight	Moderate	Marked	Major
Nearly always					5
Frequent				4	
Common			3		
Not uncommon		2			
Rare	1				

Smallest benefit

Degree of benefit

Source: Reproduced by permission from Council for International Organizations of Medical Sciences (CIOMS) Working Group IV, *Benefit-Risk Balance for Marketed Drugs: Evaluating Safety Signals* (Geneva, Switzerland: Council for International Organizations of Medical Sciences, 1998), 153, https://cioms.ch/wp-content/uploads/2017/01/benefit-risk.pdf.

Benefit = impact on indication as reflected by change(s) in health status and socio-professional capabilities

E.g., five scores; treated condition becomes (definitions are tentative):

1 = less hindering, but capabilities remain unchanged
2 = less frequently incapacitating or incapability lasts shorter
3 = less incapacitating, but no change in life expectancy
4 = less life-shortening
5 = less immediately life-threatening

Score refers to benefit associated with correctly used medicine (and leaves out of consideration aspects such as noncompliance).

$$\text{The adjusted “B” score} = \text{the “B”-factor} \tag{36.13}$$

Consider whether the medicine has relevant ancillary properties and assign a value to the correction factor as indicated below:

$$\text{“B”-factor} = \text{Bo} + \text{correction factor (Bc) for ancillary property} \tag{36.14}$$

Correction factor Bc (tentative example)

= +2 if ancillary medical property relevant to the indication
(e.g., cholesterol lowering effect for antidiabetic or for antihypertensive medicine)

= +1 if ancillary practical property
(e.g., once-daily dosage schedule or fast onset of action, etc.) (36.15)

TABLE 36.4 RB balance: the TURBO diagram.

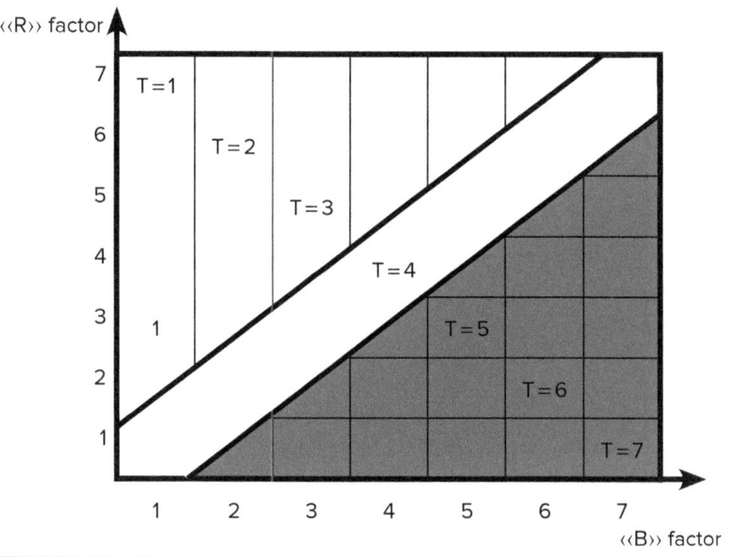

Source: Reproduced by permission from Council for International Organizations of Medical Sciences (CIOMS) Working Group IV, *Benefit-Risk Balance for Marketed Drugs: Evaluating Safety Signals* (Geneva, Switzerland: Council for International Organizations of Medical Sciences, 1998), 154, https://cioms.ch/wp-content/uploads/2017/01/benefit-risk.pdf.

The R and B factors are then plotted on the matrix shown in Table 36.4 and a risk-benefit number is obtained. These scores can be compared for a number of treatments. The matrix above suggests that the favorable treatments should have a score greater than 4.

GENERALIZED METHOD FOR RISK-BENEFIT ASSESSMENT FOR DRUGS, MEDICAL DEVICES, AND COMBINATION PRODUCTS

Risk Matrix Approach and Weighted Counts

In earlier chapters I elaborated on the risk matrix approach and presented various versions of risk matrices. Table 36.5 shows a version of a matrix that is also presented in ISO 14971:2019. The severity scales have been replaced with the Clavien-Dindo grades of harm as shown in Table 36.6.

Any five-level probability scale can be used with this method. The scale shown in Table 36.7 is used to demonstrate this method here. We are most concerned with the rank/weight in the second column and will use this later in risk and benefit calculations.

TABLE 36.5 Clavien-Dindo-based risk matrix.

		Clavien-Dindo severity level				
		Grade I	**Grade II**	**Grade III**	**Grade IV**	**Grade V**
Probability level	**Frequent (5)**	M	M	H	H	H
	Probable (4)	L	M	H	H	H
	Occasional (3)	L	M	M	H	H
	Remote (2)	L	L	M	M	M
	Improbable (1)	L	L	L	L	L

TABLE 36.6 Clavien-Dindo severity scale.

Grade	Definition
Grade I	Any deviation from the normal postoperative course without the need for pharmacological treatment or surgical, endoscopic, and radiological interventions
	Allowed therapeutic regimens are: drugs as antiemetics, antipyretics, analgetics, diuretics, electrolytes, and physiotherapy. This grade also includes wound infections opened at the bedside
Grade II	Requiring pharmacological treatment with drugs other than such allowed for grade I complications
	Blood transfusions and total parenteral nutrition are also included
Grade III	Requiring surgical, endoscopic, or radiological intervention
Grade IIIa	Intervention not under general anesthesia
Grade IIIb	Intervention under general anesthesia
Grade IV	Life-threatening complication (including CNS complications)* requiring IC/ICU management
Grade IVa	Single organ dysfunction (including dialysis)
Grade IVb	Multiorgan dysfunction
Grade V	Death of a patient

*Brain hemorrhage, ischemic stroke, subarachnoidal bleeding, but excluding transient ischemic attacks.
CNS, central nervous system; IC, intermediate care; ICU, intensive care unit.

Source: Used with permission of Wolters Kluwer Health, from D. Dindo, N. Demartines, and P. A. Clavien, "Classification of Surgical Complications: A New Proposal with Evaluation in a Cohort of 6336 Patients and Results of a Survey," *Annals of Surgery* 240, no. 2 (2004): 206, https://doi.org/10.1097/01.sla.0000133083.54934.ae; permission conveyed through Copyright Clearance Center, Inc.

The output risk index in this matrix can take three values:

1. High (H)
2. Medium (M)
3. Low (L)

The basis for a risk matrix is the definition of risk itself, which, as defined earlier, is the combination of the probability (chance) of occurrence of harm and the severity of

TABLE 36.7 Probability scale.

Occurrence	Rank/weight	Approx. rate of incidence	
Nonexistent	0	0	0
Least probable	1	≥0	<0.4%
Remote	2	≥0.4%	<2.0%
Occasional	3	≥2.1%	<7%
Probable	4	≥7.1%	<18%
Frequent	5	≥18.1%	

that harm. Thus, the combination of these two input variables leads to the single output variable of risk, which, according to its assigned value, is classified as high, medium, or low. The logic used in this risk calculation is simple and shown below:

IF probability of occurrence is O **AND** severity is S, **THEN** risk is R. (36.16)

The Model

Risk R, in its most simple form, is given in Equation 36.17:

$$\text{Risk (R)} = \text{Occurrence (O)} \times \text{Severity (S)} \tag{36.17}$$

This relationship gives equal weight to both parameters for probability of occurrence and severity. For medicinal applications, this occurrence-severity relationship may not be linear since the value of the severity parameter could be much higher. As a result, this formula must be modified. HB 436:2004: Risk Management Guidelines gives the formula shown in Equation 36.18.

$$Risk = (Severity \times W)^x \times (Occurrence)^y \tag{36.18}$$

Here, W is the weighing factor.

For purposes of this chapter, let us consider $W=2$, $x=2$, and $y=1$. The basis of choice of these variables should be the degree of resolution needed in the spectrum of risk calculations. The maximum level of severity and occurrence per the five-level scales defined in this chapter (see Tables 36.6 and 36.7) is 5. Hence, the lowest level of risk product per Equation 36.18 is 4, while the highest is 500. If we had chosen $W=2$, $x=3$, and $y=1$, the lowest level of risk would have been 8 and the highest would have been 5000, giving a tenfold increase in risk range.

For the risk-benefit model, this formula of risk will be used for calculation of both risk of treatment and risk of illness without treatment. Each of these risks is compiled of constituent risk factors derived from the Clavien-Dindo grades as shown in Equations 36.19 and 36.20.

$$\begin{gathered} Risk\ of\ treatment = Treatment\ Risk\ Factor\ A + Treatment \\ Risk\ Factor\ B + Treatment\ Risk\ Factor\ C + Treatment \\ Risk\ Factor\ D + Treatment\ Risk\ Factor\ E \end{gathered} \tag{36.19}$$

$$\begin{aligned} \textit{Risk of illness without treatment} = \textit{Illness Risk Factor } A' + \textit{Illness} \\ \textit{Risk Factor } B' + \textit{Illness Risk Factor } C' + \textit{Illness Risk Factor } D' \\ + \textit{Illness Risk Factor } E' \end{aligned} \tag{36.20}$$

These risk factors are resolved per the Clavien-Dindo severity grades as shown in the model detailed in Figure 36.2.

The mathematical conversion of this model can be realized by using Equation 36.18 as shown in Equation 36.21:

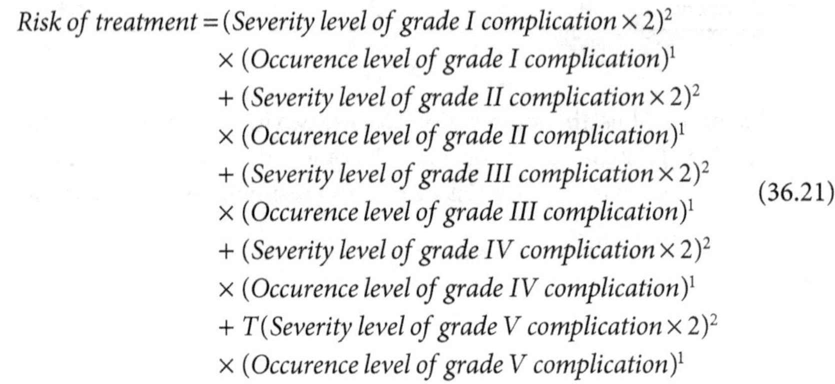

$$\begin{aligned} \textit{Risk of treatment} = {} & (\textit{Severity level of grade I complication} \times 2)^2 \\ & \times (\textit{Occurence level of grade I complication})^1 \\ & + (\textit{Severity level of grade II complication} \times 2)^2 \\ & \times (\textit{Occurence level of grade II complication})^1 \\ & + (\textit{Severity level of grade III complication} \times 2)^2 \\ & \times (\textit{Occurence level of grade III complication})^1 \\ & + (\textit{Severity level of grade IV complication} \times 2)^2 \\ & \times (\textit{Occurence level of grade IV complication})^1 \\ & + T(\textit{Severity level of grade V complication} \times 2)^2 \\ & \times (\textit{Occurence level of grade V complication})^1 \end{aligned} \tag{36.21}$$

FIGURE 36.2 Clavien-Dindo grade-based risk factor model for risk-benefit analysis.

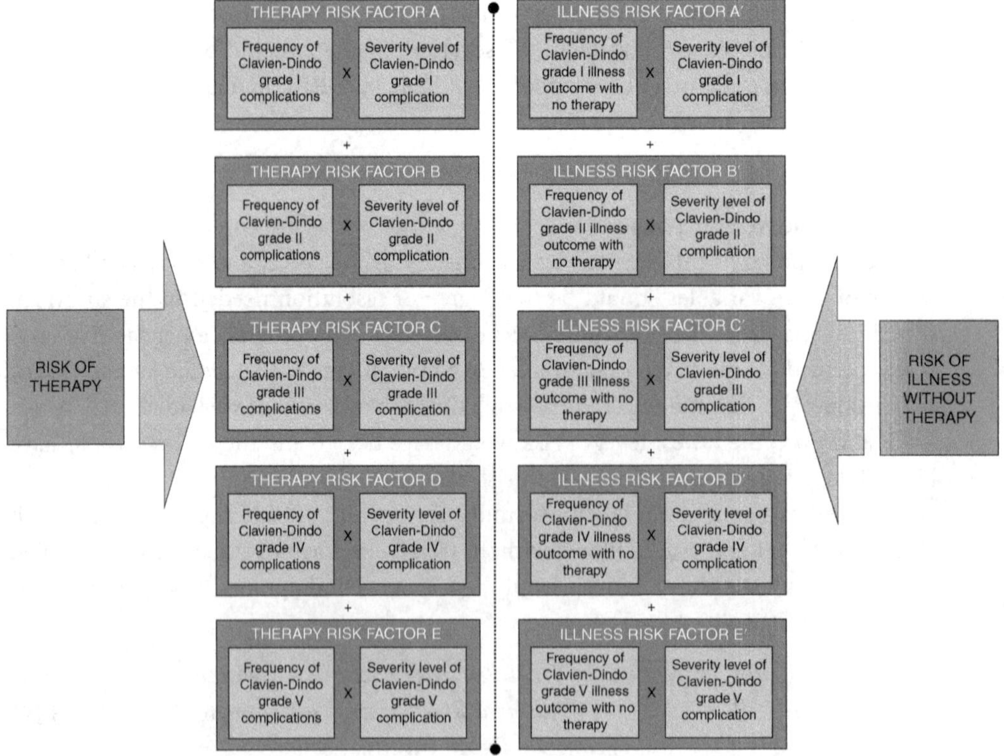

This can be mathematically represented as shown in Equation 36.22:

$$Risk\ of\ treatment = \sum_{i=Grade\ I}^{Grade\ V} (2S_i)^2 \cdot O_i \tag{36.22}$$

Thus, the risk of treatment is composed of the individual risk levels of each of the Clavien-Dindo harms (outcomes). To calculate this, the clinical end point or events must be graded per the Clavien-Dindo grades shown in Table 36.6 and assigned an occurrence level per Table 36.7. Then these numbers must be applied to the formula above for all grades of harms to obtain the aggregate risk.

Similarly, the risk of illness without treatment is the sum of illness risk factors shown in Figure 36.2 and can be mathematically represented as shown in Equation 36.23:

$$Risk\ of\ illness\ without\ treatment = \sum_{j=Least\ probable}^{Frequent} (2S_j)^2 \cdot O_j \tag{36.23}$$

The risk of illness without treatment is the risk level of the probability of each Clavien-Dindo grade outcome without treatment. To calculate this, events from least probable to frequent must be categorized in terms of the Clavien-Dindo grade per Table 36.6. For example, if a patient has the flu, it is least probable that a grade V event will occur and more likely that a grade I event will occur. There is a subjective aspect to assignation, and care must be taken to ensure inclusion of expert opinions.

With the weights assigned for different levels of probability and severity in column two (from 1 to 5) in Tables 36.6 and 36.7, this multiplication using Equation 36.18 yields the values of risk for sets of probability and severity levels as shown in Table 36.8. This has been done for ease of calculation for the practitioner.

Finally, the risk-benefit ratio can be shown as follows:

$$\begin{aligned} Risk\text{-}benefit\ ratio &= \frac{Risk\ of\ illness\ without\ treatment}{Risk\ of\ treatment} \\ &= \frac{\sum_{j=Least\ probable}^{Frequent} (2S_j)^2 \cdot O_j}{\sum_{i=Grade\ I}^{Grade\ V} (2S_i)^2 \cdot O_i} \end{aligned} \tag{36.24}$$

TABLE 36.8 Weighted Clavien-Dindo risk matrix.

		Clavien-Dindo severity level				
		Grade I	Grade II	Grade III	Grade IV	Grade V
Probability level	Frequent (5)	20	80	180	320	500
	Probable (4)	16	64	144	256	400
	Occasional (3)	12	48	108	192	300
	Remote (2)	8	32	72	128	200
	Least probable (1)	4	16	36	64	100

Cost Effectiveness Analysis (CEA)

A cost effectiveness analysis (CEA) is carried out to measure cost per incremental unit of outcome. The incremental cost can be calculated by:

$$\frac{\textit{Incremental cost of Outcome B}}{\textit{over Outcome A}} = \frac{\textit{Net Cost}_B - \textit{Net Cost}_A}{\textit{Outcome}_B - \textit{Outcome}_A} \tag{36.25}$$

The outcome or effect must be measured in terms that apply to both B and A.

CEA in Healthcare

CEA is a method to compare the cost and health outcomes of one or more therapies with a standard of care or other therapies. The comparison is done by estimating the amount of monetary cost per unit of health gain. The analysis is usually done in standardized health units such as quality adjusted life years (QALYs) and disability adjusted life years (DALYs).

QALY is composed of two submeasures:

1. Length of life
2. Quality of life

QALYs are simply calculated by multiplying the length of life by the quality of life.

Quality of life is usually plotted on a scale of zero to one, with one being perfect health and zero being death. Length of life is plotted in years. In Figure 36.3, Treatment A increases the length of life by three years and offers perfect health, while Treatment B increases the length of life by five years but decreases the quality of life by half. The former treatment has three QALYs while the latter treatment has five.

The incremental cost effectiveness ratio (ICER) aims to calculate the incremental cost per standardized unit (QALY or DALY) of health. It effectively calculates the

FIGURE 36.3 Calculation of QALY.

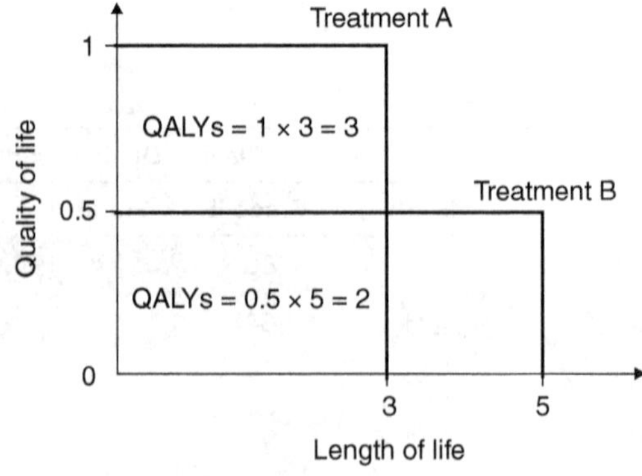

added cost of a year of life. ICER is the calculated value that summarizes the cost-effectiveness of one treatment compared with another.

For QALY, the ICER is

$$ICER = \frac{Net\ Cost_{Treatment\ B} - Net\ Cost_{Treatment\ A}}{QALY_{Treatment\ B} - QALY_{Treatment\ A}} \tag{36.26}$$

Let us continue the example from the chart above. The cost and QALYs are summarized in Table 36.9.

The ICER was calculated as:

$$ICER = \frac{\$175{,}000 - \$35{,}000}{5-3} = \frac{\$140{,}000}{2} = \$70{,}000 \tag{36.27}$$

Certain thresholds for ICER are set by agencies such as the National Institute for Health and Care Excellence (NICE) in London, UK, which adopts an ICER threshold of £20,000 to £30,000 to gauge fundable treatments.

Let us move on to DALYs. DALY is the standardized unit measure of the burden of a disease. It is composed of the following:

1. Mortality
2. Morbidity

Mortality essentially refers to the loss of life years due to the disease and can be given by the formula:

$$\text{Mortality} = \text{Life expectancy} - \text{Age of death} \tag{36.28}$$

Morbidity is rated on a scale of zero to one, where zero means perfect health and one means complete disability. Morbidity takes into account all the short- and long-term illness effects except death. A disability adjustment score can be multiplied, in some cases, to factor in short- or long-term disability.

TABLE 36.9 Cost and QALYs.

Treatment	Cost	Cost difference	QALY	QALY difference	ICER
Treatment A	$35,000	$140,000	3	2	$70,000
Treatment B	$175,000		5		

TABLE 36.10 Cost and DALYs.

Treatment	Cost	Cost difference	DALY	DALY difference	ICER
Treatment X	$50,000	$20,000	6	1.5	$13,333
Treatment Y	$70,000		4.5		

For example, for a specific cardiovascular disease, the mortality can be 15 (80–65), while morbidity can be 6 if the person is 30% disabled for the last 20 years of his or her life. The total disease burden for this person is 21 DALYs.

It must be noted that QALY gives a measure of health, while DALY give a measure of disability. Let us look at an example of ICER with DALY.

$$ICER = \frac{\$70{,}000 - \$50{,}000}{6 - 4.5} = \frac{\$20{,}000}{1.5} = \$13{,}333 \tag{36.29}$$

One DALY can be seen as one healthy life year lost. With Treatment Y, a person can gain 1.5 healthy years at the cost of $13,333 per year.

CEA Plane

The results of the CEA can be graphically visualized using the CEA plane shown in Figure 36.4. The ideal situation is the lower-right quadrant, where the new treatment is found to be less costly and more effective. This means the new treatment is "dominant." In straight contrast is the upper-left quadrant, where the cost of the new treatment is more and effectiveness is less. This means that the new treatment has been "dominated" by the old treatment. Multiple treatments can be compared using this graph, and sometimes an upper limit of ICER is set, as shown in the graph. Most new treatments will be more expensive than older treatments and fall in the upper-right quadrant. Here, the threshold ICER becomes important. In the United States, $50,000 to $60,000 is an often quoted range. In the UK, an ICER less than £20,000 is considered cost-effective per NICE. In the Netherlands, the Dutch Council for Public Health and Care suggests a threshold that depends on the disease burden of the patient and ranges

FIGURE 36.4 CEA plane.

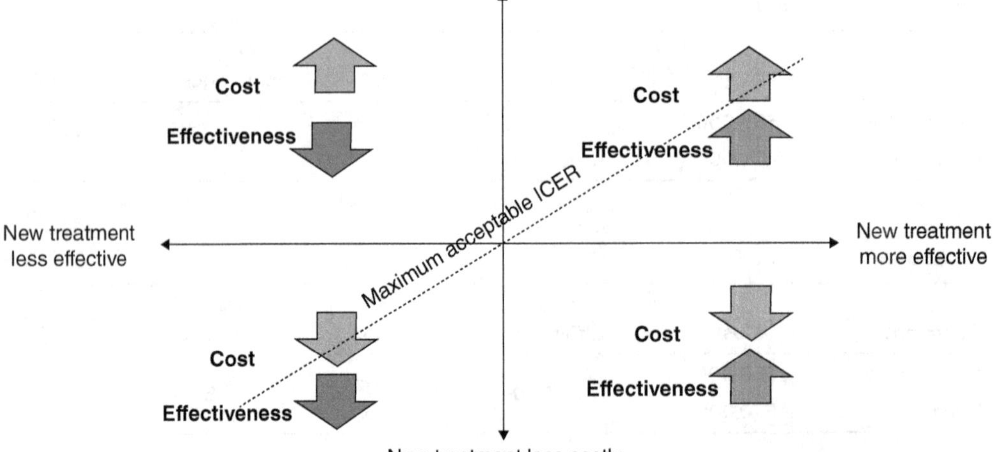

from €10,000 to €80,000 per QALY.[5] It must be noted that in the United States, the Patient Protection and Affordable Care Act of 2010 forbids usage of a measure that discounts the value of a life because of an individual's disability as a threshold to establish cost-effectiveness of healthcare.

5. T. Shiroiwa, A. Igarashi, T. Fukuda, and S. Ikeda, "WTP for a QALY and Health States: More Money for Severer Health States?," *Cost Effectiveness and Resource Allocation* 11 (2013): https://doi.org/10.1186/1478-7547-11-22.

CHAPTER 37

Cognitive Science of Risk-Based Decision Making

TO TRULY UNDERSTAND THE FUNDAMENTALS of risk-based decision making, one must study the underlying factors and motivations of human decision making in the context of the following:

1. Cognitive biases
2. Emotional intelligence
3. Heuristics

These three factors are major drivers of perception-driven risk attitudes.

Let us start by analyzing heuristics:

Heuristics are subconscious mental connections that allow people to make judgments quickly.

The concept was introduced by Nobel Prize–winning cognitive psychologist Herbert Simon, who gave us the concept of bounded rationality, which postulates that during human decision making, rationality is limited. The theory goes on to say that a fully rational decision cannot be made due to cognitive limitations and time shortage. Instead, the human mind often makes a satisfactory decision rather than an optimal one—this is known as *satisficing*. The process of making a less than optimal decision is based in heuristics. Following are a few examples:

1. Anchoring and adjustment heuristic: An estimate by an individual based on the "first" piece of provided or available information. Humans will not make random guesses regarding estimates but instead will anchor their thought process to some readily available information and adjust their outlook accordingly based on surrounding information.
2. Availability heuristic: Information related to a decision that is most easily recalled influences the decision the most.
3. Escalation of commitment: When people justify increased investment in an earlier decision based only on prior aggregate investment despite new information that may not present the investment favorably. This heuristic tricks the mind into ignoring the risk-benefit propositions.

4. Representativeness heuristic: When people make decisions based on a likeness or similarity of the current situation to a previous representative situation.
5. Familiarity heuristic: A subset of the availability heuristic, the familiarity heuristic judges events that are more frequent and more familiar in memory to be more important.
6. Affect heuristic: This comes into play when judging the risks or benefits of a decision. The emotions affected by connotation of a word or a situation primarily are the reason for a decision. If the affect is positive, then the person perceives the risk to be low and the benefits to be high and vice versa.

A systematic error in judgment or decision making that results from these heuristics is known as a *cognitive bias*. The mental processing of new evidence is not a simple step of input of information, objective logical processing, and rational output. Instead, the new information or evidence is passed through the heuristic lens and undergoes subjective processing based on the individual's own experiences and interactions. Common biases that a risk management professional may encounter are described below:

1. Confirmation bias: This often hinders risk-based solution determination and root cause analysis. The person assumes an answer to a problem based on various other heuristics and attempts to find evidence to prove this assumption correct.
2. Overconfidence bias: The illusion of more confidence in a decision or more control of a system than is actually present.
3. Loss aversion: Excessive and unfounded fear of loss leading to risk avoidance rather than a focus on opportunity for profit.
4. Planning fallacy: Underestimation of time needed to complete a task due to optimism bias (overconfidence and confirmation).

Flawed decision making results from flawed judgment that itself results from flawed assumptions based on heuristics. Campbell, Whitehead, and Finkelstein define *emotional tagging* as the process by which emotional information attaches itself to thoughts and experiences stored in our memories.[1] It is this tag that, in large part, governs the action to be contemplated in the face of uncertainty. Thus, the heuristical pattern recognition and the emotional tag together guide any decision, and this concert happens instantaneously.

These two things form the basis for risk perception, which drives the subconscious individual risk attitudes of seeking risk, aversion, tolerance, neutrality, or avoidance. The formation of this attitude is also influenced by the organizational risk attitude, which in turn is shaped by executive, top management, and leadership risk attitudes.

How does one minimize these biases and heuristics?

In humans, irrational behavior arises as a consequence of emotional reactions evoked when faced with difficult decisions, according to research at University College

1. A. Campbell, J. Whitehead, and S. Finkelstein, "Why Good Leaders Make Bad Decisions," *Harvard Business Review* 87, no. 2 (2009): 60–66.

London.[2] People are often faced with such difficult decisions and thus are subject to internal emotional turmoil on almost a daily basis. Emotional intelligence, as opposed to harsh Stoic rationalism, is a tool for leveraging and regulating the autosomatic emotional upheaval for effective decision making and thereby effective leadership. Emotional intelligence is based on three pillars:[3]

1. **Self-Awareness**

   Being mindful of one's emotions (impulsive and nonimpulsive). Consciously studying the negative and positive thoughts and their drivers. Understanding the impact of emotions on one's behavior and decision making, thereby knowing one's limitations and strengths.

2. **Self-Management**

   Emotional self-control: Keeping disruptive emotions and impulses in check
   Transparency: Maintaining integrity, acting congruently with one's values
   Adaptability: Flexibility in handling change
   Achievement: Striving to improve or meeting a standard of excellence
   Initiative: Readiness to act on opportunities
   Optimism: Persistence in pursuing goals despite obstacles and setbacks

3. **Social Awareness**

   Empathy: Sensing others' feelings and perspectives, and taking an active interest in their concerns
   Organizational awareness: Reading a group's emotional currents and power relationships
   Service orientation: Anticipating, recognizing, and meeting customers' needs

All major aspects of the decision-making process can be positively influenced by emotional intelligence. It is incumbent on the emotionally agile decision maker to consider multiple risk factors before making any critical decision. The accuracy and effectiveness of such a risk-based decision greatly depend on the level of emotional maturity of the decision maker. Emotional literacy acts as a baseline and/or autocorrects the risk perception, thereby allowing the leader to make a well-rounded and balanced decision. As discussed in Campbell, Whitehead, and Finkelstein, subconscious bias in the form of emotional tags and heuristic patterns automatically contributes to risk perception and is a major part of the immediate perception of uncertainty.[4] Here, instead of giving in to "instinct" or "hunches," an emotionally enlightened decision maker would practice

---

2. University College London, "Irrational Decisions Driven by Emotions," ScienceDaily, August 3, 2006, www.sciencedaily.com/releases/2006/08/060803171138.htm.
3. D. Goleman, R. E. Boyatzis, A. McKee, and S. Finkelstein, *HBR's 10 Must Reads on Emotional Intelligence (with featured article "What Makes a Leader?" by Daniel Goleman)* (Harvard Business Review Press, 2015), 3.
4. A. Campbell, J. Whitehead, and S. Finkelstein, "Why Good Leaders Make Bad Decisions," *Harvard Business Review* 87, no. 2 (2009): 60–66.

FIGURE 37.1 Uncertainty, risk attitude, and decision making.

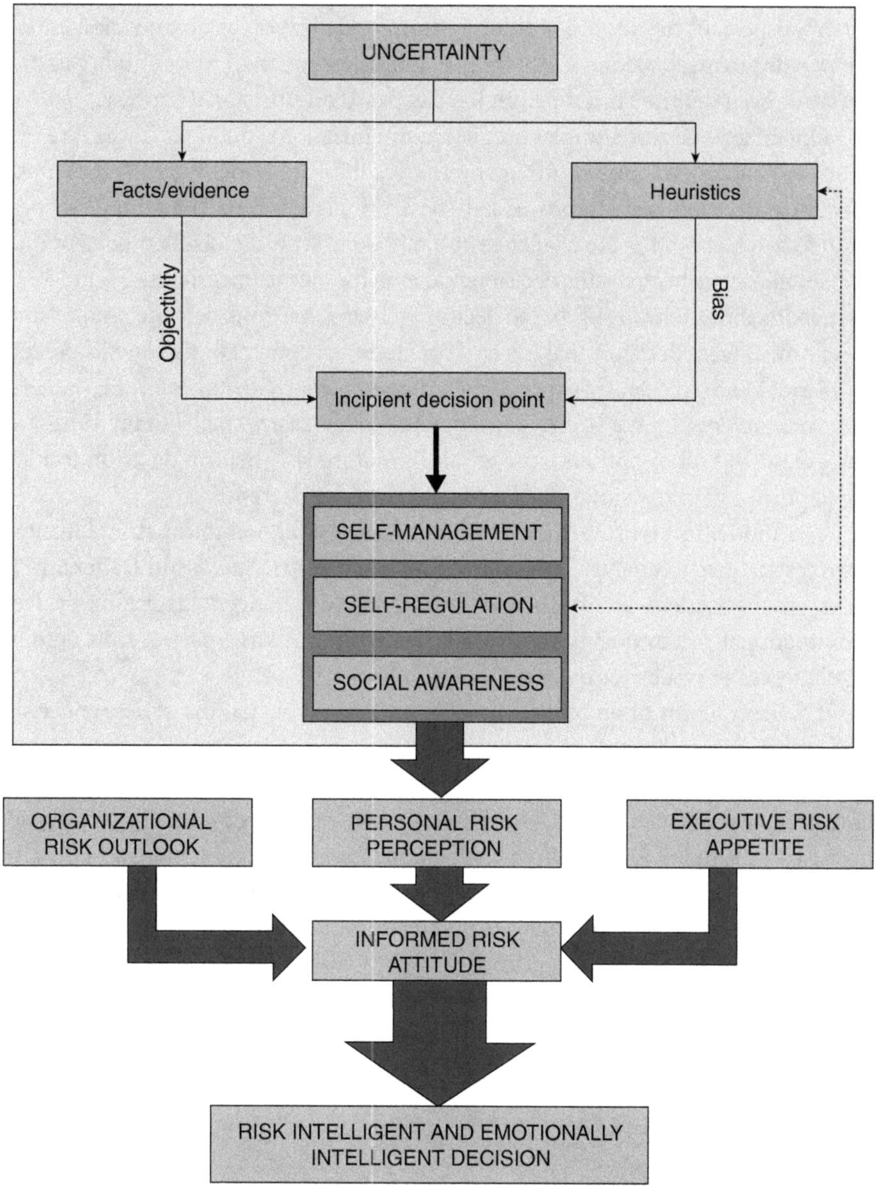

a certain level of self-management, regulation, and empathic behavior to prevent a rash decision. The act of stopping to think is governed in the background and sometimes in the foreground by the risk attitude. Weber, Blais, and Betz proved that risk attitudes differ from domain to domain and do not derive from specific traits of the person.[5] The

5. E. U. Weber, A. R. Blais, and N. E. Betz, "A Domain-Specific Risk-Attitude Scale: Measuring Risk Perceptions and Risk Behaviors," *Journal of Behavioral Decision Making* 15, no. 4 (2002): 263–290.

situation context and personality together contribute in varying degrees to a risk-based decision, and the difference in risk attitude is in part due to the perception of risk. Thus, when we speak of risk attitudes differing from organization to organization and department to department, we must recognize that the perception of risk attitude can differ day by day or even multiple times within the day based on situational context.

Organizational risk attitudes are macro-organizational outlooks in the face of uncertainty, which are only one of the many feeders into the leader's own risk response and situational decision-making process, as shown in Figure 37.1. The attitude or perceived attitude of superiors for the challenge at hand along with the distilled perception of risk decides the stance taken by the decision maker in the face of uncertainty. Figure 37.1 shows an individualized flow of risk-based decision making that considers the rational and emotionally intelligent decision-making approaches in the context of risk and its perception.

Leaders are frequently exposed to situations where mistakes in risk-benefit decision making could have severe consequences. The easiest path, many times, is to be risk averse, but often options exist to take a mature risk-neutral decision to maximize the opportunity of the situation by going against the current.

The model in Figure 37.1, which integrates risk and emotional intelligence, provides a structure to analyze judgment of such scenarios. Successful leadership heavily relies on the leader's ability to make emotionally intelligent decisions by weighing the situational risk and aligning the risk perception. A large part of this includes self-regulation of perspectives by open-loop feedback.

The interaction of emotional intelligence, decision-making styles, and risk management is a complicated subject but one that has significant potential to contribute to enhancing leadership effectiveness. Emotionally intelligent transformational leaders have greater resistance to decisions based on subconscious bias and unmanaged emotional risk attitudes. By practicing self-awareness, self-regulation, and empathy, one can recognize and understand gaps in the decision-making process and enable oneself to take balanced risk-based decisions. The key to risk-based emotionally intelligent behavior is to engender awareness of thought, awareness of choice, and awareness of mental and material consequences.

CHAPTER 38

Risk-Based Design Thinking: Risk Mitigation by Design

A DESIGN OF A PRODUCT, process, or service starts with an end goal. A system framework is created to enable the design process such that the end objectives may be achieved with a high likelihood of success.

Whether it be a small company, a start-up, a bank, a hospital, or a manufacturing firm, the design of systems for achievement of end goals is an activity whose success is critical to ensure output relevant to the mission and strategic objectives of the company. Design is by nature a creative process that is based on gathering requirements, refining them, and creating an end output that satisfies all the predefined requirements. If the design process is unstructured, then all the requirements may not manifest in the final output or may be transformed to an unusable feature. In addition, if risk-based thinking is not inherent in the design process or not enforced by a risk management function, then the inherent risks of the design could be under- or overstated, or missed completely. Early mismanagement of risk can prove to be costly and time-consuming.

Risk management is a natural companion to the creative process and provides a structure to refine the initial system requirements. One can use the risk management principles to modify risk to reduce threats and increase opportunities at all design stages. It must be remembered that the avenues for capitalizing on opportunities decrease as one moves toward design completion.

On a macro level, a risk-based approach to design entails analyzing the effect of uncertainty on design in terms of the following:

1. Identifying requirements and their associated risks
2. Organizing requirements based on risk
3. Recognizing uncertainties related to the design and stages of design framework, including identification of hazards
4. Using risk to refine design requirements
5. Using risk-based verification of design output

ANSI/ASSE Z590.3-2011 (R2016) mentions that the goals of applying prevention through design are not only to achieve acceptable risk levels but also to "*reduce the cost of retrofitting necessary to mitigate hazards and risks that were not sufficiently addressed in the design or redesign process.*"[1]

The process of risk-based design thinking starts by setting the context of the design process, which begins by understanding the needs of the business and of the customer. From this set of identified needs, a list of requirements is generated. This is the ideation stage of the design. At this stage, these requirements may encompass a range of possibilities—some realistic and others not. Here, a prioritization of requirements is needed based on the most critical needs and business objectives. Once the set of requirements is finalized, one must anticipate the resistance to their fulfillment and identify in specific terms the internal and external drivers of that resistance. This process can be done using a tool such as the House of Quality or the Pugh matrix. The anticipated nonfulfillment of the requirement must be assessed in terms of impact to the final design outcome. From this, an impact assessment of requirements must be created, and a further filtering of requirements may occur in this scoping phase. This assessment should look at requirements from the standpoint of threats and opportunities. There might be some requirements that are difficult and a threat to the success of objectives but are absolutely essential, or, a requirement may involve extra effort but improve design output manifold. An example of a risk matrix for rating requirements is shown in Table 38.1.

After a set of requirements has been finalized, it is converted into inputs of the design. *Design inputs* are refined requirements that are input characteristics that dictate in detail the nature of the design outcome, which could be the product, process, or service performance requirements, physical requirements, or operational characteristics. These characteristics should follow the risk profile of the requirements, but at times, introduction of boundary parameters and additional clarifying details may increase the risk impact or probability levels initially associated with the requirement. In such a case, the attention to the input stemming from the requirement may need to be adjusted. Table 38.2 can help guide this process by prioritizing the requirements in terms of the probability of their realization and their consequence on the design objective.

The creative design process that follows is meant to convert these inputs into design outputs. Design outputs are practical limits of the desired input characteristics. This is the defined system designed to achieve the objective itself with defined workable boundaries. The outputs of the design process can have many features, each of which may have a separate risk profile of its own. A risk assessment must be done at this stage to evaluate the inherent risk of the designed system. These features must be assessed for risk in terms of failures, and efforts must be directed at unacceptable risks for mitigative measures.

Where the risk is considered unacceptable, system redesign or fail-safes should be implemented to reduce the risk to an acceptable level. After choosing from alternate risk mitigation options and reducing risk as much as practicable, the final design

---

1. *Prevention through Design: Guidelines for Addressing Occupational Hazards and Risks in Design and Redesign Processes*, ANSI/ASSE Z590.3-2011 (New York: American Society of Safety Engineers, 2011), 10.

TABLE 38.1 Risk matrix for rating requirements.

		Consequence of requirement on objective				
		Very low	Low	Medium	High	Very high
Probability for successful realization	Very high	Consider	Consider	Capitalize	Capitalize	Capitalize
	High	Consider	Consider	Review	Capitalize	Capitalize
	Medium	Discard	Consider	Consider	Review	Capitalize
	Low	Discard	Discard	Consider	Review	Review
	Very low	Discard	Discard	Discard	Consider	Review

TABLE 38.2 Risk matrix for rating requirements based on consequences of design input on objective.

		Consequence of input on objective				
		Very low	Low	Medium	High	Very high
Probability for successful realization	Very high	Medium	Medium	Very high	Very high	Very high
	High	Medium	Medium	High	Very high	Very high
	Medium	Low	Medium	Medium	High	Very high
	Low	Low	Low	Medium	High	High
	Very low	Low	Low	Low	Medium	High

TABLE 38.3 Risk matrix for rating requirements based on consequences of output on objective.

		Consequence of failure of output feature on objective				
		Very Low	Low	Medium	High	Very High
Probability of feature failure	Very high	ALARP	ALARP	Unacceptable	Unacceptable	Unacceptable
	High	Acceptable	ALARP	Unacceptable	Unacceptable	Unacceptable
	Medium	Acceptable	ALARP	ALARP	Unacceptable	Unacceptable
	Low	Acceptable	Acceptable	ALARP	ALARP	ALARP
	Very low	Acceptable	Acceptable	Acceptable	Acceptable	Acceptable

must be evaluated again to verify the acceptable risk profile using tools such as FMEA, HACCP, or HAZOP. The risk that remains after mitigation is the residual risk. When the decision is made to accept a certain level of risk, plans should be in place to monitor that risk for escalations. A plan should be in place to identify and escalate risks that escaped the risk identification process. Such risks are known as emergent risks, and they arise after the launch of a system. These must be managed reactively and thus require flexibility on the part of the organization to ensure their successful mitigation. The process of risk mitigation by design is summarized in Figure 38.1.

ANSI/ASSE Z590.3-2011 (R2016) Standard for Prevention through Design introduces the concept of hierarchy of controls, which is defined as:

FIGURE 38.1 A process for risk mitigation by design.

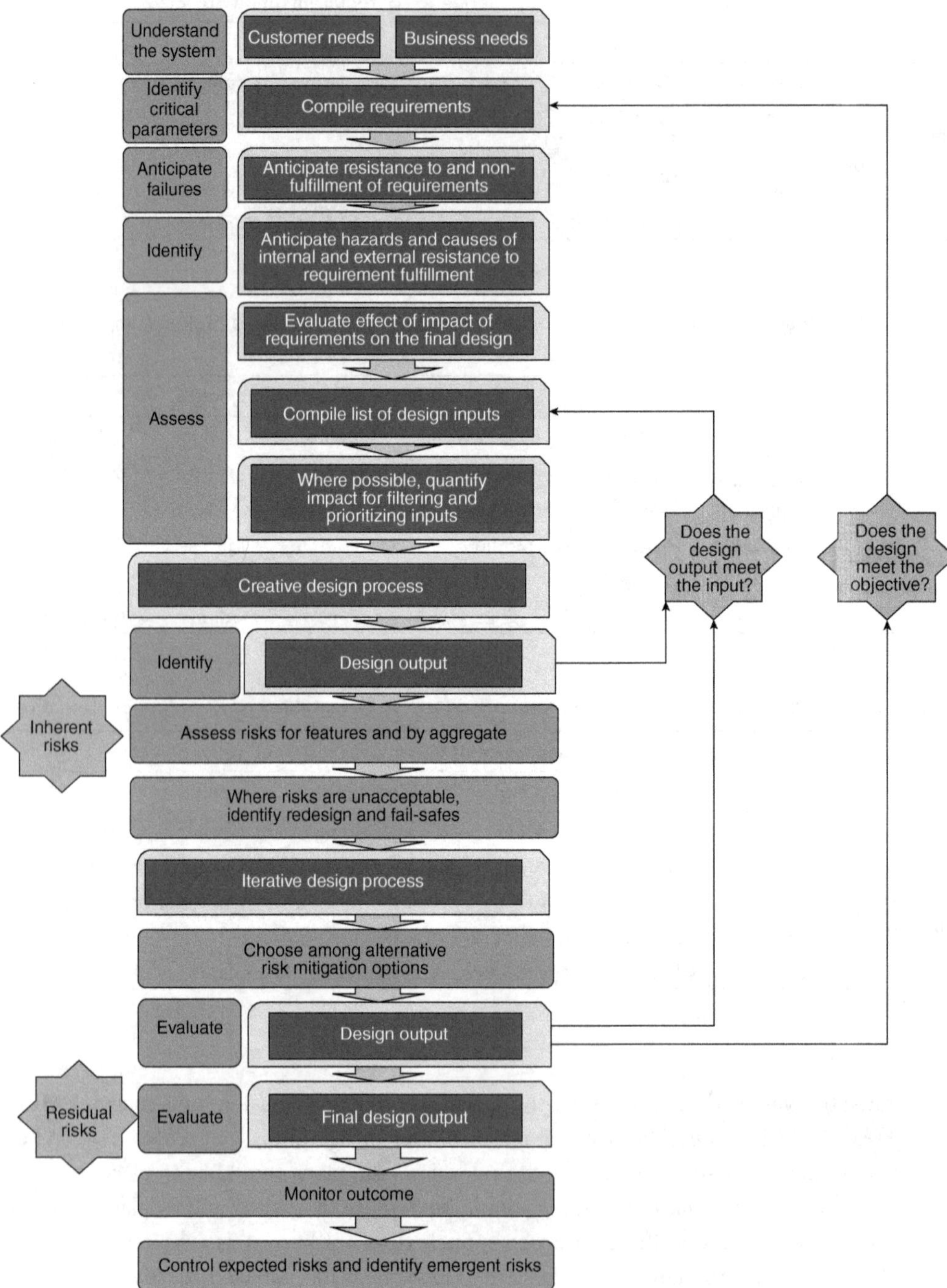

FIGURE 38.2 Hierarchy of controls for risk mitigation by design.

AVOIDANCE — First line of prevention

- By using risk-based thinking and choosing appropriate methods, techniques, designs, technology, etc. during successive stages of the design process, the potential hazards are avoided.

ELIMINATION — Remove adverse possibilities

- By anticipating failures and conducting initial level of risk and hazard assessments, eliminate the possibilities of hazards discovered so far.

SUBSTITUTION — Reduce risks

- When some risk sources or drivers cannot be avoided, substitute the features or materials with less hazardous options.

EMBEDDED CONTROLS — Reduction without substitution

- Where possible, design controls into the system such that the risks may be diffused internally by design.

WARNING — Red flag

- Where the hazard and probability for risk realization still exist, design early warning systems into the design as leading indicators of risky events.

OPERATIONAL CONTROLS — Last level of defense

- These include procedural- and operational-level controls like training, supervision, standard operating procedures, and work instructions where indications for safe use are provided for the users to avoid risky events.

A systematic approach to avoiding, eliminating, controlling, and reducing risks, considering steps in a ranked and sequential order, beginning with avoidance, elimination, and substitution.[2]

While this standard is focused on occupational hazards, this concept can be applied to all design processes. Figure 38.2 is an adaptation of a table from the standard that shows the risk reduction hierarchy of controls for risk mitigation by design.

From top to bottom, these actions are listed from most preferred to least preferred. The first four controls are more effective than the last two since they are proactive and do not rely on human behavior.

The main goal of risk mitigation by design is to reduce risks during the design phase by risk intelligent design. This has two parts: the first is the inherent functioning of the designed system itself, and the second is the usability aspect, whereby the interaction of the system with the user is considered. For the latter, the goal must be to minimize user errors by focusing on the first four controls listed above, which attack system inadequacies by ensuring robust preventive design.

2. *Prevention through Design: Guidelines for Addressing Occupational Hazards and Risks in Design and Redesign Processes*, ANSI/ASSE Z590.3-2011 (New York: American Society of Safety Engineers, 2011), 12.

CHAPTER 39

Supplier or Vendor Risk Oversight

WITH THE INCREASE IN GLOBAL OUTSOURCING and contract manufacturing, there has been a proliferation of suppliers in every industry. There is a need to engage these suppliers not only in terms of acceptability of their final outputs but also in terms of having an operational oversight to ensure proactive supplier or vendor quality management.

Before talking about risk management, it is important to understand *the extent of the obligations that a company has to manage the supplier*. Usually, supplier agreements spell out certain stipulations, contractual clarifications, and terms of oversight—for example, vendor auditing and return or refund terms. This is a good place to set a baseline for mutual expectations since supplier agreements can be legally enforceable. Another important item is to *assess whether the current processes in place are sufficient to deliver on those obligations*. And finally, one must ask, *are the obligations in the supplier agreement sufficient to ensure efficient and sustained high-quality output?*

To create a risk-based supplier management system, the first step is to segment the supplier in terms of its impact on the organization. A proven tool in this regard is the Kraljic matrix, shown in Figure 39.1.

In the classic Kraljic matrix, published by Peter Kraljic,[1] there are four quadrants divided per the supply risk and profit impact. These quadrants describe different buyer-vendor relationships as follows:

1. **Noncritical (low profit impact and low supply risk)**

   The buyer can choose to devote low-to-medium-risk management resources to this category since the supplier not only has low profit impact but this supply chain is also very secure. A reactive strategy to manage risks, which saves costs, may be justified for some suppliers in this category. For example, a nuclear power plant may not need a risk management program for an office stationery vendor.

1. P. Kraljic, "Purchasing Must Become Supply Management," *Harvard Business Review*, 61, no. 5 (1983): 109–117.

FIGURE 39.1 Kraljic matrix.

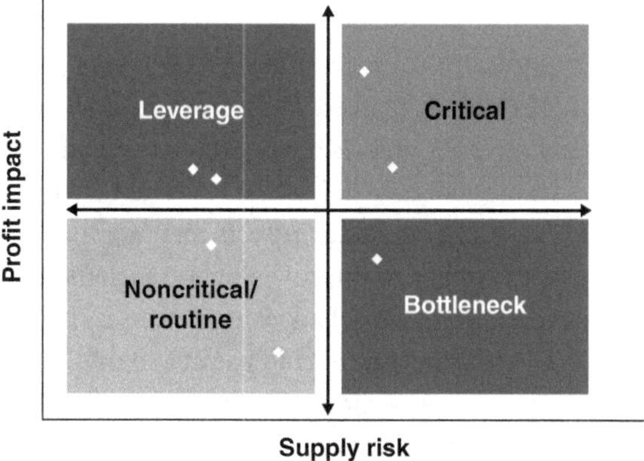

2. **Leverage (high profit impact and low supply risk)**

   The buyer should consider devoting medium-to-high-risk management efforts to this category of suppliers. The purchasing team will push to leverage this relationship for even higher profits since the supply risk is low (and strength as a buyer is high), but due to high profit impact, the risk professional must ensure that the exploitation of the supplier does not result in loss of quality. The balance can be maintained using supplier risk management.

3. **Bottleneck (low profit impact and high supply risk)**

   Purchasing departments will make efforts to control output of these kinds of suppliers by overordering. These suppliers are sometimes the only purveyors of required goods and services and therefore have certain power to impact organizational objectives and goals. Since the impact on profit is low, it is the likelihood of a damaging situation that needs to be decreased with this segment. Risk management to ensure service and volume assurance can help manage this relationship.

4. **Strategic (high profit impact and high supply risk)**

   These suppliers already have the most attention of the purchasing managers and need more attention of the risk managers. Risk must be planned and actively managed with structured steps for assessment, treatment, monitoring, and communication. Risk management must be viewed as a life-cycle activity and should be collaboratively carried out. These items and their suppliers should feature in the strategic risk management plans, and outcomes and steps must be taken to develop long-term relationships and, as needed, a plan for contingencies.

The segmentation of the supplier as shown above should guide the level of risk management efforts and the rigor of implementation of risk controls from an enterprise level. But from an operational standpoint, a risk-based supplier relationship begins with tiering the suppliers based on various quality parameters that are led by the supplied product risk.

A risk index is useful to not only add a layer of risk-based segmentation to the vendor base but also track key indicators of risk as they apply to suppliers and consolidate them in one metric that can be resolved as needed. These indicators are shown in Figure 39.2.

The reactive quality includes aspects that are discovered after the delivery of product or service. It includes things like complaint events related to the product and failures at inspection. The proactive quality includes aspects that are discovered as part of a proactive engagement with the supplier to improve quality, such as process capability, service levels, responsiveness, and quality of change notifications. The enterprise parameters draw from the Kraljic risk matrix and include parameters on the enterprise effect of the supplier on profit impact and supply chain risk. Finally, the product risk is the actual level of risk of the supplied product in terms of cost or criticality to the end user.

Example 1

For a manufacturing facility, the model shown in Figure 39.3 may apply, which includes parameters for audit nonconformances (NCs), supplier corrective action requests (SCARs), delivery timeliness, acceptance rate of the products, and finally the risk level of the product itself. Based on a cumulative score of these criteria, the suppliers can be segmented into three tiers.

Example 2

A Comprehensive Risk Index

These parameters can be drawn into specific KRIs as shown in Table 39.1. It considers the risks previously discussed and presents them in a standardized format that can be charted and used for comparison.

Objective comparative analysis is very important when we are making quality decisions, and a standard metric makes the presentation of metrics to top management very easy and effective. In this case, the first set of elements is classic supplier scorecard

FIGURE 39.2 Risk indicators for a supplier.

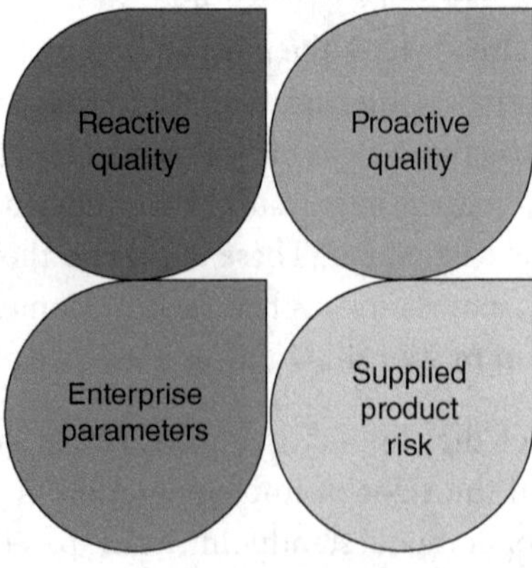

FIGURE 39.3 Risk indicators, risk level, and tiers.

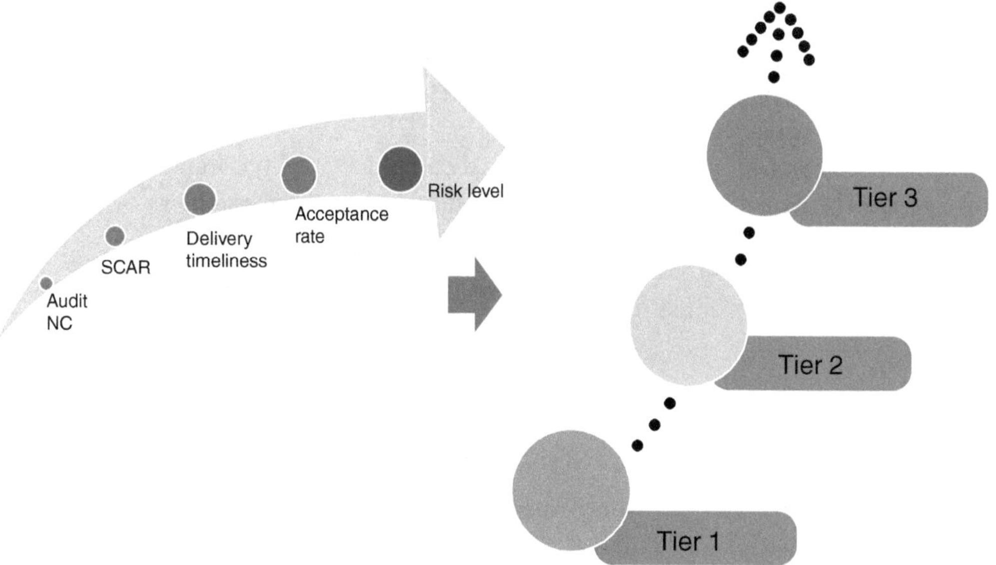

TABLE 39.1 Elements of a comprehensive risk index.

Element	Max points	Supplier A	Supplier B	Supplier C
Audit findings	10	7	9	5
SCAR quality	20	6	9	6
Delivery timeliness	10	3	5	8
Process health	15	7	7	8
Responsiveness	5	5	5	2
Compliance maturity	20	6	4	3
Field complaint allegations	10	7	3	4
Change notifications	10	9	7	7

Element	Max points	Supplier A	Supplier B	Supplier C
Strategic level	50	25	10	5
Leverage level	20	20	0	5
Diversification level	30	5	5	5

Element	Max points	Supplier A	Supplier B	Supplier C
Product risk	100	75	50	25

$$\text{Supplier risk index} = \frac{3 \times \text{Quality risk level} + 2 \times \text{Enterprise risk level} + 5 \times \text{Product risk}}{5 \times \text{Total score}}$$

elements. The second set of elements is the Kraljic elements. They heavily borrow from the paper Kraljic wrote for *Harvard Business Review*[2]—these elements capture enterprise risk, so we have now gone beyond the realm of traditional quality. The final element is the element with the most weight: the product risk. This is mainly the risk of use of bad product that is shipped out to the customer. This risk has to be relative. A cough syrup will have less risk than an arthritis drug.

A comprehensive supplier index based on product quality parameters, enterprise supply risk parameters, and the product risk can be calculated as follows:

$$\text{Supplier risk index} = \frac{3 \times \text{Quality risk level} + 2 \times \text{Enterprise risk level} + 5 \times \text{Product risk}}{5 \times \text{Total score}} \tag{39.1}$$

GRAPHICAL SUPPLIER RISK REPRESENTATION

The bubble charts shown earlier can be used as a graphical indicator of risk exposure of individual supplier risks. If two suppliers are supplying the same service or product, their risk exposures can be compared using these charts by quantifying them in consequence and likelihood terms as shown in Figure 39.4.

The area of the circle is the risk exposure, which is the multiplication of consequence and likelihood of the individual risks.

FIGURE 39.4 Bubble chart as graphical indicator of supplier risk exposure.

Risk	Severity	Occurrence	Risk level	Supplier
Risk 1	1.4	1.2	1.68	A
Risk 2	2.7	1.9	5.13	A
Risk 3	2.6	0.8	2.08	A
Risk 4	4.2	4.6	19.32	A
Risk 5	1.9	3.9	7.41	A
Risk 6	0.5	4.3	2.15	A
Risk 7	0.4	2.9	1.16	B
Risk 8	3.6	3.6	12.96	B
Risk 9	2	3	6	B
Risk 10	2	1	2	B
Risk 11	1	2	2	B
Risk 12	4	3	12	B
Risk 13	4	2	8	B
Risk 14	4.5	5	22.5	B

Supplier	Pattern
A	
B	

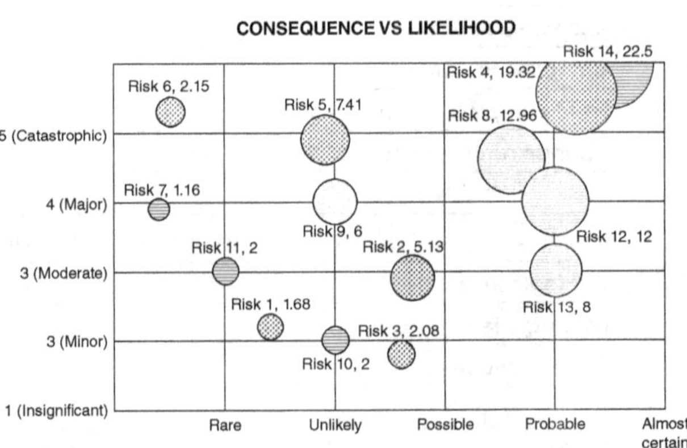

2. P. Kraljic, "Purchasing Must Become Supply Management," *Harvard Business Review* 61, no. 5 (1983): 109–117.

PREPARING FOR UNANTICIPATED SUPPLIER RISKS

We have evaluated risk often in this book by assessing the probability of occurrence and severity of impact. This method will work for only those risks that are anticipated. Some risks, as illustrated by the COVID-19 pandemic and 9/11 terrorist attacks, for example, are unanticipated by many companies and organizations. Dealing with such unanticipated risks requires organizational risk resilience. In the context of supplier risk management, this involves assessment of organizational supply chain and assessing the overall outcome when each part of the supply chain is disrupted. This concept was first presented by Simchi-Levi and colleagues in their 2014 article "From Superstorms to Factory Fires" in *Harvard Business Review*.[3] The method involves calculation of time to recovery (TTR) for each piece of the supply chain after a disruption and gauging its effect on the business.

The first step in assessing the risk associated with a particular supplier is to calculate TTR for each of its sites under various disruption scenarios.

Companies can develop a simple survey to collect key data, including:[4]

1. Supplier
   - Site location (city, region, country)
2. Parts from this site
   - Part number and description
   - Part cost
   - Annual volume for this part
   - Inventory information (days of supply) for this part
   - Total spend (per year) from this site
3. End product
   - OEM's end product(s) that uses this part
   - Profit margin for the end product(s)
4. Lead times from supplier site to OEM sites
   - Days
5. Time to recovery (TTR)

   The time it would take for the site to be restored to full functionality:

   - If the supplier site is down, but the tooling is not damaged
   - If the tooling is lost

3. D. Simchi-Levi, W. Schmidt, and Y. Wei, "From Superstorms to Factory Fires: Managing Unpredictable Supply Chain Disruptions," *Harvard Business Review* 92, no. 1–2 (2014): 96–101.

4. Questionnaire reprinted with permission from *Harvard Business Review*. Originally from D. Simchi-Levi, W. Schmidt, and Y. Wei, "From Superstorms to Factory Fires: Managing Unpredictable Supply Chain Disruptions," *Harvard Business Review* 92, no. 1–2 (2014): 96–101.

6. Cost of loss
    - Is expediting components from other locations possible? If so, what is the cost?
    - Can additional resources (overtime, more shifts, alternate capacity) be organized to satisfy demand? If so, what is the cost?
7. Supplier risk assessment
    - Does the supplier produce only from a single source?
    - Could alternate vendors supply the part?
    - Is the supplier financially stable?
    - Is there variability in performance (lead time, fill rate, quality)?
8. Mitigation strategies for this supplier–part combination
    - Alternate suppliers
    - Excess inventory
    - Other

After the TTR of each supply node is calculated, the disruption to the whole supply chain due to node failure should be calculated with the relationship of the supply node to the other parameters, such as hierarchical relationships and inventory levels, in mind.

Basically, this exercise will show how resilient the supply chain is to external disruptions, how much disruption it can withstand and where. Oftentimes, results of this exercise are surprising. Parts that are traditionally considered low risk (due to low product-specific risk) or low cost sometimes do not get the attention of purchasing and supplier quality teams and end up being the bottleneck due to reasons such as poor quality or single sourcing.

TTRs can also be calculated for service workflows by dividing a team that provides a particular service by subfunctions and calculating impact of disruption to a particular group.

By understanding TTRs for various nodes in a supply chain due to various cases of disruption from worst case to best case, the company can understand its risk exposure and consequently create redundant systems where necessary or adjust operations parameters such as inventory, spend, cash in hand, and work in progress.

CHAPTER 40

Risk in Industry 4.0

INDUSTRY 4.0 REFERS TO THE FOURTH INDUSTRIAL REVOLUTION. Despite being the most silent, compared with the earlier revolutions of industrial steam, mass manufacturing, and electric systems, 4.0 is the most pervasive. Industry 4.0 takes the digitization engendered by 3.0 and magnifies it to provide near-universal accessibility and connectivity. The capacity for accurate data gathering has increased like never before, entering our personal devices, homes, cars, and sometimes on and even into our bodies.

These increased data points and enhanced analytics can together be used to enhance predictive decision making. The effect of 4.0 is only as good as the ability of an organization's infrastructure to leverage the connectedness of systems.

Of particular note are developing technologies that have tremendous potential to effect a paradigm shift in the conduct of business. Artificial intelligence (AI) and machine learning, for example, can affect all phases of design, development, and execution of systems and processes.

The reach of AI is tremendous, though its potential intelligence has yet to be completely realized. For example, Google brain has an IQ of 47, which is less than that of a six-year-old child, but it can acquire knowledge at lightning speed. At least for now, reasoning creativity and critical thinking will remain domains of humans and not androids.

Even if an AI could be provided with an IQ greater than 200, smartness in terms of business decision making involves futures thinking and consequences analysis. It means processing the final decision by taking into account multiple parameters that include cascading effects, material outcomes, financial outcomes, and emotional outcomes to assign a probability of success to one decision.

In short, the ultimate AI is equipped with risk-based thinking.

While this may happen sometime in the distant future, in practical terms, for the present, it will not be human versus machine but, instead, human versus human with 4.0 tools to aid decision making. On a more basic level, 4.0 technologies such as mobile technology, virtual reality, augmented reality, the cloud, big data, Internet of Things, and social media do not engender a revolution by themselves but provide a tremendous opportunity to leverage information.

FIGURE 40.1 Sources of data and decision making in industry from 2.0 to 4.0.

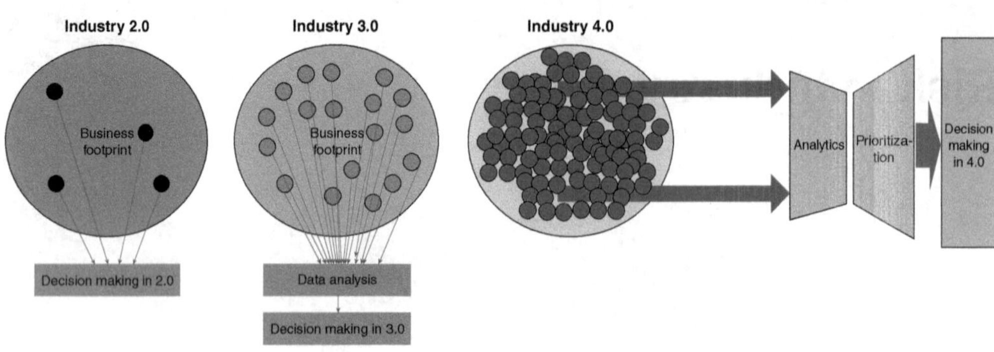

4.0 is often confused for only technology or digitization. This is a simplistic view. 4.0 is the effect of digitization on the market. Installing a technology that uses the cloud on service center computers or on a manufacturing floor does not guarantee an effect on the company's bottom line. Indeed, many such information technology implementation projects fail at large expense to the company. It is the strategy behind these projects that decides the objectives and goals that lead to its success.

Technology is only the means to an end, and in 99% of cases it does not make the decisions for us. It is an enabler that enriches the informed decision by providing accurate and precise data. In Industry 2.0, value chains were smaller, local, and simpler. A decision could be made by a few pieces of information from specific preidentified points. In 3.0, transistors and related electronics ushered in a digital age in which computer systems provided a yet unseen data processing and transfer power that in turn allowed for greater value addition with associated value chain expansion. The focus in 3.0 was to install a digital system at critical points to collect data and monitor systems. This multiplied data points required for accurate decision making. Companies that relied on local data points ended up taking risk-uninformed decisions based on incomplete data and lost business.

In 4.0, with the inherent connectedness of systems, there is no dearth of data points. The challenge is to rank and filter them for provision of diagnostic and predictive analytics to enable inclusive decision making. Sources of data and decision making from 2.0 to 4.0 are summarized in Figure 40.1. Data inputs in 4.0 and the generated data's transformative processing to enable decision making is shown in Figure 40.2.

On one side, risk management is a tool that can make sense of the pervading information and ensure visualization of the state of business by ranking and filtering. On the other side, risk management can help effect and manage the connectedness of the business footprint by exposing gaps and prioritizing actions.

To navigate the 4.0 landscape, enterprise risks of connectedness in aspects of the business process and technology must be considered. The change from a paper-based process to a software process in 3.0 seems small when compared with the connected autonomous processes in 4.0. When done correctly, an organization can see a large

FIGURE 40.2 Data points in 4.0.

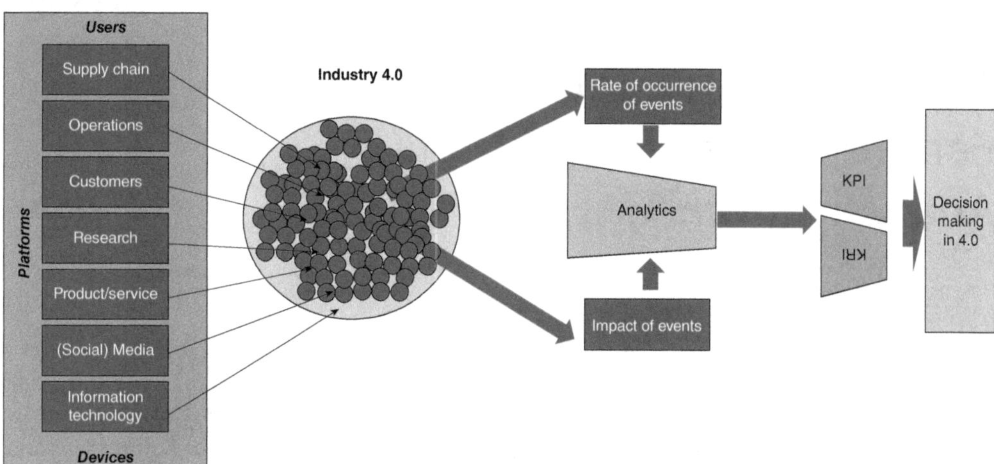

increase in productivity; but when the changeover is sluggish, the opposite can occur. Mismanagement of transition to 4.0 can lead not only to loss of opportunity but also to loss of currently available resources, leading to overall business loss. Thus, 4.0 transition must be managed as an upside opportunity risk.

Technology risks are associated with mismanagement of the transition from traditional data to big data. In 3.0, businesses had the luxury to analyze value chains and place data monitors at select positions. In 4.0, the data are there, and there are a lot. During the transition to 4.0, risk associated with scalability of the data, connectedness, structure of reporting, volume of reporting, and integrity must be analyzed. It has become very easy to get lost in data and get caught up with a false alarm. The risk of an analytic process in terms of its scope and constraints must be taken into account.

Data measurement systems must be validated, with measures and countermeasures defined before a data stream is used for decision making. Risk management, by virtue of its analyzing and assessing both opportunities and threats, provides an avenue for this objective assessment.

For example, many car insurance companies use an app on a consumer's phone to track markers of safety like braking, accelerating, speeding, and so on to decide their insurance rates. This is an excellent method to leverage the connectedness of 4.0 to reduce the insurer's risk. But this is based on the assumption that the driver will carry the same phone in each and every car ride. A person may install the app on one phone and use it sparingly and drive cautiously on purpose while using another phone at other times. Thus, countermeasures must be developed to check such misuse. Many such fallacies can be revealed when a structured risk management process is applied.

4.0 is not an option to consider. It is here. And the speed with which a business adapts to it will determine its future success in the connected marketplace.

CHAPTER 41

Advanced Risk Tools: Failure Modes and Effects Analysis (FMEA)

FAILURE MODES AND EFFECTS ANALYSIS (FMEA), as the name denotes, is a systemic process for the analysis of the failure modes of a system, subsystem, or component and the local or global (immediate or end) effects (consequences) of the analyzed failures. While FMEAs also provide a framework for risk identification, analysis, and evaluation, the main intent of the FMEA is the identification of the mitigations or modifications to a system or subcomponents that can act as preventive action to mitigate or reduce the severity of the failure mode. It is a method for bottom-up or inductive assessment of downside risk and focuses on analysis of the various ways in which the system or component under study can become faulty and fail..

The system is an entity that, by virtue of its function, converts an input into a desired (expected) output (see Figure 41.1). The system accomplishes this by going through process steps that may use various subsystems and components to realize the output. Most systems have some output variability, and at times, the variance can go beyond the accepted levels. This may or may not lead to a system failure. Before the system failure, the subsystems and components within the system start misbehaving and providing unacceptable intermediate outputs due to a variety of internal and external causes. Some of these unacceptable intermediate outputs may not lead to system failure but may contribute to variance.

Failure is defined by IEC 60812:2006 as:

> *Termination of the ability of an item to perform a required function.*[1]

Various parts of the system may fail while the system itself may still operate. The analysis of failures within FMEAs can include analysis of the system, process, subpart, or subprocess and can go down to the smallest resolvable element of the system as required. A failure can be preceded by faults in the system that can cause increased variance but do not cause outright failure.

1. *Failure Modes and Effects Analysis (FMEA and FMECA)*, IEC 60812:2006 (Geneva, Switzerland: International Electrochemical Commission, 2006), p. 13. Copyright © 2006 IEC Geneva, Switzerland. www.iec.ch.

FIGURE 41.1 System output and variability.

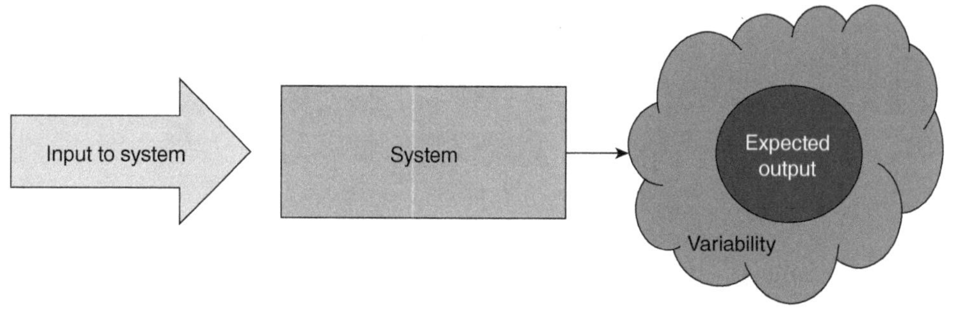

FIGURE 41.2 Cause and effect.

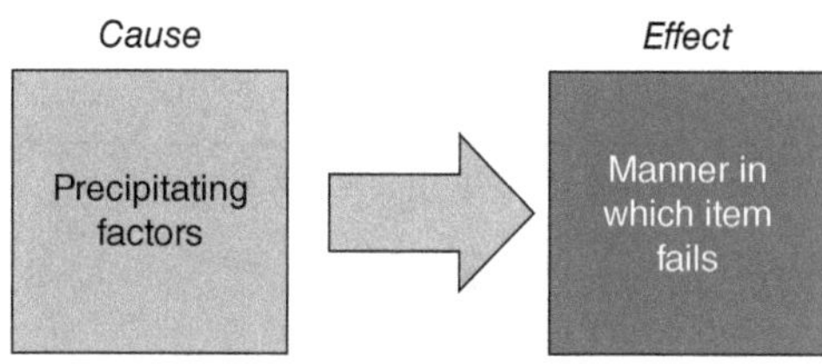

The *failure mode* is defined as:

The manner in which an item fails.[2]

The failure mode simply uses verbiage to describe the fashion, method, or manner in which the failure occurs. This can be used to describe the state of the system under study (e.g., the device does not turn on) or can describe the failure as a sequential event (e.g., device develops microcracks upon load application).

It is useful to view the system, subsystem, or component under study and its outcomes in terms of causes and effects to understand the theory of FMEA.

Real-world systems are complex, and the diagram in Figure 41.2 can be resolved to show the faults generated by precipitating factors that do not lead to an effect. One must consider whether every failure under analysis will actually lead to an effect. The illustration in Figure 41.3 clarifies this concept.

Per IEC 60812:2008, the *failure effect* is defined as:

Consequence of a failure mode in terms of the operation, function or status of the item.[3]

2. *Failure Modes and Effects Analysis (FMEA and FMECA)*, IEC 60812:2006 (Geneva, Switzerland: International Electrochemical Commission, 2006), p. 13. Copyright © 2006 IEC Geneva, Switzerland. www.iec.ch.

3. *Failure Modes and Effects Analysis (FMEA and FMECA)*, IEC 60812:2006 (Geneva, Switzerland: International Electrochemical Commission, 2006), p. 13.

FIGURE 41.3 Failure mode, cause, and effect.

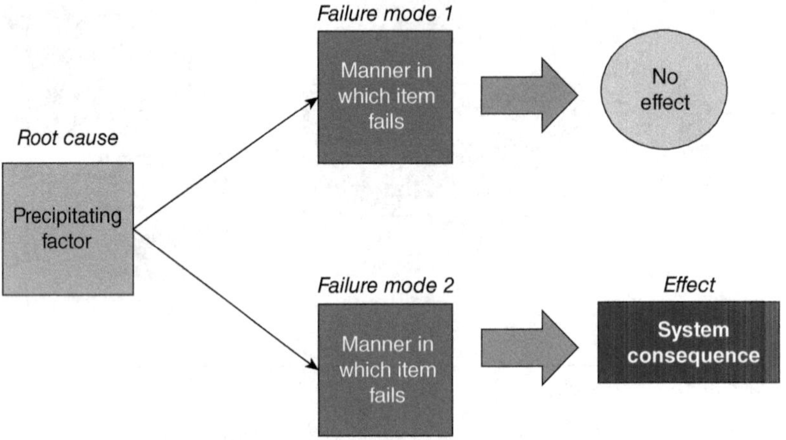

FIGURE 41.4 Cause, effect, and failure mode.

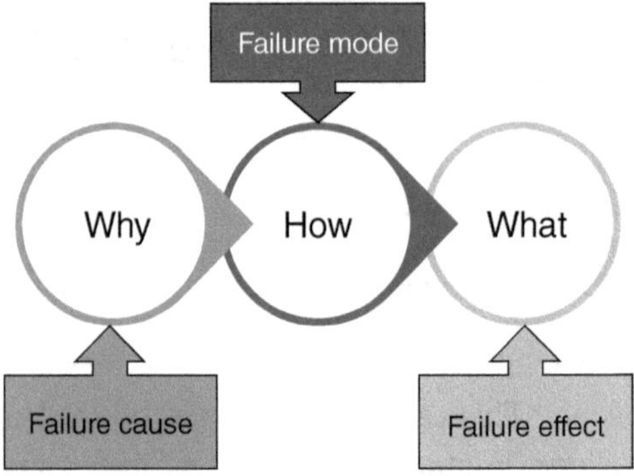

The failure effect can be local or systemic or can even be a "no effect." The effects must be considered for both the short and long term to get a holistic picture. Figure 41.4 shows a very high-level view of FMEA process fundamentals. The failure mode is the "how" of the failed state (i.e., how did the failure occur?). The failure effect is the "what" of the failed state (i.e., what was the result of the failure?). Finally, the root cause of the failure is the "why" of the failed state (i.e., why did the failure under study occur?).

FMEAs can be applied at various levels starting from the system, subsystem, or discrete component level. It is important to understand and identify the elements that define a system and how the subclusters of these elements become subsystems and components. Similarly, the function of each of these elements should be studied, and, more importantly, states of elements (higher or lower in the system hierarchy) that can adversely affect the function should be noted as well. For example, a component failure can affect a few downstream subcomponents in one way and affect the upstream subsystem in a different way.

Once the system (and associated elements) and its failure modes are mapped, an occurrence rate or probability is assigned to the failure mode. The following may feature in the assignation of this occurrence rating:

1. Probability of failure mode
2. Probability of cause leading to failure mode
3. Probability of failure mode leading to failure effect

Every system is unique, and these three or other probabilities may feature in calculation of the final probability of occurrence of the failure mode. Normally, all preceding probabilities before the failure mode are multiplied to give the probability of occurrence of the failure mode.

An example of failure modes and their causes for hip implants is shown in Figure 41.5.

Here, the horizontal probabilities are multiplied to give us the probability of failure mode. For example, the probability of the hip implant fracturing into pieces due to poor strength of material is $0.1 \times 0.1 = 0.01$. The multiplicative logic has been applied here since the sequence of events can be broken down to the probability of poor material strength leading to poor standalone mechanical integrity and that of poor mechanical integrity leading to microcracks.

Another method is shown in Figure 41.6.

Here, the probability of the cause (Pc) is the probability of each "cause" leading to failure mode. The failure mode probability is the overall probability of all the identified causes leading to failure mode (PFM). Probability of the failure mode leading to failure effect is failure mode probability divided between all the failure effects that could happen from the failure mode.

The above discussed methods of calculating probabilities may not apply to all systems and can be adjusted per the system under study.

FIGURE 41.5 Example of failure modes and their causes.

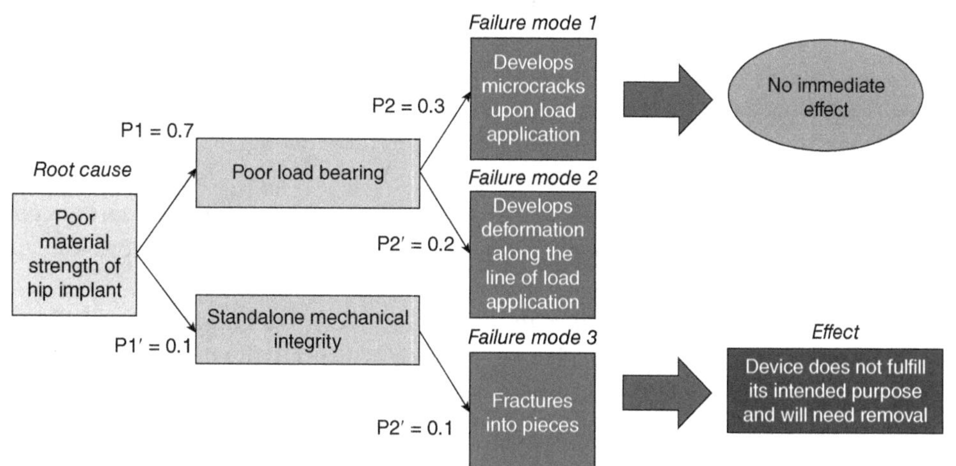

FIGURE 41.6 Probability tree for failure mode and failure effects.

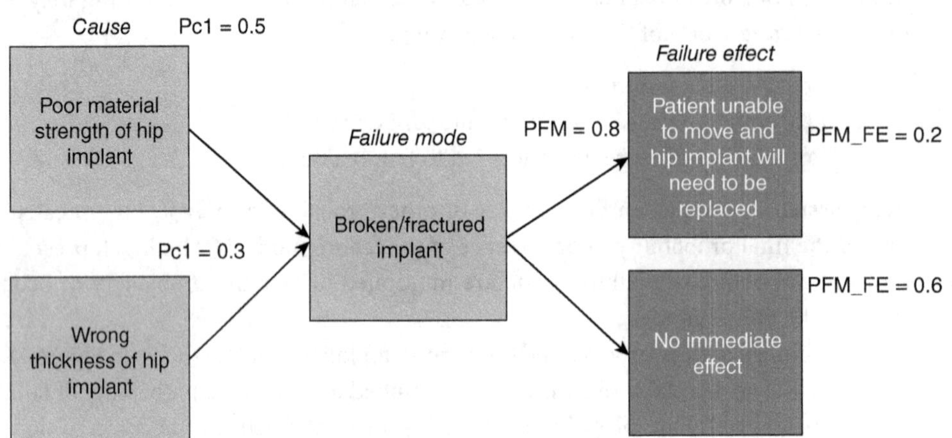

TABLE 41.1 Occurrence scale.

Occurrence (O)	Frequency of the failure mode	Ranking
Frequent	1 in 10	5
Probable	1 in 100	4
Occasional	1 in 1000	3
Remote	1 in 10,000	2
Improbable	1 in 100,000	1

The probabilities can be assigned based on either rigorous quantitative analysis or informed assumptions/beliefs based on available data and opinions from subject matter experts.

In either case, it is essential to rank the probabilities per the level of occurrence on a graded scale. An example is shown in Table 41.1.

Next, we need to understand the failure effect and the failure severity.

For purposes of the FMEA, the severity is the grade of effect of the failure. This means that while the effects of the failure could be very specific to the system outcomes, the assignation of severity must accomplish a relative grading of these effects using a common scale with descriptors that are general enough to apply to the system. Samples of severity are shown in Table 41.2.

It is common to rank the levels of severity by number, which makes the consequence parameter semiquantitative and lends it to multiplicative operations for calculation of risk.

Failure modes and effect criticality analysis (FMECA) is an extension of FMEA that includes the failure mode criticality. This criticality is primarily driven by the severity of the consequence and the probability of the failure mode and may include the risk factor for detectability. The criticality helps in deciding the level of acceptability of the risk and prioritizing the mitigations.

TABLE 41.2 Severity scale.

Severity (S)	Description	Ranking
Catastrophic	Very high severity, can affect safe vehicle operation and/or involves noncompliance with government regulation	5
Critical	Item is inoperable (loss of primary function)	4
Major	Operable but a reduced level of performance; customer very dissatisfied	3
Moderate	Fit and finish/squeak and rattle item does not conform	2
Minor	No discernible effect	1

FIGURE 41.7 Filling out an FMEA.

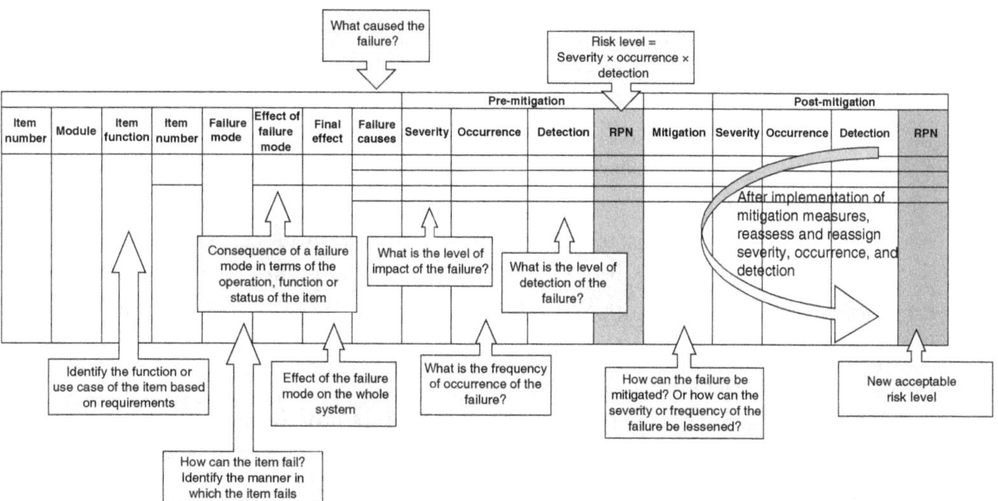

Risk is the failure criticality that, at the very minimum, combines the severity and occurrence levels of each failure mode. This is accomplished by the following:

1. Assigning (ranking) probability levels on a relative scale
2. Assigning (ranking) severity levels on a relative scale
3. Multiplying the relatively ranked probability and severity (and detection, where applicable)

Where appropriate, the detection of the failure is added as another parameter and multiplied with the probability and severity to provide risk criticality or risk level. Using a risk matrix to get a risk level and multiplying severity, probability, and detection to get a risk priority number (RPN) is the most common form of criticality assignation.

Figure 41.7 pictorially summarizes the FMEA process.

FMEA is an iterative process that gets updated throughout the life cycle of the product. FMEAs are performed at the early stages of development as soon as design details are available. Early stage identification of mitigations through FMEAs is the most effective because changes to the design are easy at this stage. FMEAs are updated based on any new information or evidence that becomes available after the launch, like feedback or complaints on the products/services, and, accordingly, additional mitigations or field actions are performed based on the FMEA outputs. There are different types of FMEAs based on their application. Commonly used ones are design FMEA (DFMEA), process FMEA (PFMEA), software FMEA, service FMEA, and use FMEA (UFMEA).

There are four main stages of FMEA:

1. Planning of the FMEA and related activities, which includes identifying the scope, purpose, and stakeholders
2. Identifying the failure modes and their consequences and causes; documenting the identified columns in the FMEA worksheet
3. Communicating the identified mitigations and detection techniques
4. Updating the FMEA throughout the life cycle of the product based on new evidence and information

Identifying the scope of the FMEA: The scope of the FMEA should be identified in the initial design phase; this will help in the collection of data and selection of the right stakeholders. The scope should clearly define the boundaries of the system under study and whether any specific features are in or out of the scope. Sometimes, for product FMEAs, one FMEA includes many parts, products, or a family of products. This must be clearly documented, and later users of the FMEA document should not be expected to assume that the FMEA applies to multiple products. In process FMEAs, if multiple products use the same process, then analysis must be done if the FMEA really does apply to all products or if some products are out of scope.

Purpose of the FMEA: The reasons for or the intent of the analysis can be to identify the mitigations for the failure modes in the early stages of the design, to create a benchmark for review of the post-launch or post-market data, to determine the sample size for the verification and validation, to identify the input parameters for process validation and reliability analysis, or to meet regulatory requirements.

Stakeholders: FMEA is a result of the team composed of the qualified stakeholders who can

- identify system, product, or process failure modes;
- assess the effects and consequences;
- and identify the causes and mitigations to eliminate and reduce the occurrence of the failure mode.

If the right stakeholders are not included, the FMEA can unfortunately become a paper exercise.

Data gathering: The following information can help in the FMEA creation process:

1. FMEAs for similar products
2. Feedback/complaints for similar product and competitor products
3. Design details, design drawings, schematics, and so on
4. Feasibility study data
5. Input/output requirements document

Relation between DFMEA and PFMEA: The failure modes in the DFMEA can be reused in the PFMEA as failure effects. The severity identified for the failure effects in the DFMEA should ideally match the severity in the PFMEA. If the PFMEA is performed by the supplier, the risk professional should foster proper cross-functional participation to ensure alignment.

FMEA process flow (including the detection factor) is shown in Figure 41.8.

Table 41.3 shows an example of a DFMEA worksheet.

FIGURE 41.8 The FMEA process.

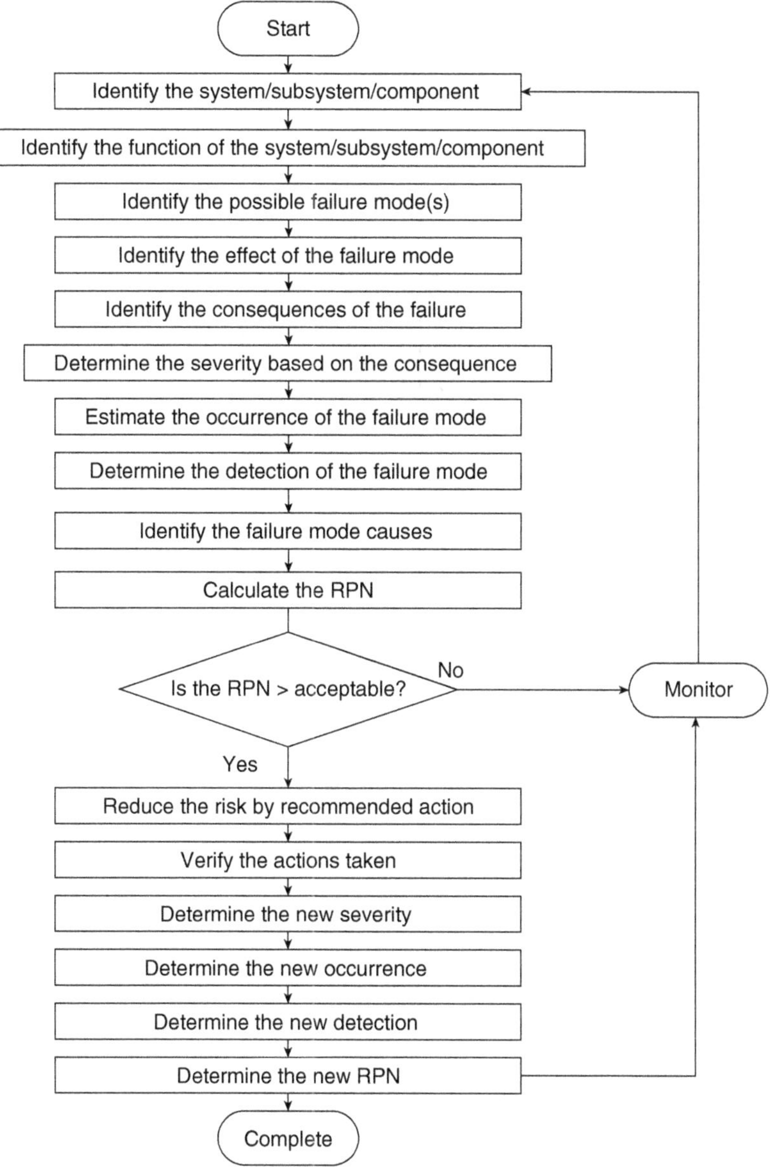

TABLE 41.3 DFMEA column headers in a worksheet.

						Prior to recommended action						Action results		
Item ref	Item function	Failure mode	Effect of the failure	Final effect	Failure causes	Severity	Occurrence	Detection	RPN	Recommended action	Action taken	Severity	Occurrence	RPN

The column headers are defined as follows:

System/subsystem/component (Item ref): defines which specific system/subsystem/component is analyzed within the FMEA. Examples of a system are a mobile phone, infusion pump, and automatic braking system. Examples of a subsystem are the display module in the mobile phone, an alarm system inside an infusion pump, and the controller system inside the automatic braking system. Examples of components are the display screen in the display module, the speaker inside the alarm system, and the central processing unit (CPU) inside the controller system.

It is sometimes helpful to construct a hierarchical diagram that lists the system, subsystem, components, and subcomponents (see Figure 41.9). Major elements within these should be subject to analysis, and a component or subcomponent failure will have a system impact and vice versa.

When analyzing hierarchy, the elements within the hierarchy and their functions and failures along with their horizontal and vertical effects can be studied for detailed failure impact analysis.

Item function: explains the function of the specific system/subsystem/component. The "reason for being" of the specific element should be written out. Table 41.4 shows examples of functions.

FIGURE 41.9 Hierarchy of elements for failure study.

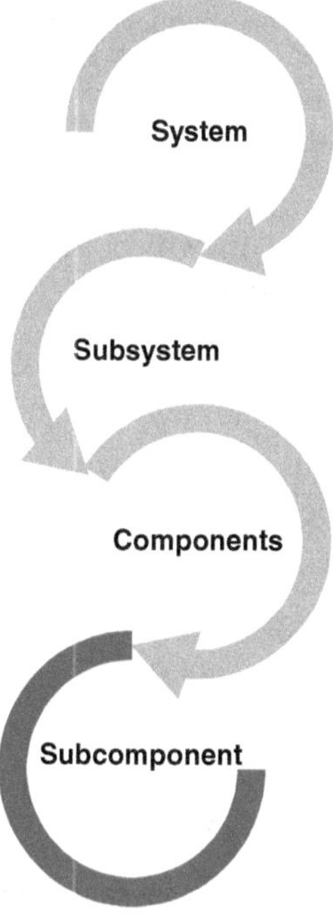

TABLE 41.4 Component and function.

System/subsystem/component	Function
Mobile phone	Receives and makes phone calls
Infusion pump	Delivers medication in the appropriate flow rate to patient
Automatic braking system	Applies brakes when obstruction is detected
Display module	Displays details to the user
Alarm system	Alerts the user of a malfunction in the device
Controller system	Controls the overall process of the automatic braking system
Display	Converts electrical signal to display
Speaker	Converts electrical signals to sound energy
CPU	Processes inputs and provides appropriate output

TABLE 41.5 Component and failure mode.

System/subsystem/component (Item)	Failure mode
Mobile phone	Unable to display caller details
Infusion pump	Delivering at an incorrect flow rate
Automatic braking system	Intermittent braking without obstruction
Display module	Erroneous display
Alarm system	False alarm
Controller system	Unable to control the automatic braking system
Display	Broken/fractured
Speaker	No sound when electrical signals are applied
CPU	No response for any inputs

Failure mode: the manner in which the system/subsystem/component fails. Table 41.5 shows examples of failure modes.

Effect of failure mode: the immediate effect of the failure mode. One failure mode can lead to multiple effects, and one effect of failure mode could happen due to multiple failure modes. This can be more categorically written as the actual condition, characteristic, or specification of the element that goes beyond acceptable bounds. Table 41.6 shows examples of failure effects.

Cause of the failure mode: the reasons for the failure mode. The most likely causes for each failure mode should be identified and documented. The earlier steps described the "how" of the failure. The cause refers to the "why" of the failure. It is important to reach this conclusion carefully as mitigative measures for failure prevention are dictated by the cause analysis. Table 41.7 shows examples of failure causes.

Table 41.8 combines the failure mode, failure effect, and failure cause.

TABLE 41.6 Component and failure effect.

System/subsystem/component (Item)	Failure effect
Mobile phone	Unable to know the caller details
Infusion pump	Patient receiving medication at an incorrect rate
Automatic braking system	Braking without obstruction
Display module	Incorrect details displayed to user
Alarm system	User incorrectly alerted
Controller system	Unable to control the automatic braking system
Display	Broken/fractured
Speaker	No sound when electrical signals are applied
CPU	No response for any inputs

TABLE 41.7 Component and cause of the failure.

System/subsystem/component (item)	Cause of the failure
Mobile phone	Keyboard not functional
Infusion pump	Incorrect motor speed
Automatic braking system	Sensor providing wrong signals
Display module	Pixel damage
Alarm system	Incorrect input from the battery
Controller system	Signal interference
Display	Unable to withstand small impacts
Speaker	Incorrect speaker for the application
CPU	Infinite loop

Consequence of the failure mode (final effect): the final or end effect of the failure mode. One effect of failure mode could lead to multiple consequences, and one consequence could happen due to multiple effects of failure modes. Examples include a mobile phone user not being able to accept or make calls (loss of functionality), a patient not receiving the medication in time and dying, and a passenger being injured in an automotive collision.

Severity (S): severity of the consequence or the final effect. The severity of the consequence is normally based on the preestablished values. See Table 41.9.

Occurrence (O): the probability of the failure mode occurring. This is based on the occurrence table established. See Table 41.10.

Detection (D): the detection of the failure mode. The detection table is based on the various detection techniques. See Table 41.11.

Table 41.9 is an example of a severity table.
Table 41.10 is an example of an occurrence table.

TABLE 41.8 Component and failure mode, effect, and cause.

System/subsystem/ component (item)	Failure mode	Failure effect	Failure cause
Mobile phone	Unable to display caller details	Unable to know the caller details	Keyboard not functional
Infusion pump	Delivering at an incorrect flow rate	Patient receiving medication at an incorrect rate	Incorrect motor speed
Automatic braking system	Intermittent braking without obstruction	Braking without obstruction	Sensor providing wrong signals
Display module	Erroneous display	Incorrect details displayed to user	Pixel damage
Alarm system	False alarm	User incorrectly alerted	Incorrect input from the battery
Controller system	Unable to control the automatic braking system	Unable to control the automatic braking system	Signal interference
Display	Broken/fractured	Broken/fractured	Unable to withstand small impacts
Speaker	No sound when electrical signals are applied	No sound when electrical signals are applied	Incorrect speaker for the application
CPU	No response for any inputs	No response for any inputs	Infinite loop

TABLE 41.9 Severity table.

Severity (S)	Description	Ranking
Catastrophic	Very high severity; can affect operation and lead to bodily user harm and/or involves noncompliance with government regulation	5
Critical	Item is inoperable (loss of primary function)	4
Major	Operable but a reduced level of performance; customer very dissatisfied	3
Moderate	Fit and finish/squeak and rattle item does not conform	2
Minor	No discernible effect	1

TABLE 41.10 Occurrence table.

Occurrence (O)	Frequency of the failure mode	Ranking
Frequent	1 in 10	5
Probable	1 in 100	4
Occasional	1 in 1000	3
Remote	1 in 10,000	2
Improbable	1 in 100,000	1

TABLE 41.11 Detection table.

Detectability (D)	Criteria	Ranking
Very high	Error proofing, poka-yoke design	1
High	Easy to detect, able to detect through visual test	2
Remote	Can be detected through specific inspection test	3
Low	Can be detected only through destructive testing	4
Almost impossible	Failure mode is very difficult to detect	5

Table 41.11 is an example of a detection table.

Current control: any existing or prevailing method to prevent the occurrence of the failure mode, or any detection method currently available, or a way to avoid the consequence due to the failure mode.

Risk priority number (RPN): the calculated value of Severity (S) × Occurrence (O) × Detection (D).

Recommended action: any additional method or technique to prevent the occurrence of the failure mode, reduce the consequence of the failure mode, or increase the detection/detectability of the failure mode.

Action taken: objective evidence on how the recommended action is implemented to prevent the failure mode, reduce the consequence of the failure mode, or increase in detection of the failure mode.

Action results: recording the final severity/occurrence/detectability after the recommended action is implemented to prevent the failure mode, reduce the consequence of the failure mode, or increase in detection of the failure mode. These are the expected outcomes of the actions. The new RPN or risk level should also be documented.

Acceptability criteria: the pre-determined acceptance criteria of a specific FMEA line. For example, if the RPN value is greater than 50 for the FMEA line, then it is required to have a recommended action to reduce or maintain the RPN to 50. Or, if the risk criticality level is high, it should be reduced to low or medium.

A sample FMEA for a mobile phone display is shown in Table 41.12.

Monitoring: The FMEA should be reviewed/updated based on any new applicable information or evidence. Examples include complaints, feedback, design changes performed on the system/subsystem/component, and periodic reviews. Any of these could trigger changes if a new failure mode, failure effect, or final effect is identified. Similarly, an increase in the estimated occurrence value could trigger a new corrective action and risk response.

TABLE 41.12 FMEA snippet for a mobile phone display.

								Pre-mitigation					Post-mitigation			
Item number	Module	Item function	Item number	Failure mode	Effect of failure mode	Final effect	Failure causes	Severity	Occurrence	Detection	RPN	Mitigation	Severity	Occurrence	Detection	RPN
1	Thin Film Transister (TFT) mobile display	To reliably function as a phone display screen by providing required contrast, resolution and color reproduction	1	Cracked screen	Portion of screen is dark	Phone is usable	User drops the phone	3	4	1	**12**	Issue user warning and provide screen protectors	2	3	1	**6**
							High temperature during charging affects glass integrity	3	1	1	**3**	None, RPN acceptable	3	1	1	**3**
			2		All of screen is dark	Phone is unusable	User drops the phone	4	3	1	**12**	Provide screen protectors	3	3	1	**9**
							High temperature during charging affects glass integrity	4	1	1	**4**	None, RPN acceptable	4	1	1	**4**

Advantages of FMEA

- Early and detailed identification of specific potential failures
- Easy assignation of a risk profile
- Easy to communicate the risk with different stakeholders
- Can be used for reliability calculations
- Can be used and updated throughout the life cycle
- Very structured tool and is easy to adopt

Disadvantages of FMEA

- Only one failure is analyzed at one line; aggregate failures cannot be analyzed
- It is qualitative or semiquantitative
- Multiple-system-level FMEAs can become complicated

WORKFLOW FOR UFMEA

UFMEA analyzes the uses and misuses of the product or process and identifies the use errors and their effects and consequences. The usability of the process or product is analyzed in detail to understand the errors that can occur during use and how they will impact the outcome of the intended function. As explained earlier in the chapter, FMEAs can be performed at different levels; the UFMEA is performed at a systems level. UFMEA usually considers the usability and human factors for the product, process, or service and considers the user interaction with the system as a whole at preset locations per design of the system. The flowchart in Figure 41.10 shows a workflow for UFMEA creation.

WORKFLOW FOR PFMEA

PFMEA analyzes the potential process failures and their effects and consequences. Process failures can greatly affect the safety and quality of the product, and therefore identification and mitigation of these failures is important. PFMEA for products is initiated with the design transfer phase, at which time the design and planning of the manufacturing processes are initiated. The PFMEA can be applied to a high-level process or can be broken down into individual process steps; this can be based on how complex the process is and what details need to be analyzed for failure prevention. Figure 41.11 shows a flowchart for PFMEA creation.

RELATIONSHIP BETWEEN DFMEA AND UFMEA

The failure modes in the DFMEA and the use errors in the UFMEA can be the failure effects in the PFMEA; the severity identified for the DFMEA and UFMEA failure effects should be the same for the PFMEA.

FIGURE 41.10 The UFMEA process.

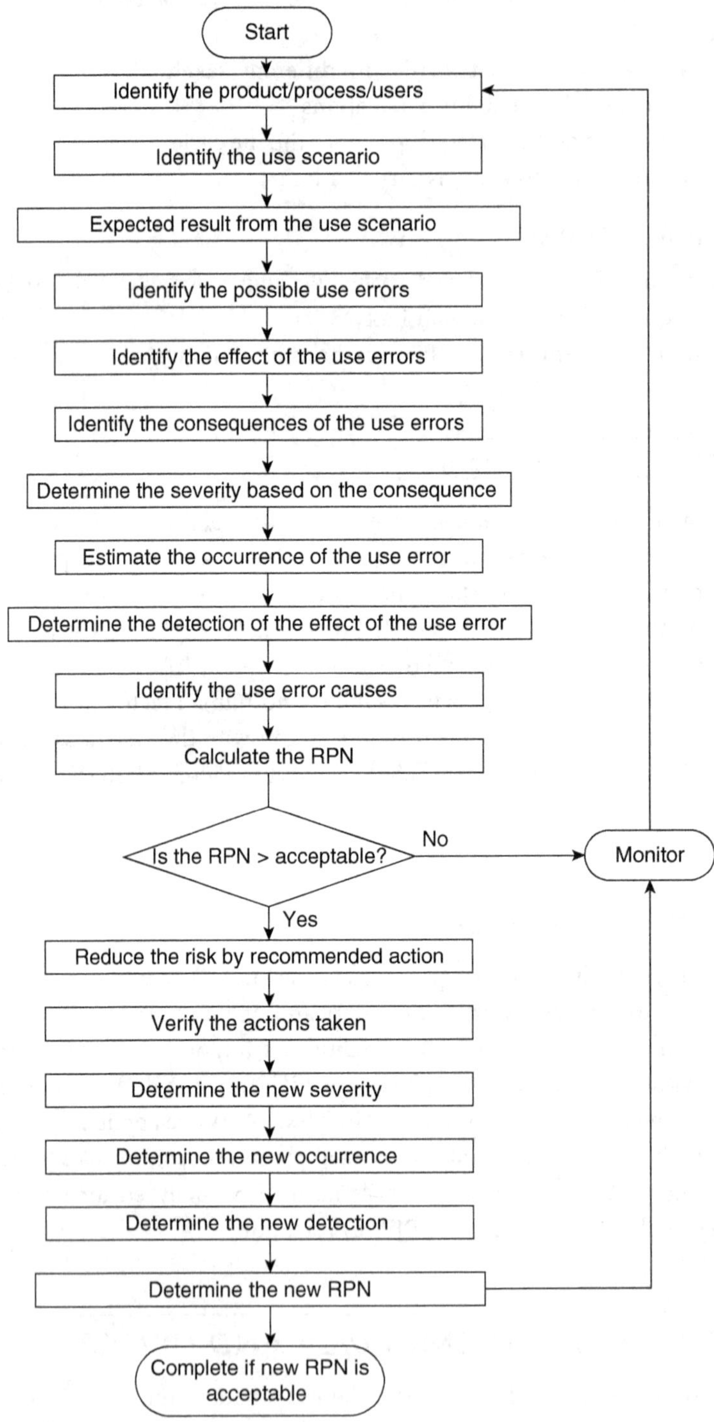

FIGURE 41.11 The PFMEA process.

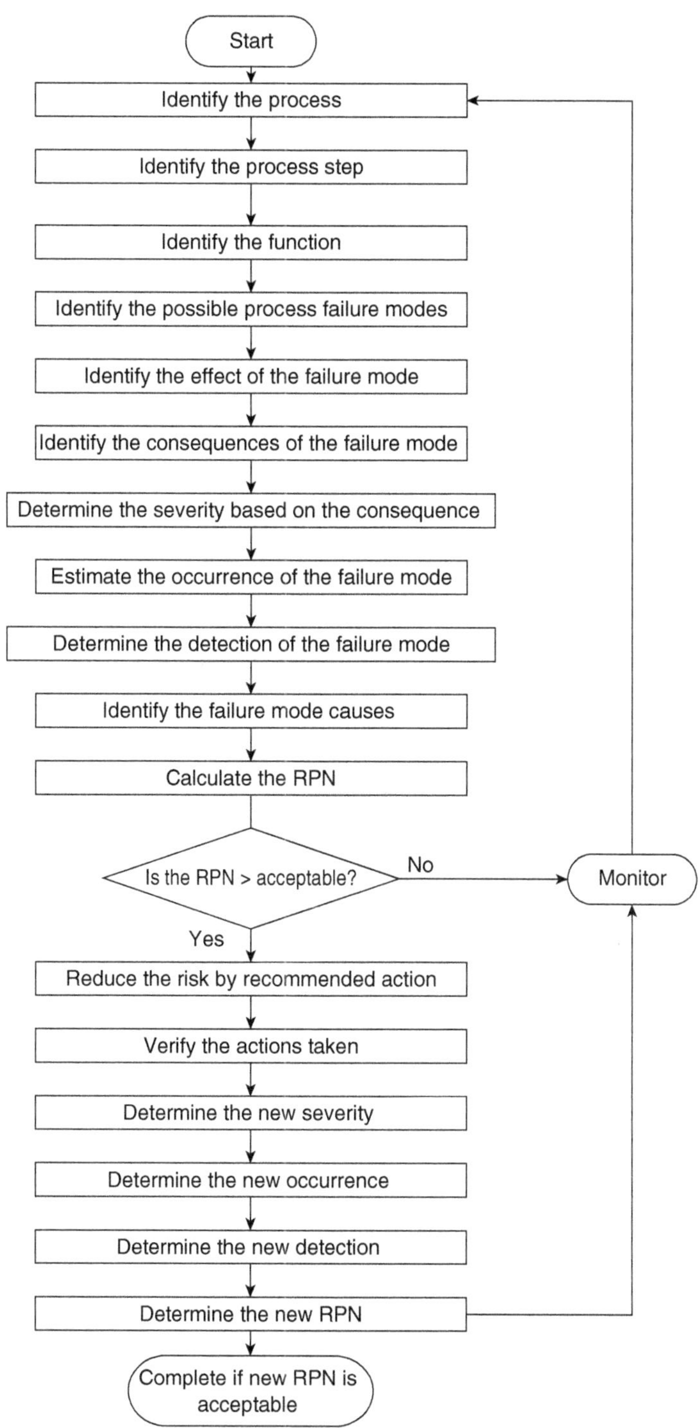

For performing PFMEA, the following information is required:

- Clear definition of the process goal (What is the intention of the process? Its desired output?)
- Understanding of the individual steps in the process
- Understanding of potential flaws in the process
- Understanding of the potential effects of and causes for the process failures (and their impact on the final output)

CHAPTER 42

Advanced Risk Tools: Hazard Analysis

HAZARD ANALYSIS IS A PROCESS to analyze the hazards and their consequences related to a product or process under study. The aim is to study the hazard, its causes, and hazardous conditions and effects such that the risks arising from them can be managed.

Let us begin by restating some relevant terminologies. Per ISO 14971:2019,[1]

Hazard is the "potential source of harm."
Hazardous situation is "a circumstance in which people, property, or environment is/are exposed to one or more hazards."
Risk is the "combination of the probability of occurrence of harm and the severity of that harm."

Figure 42.1 depicts the relation among hazard, hazardous situation, impact (harm), and risk. The probability of a hazard leading to a hazardous situation is P1, and the probability of a hazardous situation leading to an impact is P2. Therefore, the probability of the risk itself, which is the combined probability of a hazard leading to a hazardous situation and the hazardous situation leading to harm (impact), is $P1 \times P2$.

The main process involved in hazard analysis is shown in Figure 42.2.

IDENTIFY THE HAZARD

Hazard identification is the process of identifying and describing all significant system-specific hazards and hazardous situations. Some techniques for identifying hazards are the following:

- Checklists: going through a predefined generic list of hazards to identify which of them are applicable and documenting the rationale for their applicability.

1. ©ISO. This material is reproduced from ISO 14971:2019, with permission of the American National Standards Institute (ANSI) on behalf of the International Organization for Standardization. All rights reserved.

FIGURE 42.1 Relation among hazard, hazardous situation, impact (harm), and risk.

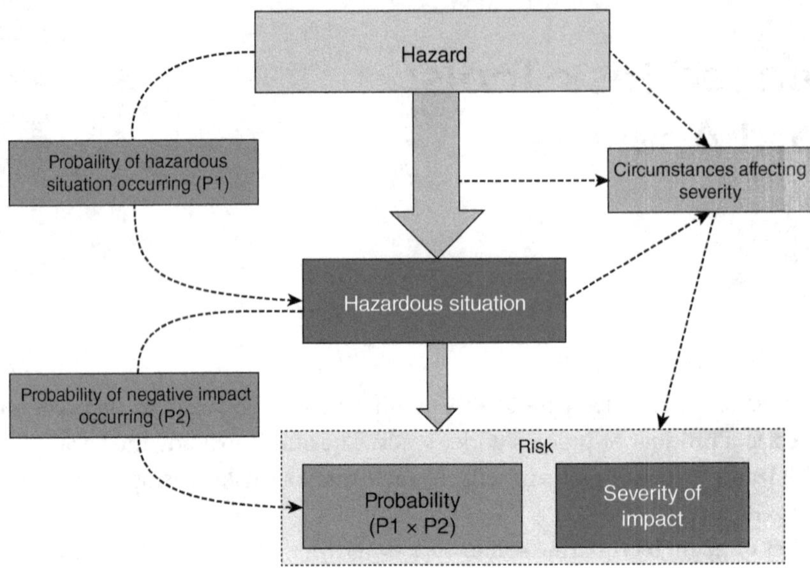

- Questionnaire: a set of questions posed to subject matter experts, process owners, operators, and others to identify the applicable hazards. The answers to the questions are documented for the details of their applicablility and further analyzed and confirmed by the hazard identification team.
- Literature review: a review of any and all published literature and industry/trade publications of interest to document the applicable hazards on similar systems and check their applicability based on system and environment similarity.
- Brainstorming: a creative team-based technique of discussing the system and using checklists, questionnaires, or prompts to decide which hazards may apply to the system and how they can progress to hazardous situations.
- What-if techniques: analyzing the system by asking what-if questions to stimulate the brainstorming session. Certain guide words can be used to direct the team discussions for faster results.
- Review of internal and external information such as complaints, reports, and so on.
- Applicable standards and guidelines: review of national and international standards and guidelines by regulatory bodies to identify any recommended hazards or their sources.

IDENTIFY THE SEQUENCE OF EVENTS

Once the hazards are identified and their applicability is verified, we identify the sequence of events that can transform the hazard into hazardous situations.

FIGURE 42.2 Hazard analysis process.

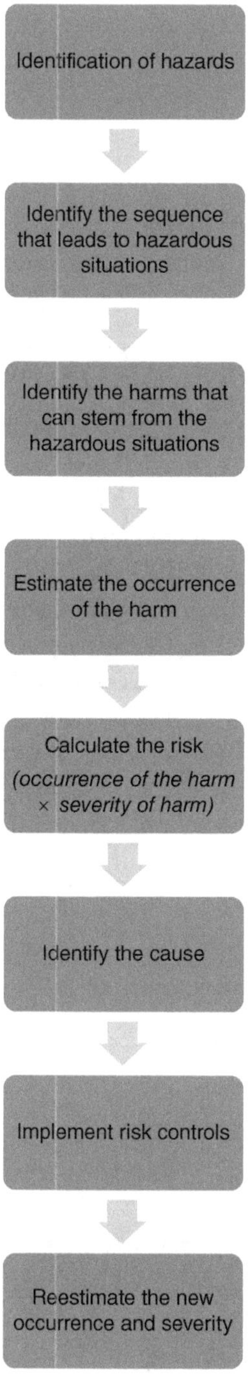

IDENTIFY THE HAZARDOUS SITUATION

For each sequence of events, we identify all possible hazardous situations. One sequence of events could lead to multiple hazardous situations and vice versa.

IDENTIFY THE HARM

We aim to identify all possible harms from the hazardous situation. One hazardous situation could lead to multiple harms and vice versa.

ESTIMATE THE OCCURRENCE OF THE HARM

The process shown in Figure 42.3 is used to estimate the probability of the harm occurring due to a specific hazard. As denoted above, a sequence of events leads each hazard to become a hazardous situation and each hazardous situation to become a harm. Both of these steps have probabilities of their own.

In the example shown below, the hazard is ice on the sidewalk, the sequence of events is a person walking on the ice to go to the office, the hazardous situation is that the person slips on the ice, the harm is the person breaking a leg or, in very rare cases, death (not all harms are considered). The probability of the person walking on ice and slipping and falling is $P1 = 0.3$. The probability of a person slipping on the ice and breaking a leg is $P2\ (\text{leg}) = 0.1$ (Figure 42.4), and the person dying due to slipping on the ice is $P2\ (\text{death}) = .0001$. The overall probability of the person breaking a leg while walking on the ice is $P(\text{leg}) = .3 \times 0.1 = 0.03$, and the overall probability of the person dying due to slipping on the ice is $P(\text{death}) = .3 \times 0.0001 = 0.00003$ (Figure 42.5).

FIGURE 42.3 Probability path from hazard to harm.

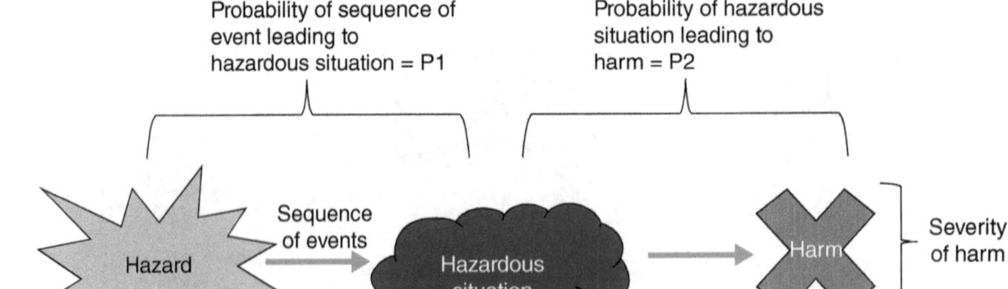

Source: ©ISO. This material is reproduced from ISO 14971:2019, with permission of the American National Standards Institute (ANSI) on behalf of the International Organization for Standardization.

FIGURE 42.4 Probability path from the hazard of slippery ice to the harm of breaking a leg.

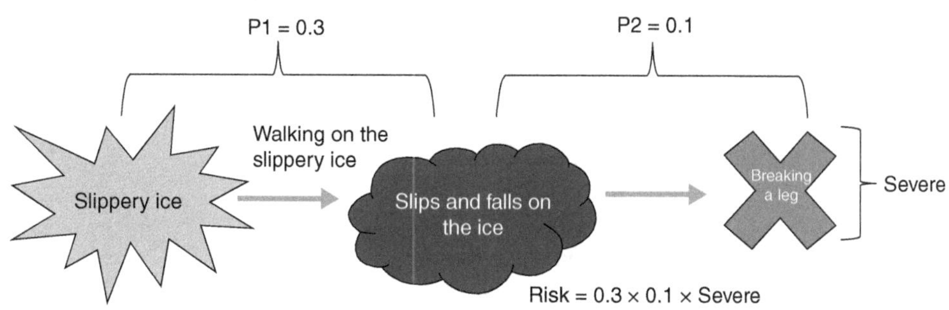

FIGURE 42.5 Probability path from the hazard of slippery ice to the harm of death.

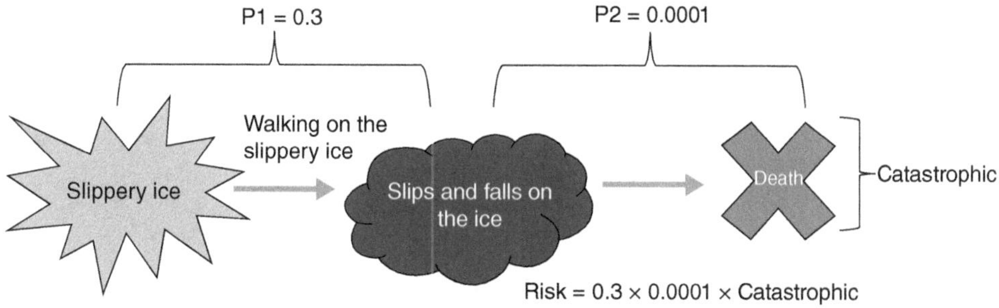

ISO 14971:2019 provides a figure, reproduced below (Figure 42.6), to show the relationship between hazard, hazardous situation, and harm.

SELECT A SCORING SYSTEM

The risk scoring system includes scales for probability of occurrence and impact as well as any risk matrices for assessing risk levels. It is important to define and document these before proceeding with the risk ranking.

ESTIMATE THE SEVERITY OF THE HARM

The severity of the harm is the measure of the impact or consequence. This must be graded using a severity scale.

CALCULATE THE RISK

We calculate the risk as follows:

$$\text{Risk (R)} = \text{The } \textit{probability} \text{ of the harm} \times \text{The } \textit{severity} \text{ of the harm.}$$

FIGURE 42.6 Pictorial example of the relationship between hazard, sequence of events, hazardous situation, and harm.

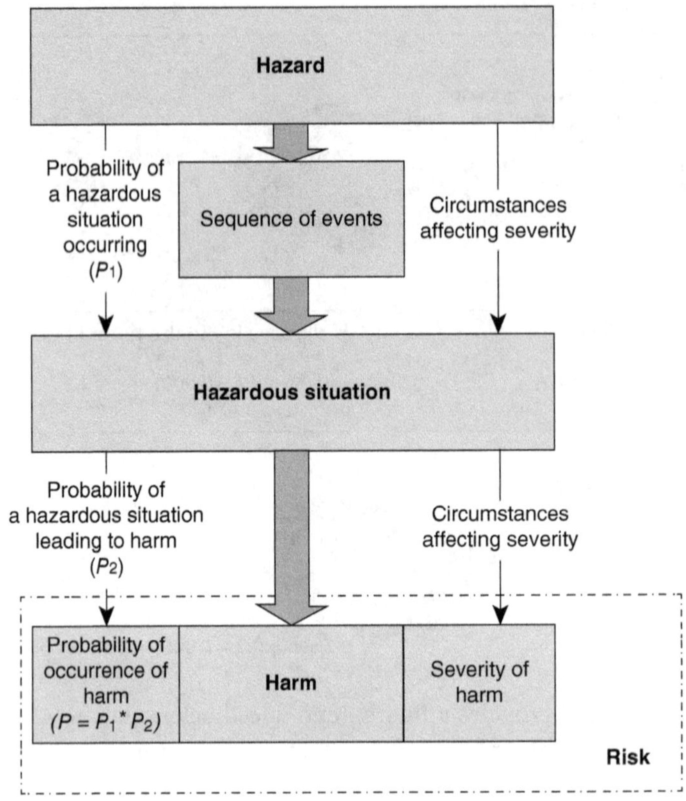

Source: ©ISO. This material is reproduced from ISO 14971:2019, with permission of the American National Standards Institute (ANSI) on behalf of the International Organization for Standardization.

IDENTIFY THE CAUSE

We aim to identify the causes for the sequence of events or hazardous situations and in some cases for the hazard itself. Root cause analysis should be carried out where needed using tools such as 5 Whys and the Ishikawa diagram.

IMPLEMENT RISK CONTROL

Risk control is the process in which decisions are made and measures implemented by which risks are reduced to, or maintained at, specified levels.

Based on the levels of the risks, we identify the ones that require mitigations or modifications. Once the new risk control measures are implemented, we reestimate the

TABLE 42.1 Column headers for hazard analysis worksheet.

					Pre-mitigation					Post-mitigation			
Line number	Hazard	Sequence of events	Hazardous situation	Harm	Occurrence	Severity	Risk	Risk control	Verification	Occurrence	Severity	Risk	Risk control (if needed)

TABLE 42.2 Hazard analysis for infusion pump.

Line number	Hazard	Sequence of events	Hazardous situation	Harm	Pre-mitigation Occurrence	Pre-mitigation Severity	Pre-mitigation Risk	Risk control	Verification	Post-mitigation Occurrence	Post-mitigation Severity	Post-mitigation Risk
1	Electromagnetic radiation	The infusion pump is installed near an X-ray machine, leading to interference in the infusion pump	Incorrect rate of medication	Patient condition worsens	Occassional	Serious	High	Design for electromagnetic interference	Electromagnetic interference testing	Rare	Serious	Medium
2			Criticial medicine infusion stopped	Death	Rare	Catastrophic	Medium			Rare	Catastrophic	Medium
3	Line voltage	Line wire loosened and is now touching the handle of the infusion pump	Line voltage appearing on the handle	Death	Occassional	Catastrophic	High	Design for safety per IEC 60601-1	Line fault test	Rare	Catastrophic	Medium
4				Major shock, leading to burn	Frequent	Serious	High			Rare	Serious	Low
5	User error	User trying to start a therapy and doesn't start the infusion	Critical medicine infusion stopped	Death	Rare	Catastrophic	Medium	Provide alarm when infusion not started	Testing for all warnings and alarms	Rare	Catastrophic	Medium
6		User trying to start infusion with specific rate enters an incorrect rate	Incorrect rate of medication	Patient condition worsens	Frequent	Serious	High	Design for usability	Usability testing	Occassional	Serious	Medium
7	Falling	Pump falls while the patient is being transported	Incorrect rate of medication	Patient condition worsens	Rare	Serious	Low	Design for transporting the infusion pump; impact protection	Transportation testing; fall test per standard	Rare	Serious	Low
8			Critical medicine infusion stopped	Death	Rare	Catastrophic	Medium			Rare	Catastrophic	Medium

occurrence value and the new severity. We recalculate the risk with the new occurrence and severity values, review the risk level, and document its acceptability.

PERFORM A RISK-BENEFIT ANALYSIS

For the risks that remain in the unacceptable level, we can perform a risk-benefit analysis to see whether the benefits outweigh the risks for the system and its expected objective. If the benefits outweigh the risks, we continue with the project; if the risks outweigh the benefits, we redesign the product/process.

Table 42.1 is an example of a hazard analysis worksheet.

Table 42.2 shows an example hazard analysis for an infusion pump.

CHAPTER 43

Advanced Risk Tools: Hazard and Operability Study (HAZOP)

HAZARD AND OPERABILITY STUDY **(HAZOP)** is a structured and systematic review of a process, procedure, or system for identifying the hazards, potential operability problems, and potential causes and consequences of the problems.

This tool is often used to identify hazards in industries where continuous processes can be said to have an additive design intent by virtue of process steps and their parameters. These process parameters may deviate from the intent in various common or special conditions.

HAZOP is performed through a detailed examination of the process, procedure, or system by understanding the design intent and the potential deviations from the intent that could occur in the studied locations. This detailed examination is performed through a set of guide words that help verbalize the potential deviations from the expectations. The set of guide words and their interpretations have to be defined before performing the examination of the process, procedure, or system. Finally, all information is captured in a HAZOP worksheet.

The specific locations in the process where the process parameters are studied by application of guide words are known as *study nodes*.

An example study node is shown in Figure 43.1, where the waveform conversion is the process under investigation. The intent of the process is to convert the square wave to a sine wave, but at the process step under study, we can get a distorted square wave; this is a deviation from the expected output.

The study node in this example is an electrical circuit, and causes of deviation can be investigated by analyzing this circuit, which transforms the waveform. The process parameters are the current, resistance, capacitance, and voltages, which enable the waveform conversion.

It is also important to understand the consequences of the deviation. For this, the output of the node must be tracked to the point where it becomes the input to another process or node. How does the deviated output affect the next process when it acts as an input? Does it stop the system outright? Or does it magnify the deviation? The end result of this deviation to the system must be analyzed in the HAZOP study.

Let us look at another example in Figure 43.2.

FIGURE 43.1 An example of a study node: waveform conversion.

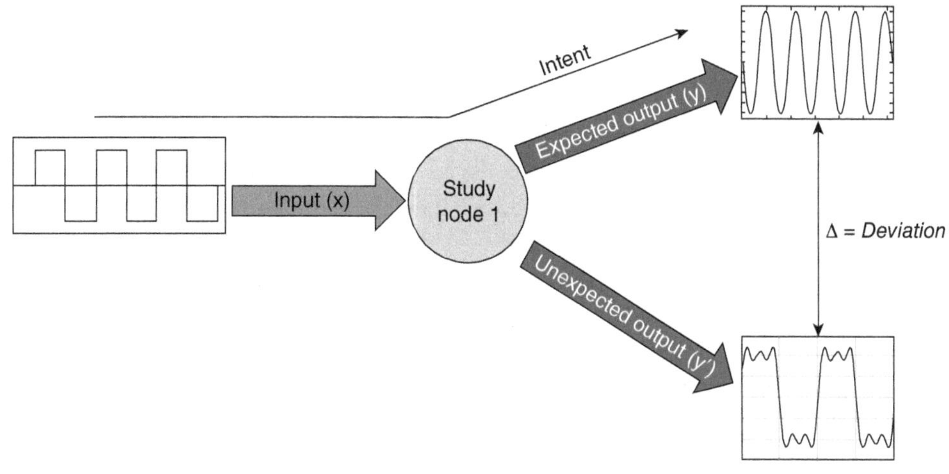

FIGURE 43.2 Another example of a study node: the chemical reactor.

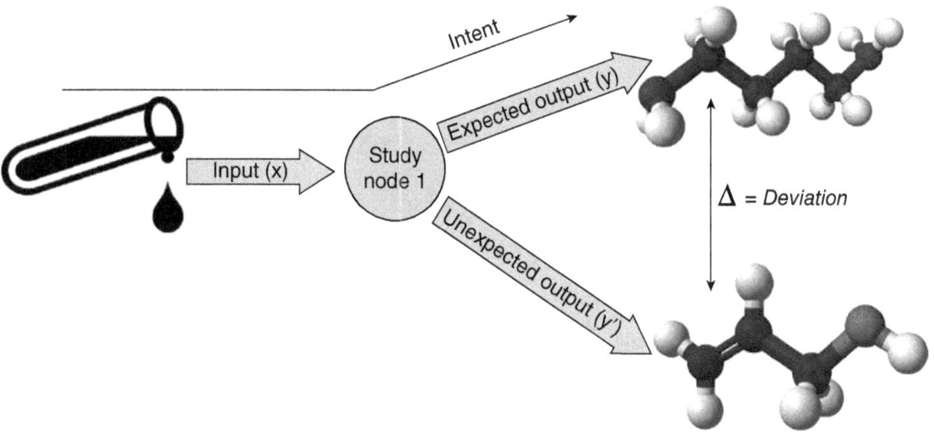

The study node is the chemical reactor, which converts an input chemical to an output chemical. The process parameter under study is the reaction time. If the time is not controlled and too much time is allowed, an unexpected output is the deviated result.

There will be multiple nodes of varying importance in the system. These nodes may be subsystems or subcomponents depending on the classification key and the nature of the system under study. The choice of nodes is dependent on the accuracy and reliability of measurement of the process parameters at the nodal location. We must attempt to study all process parameters that define the success of the process. To realize this, one nodal location may not be enough, and we may need to study the input conversion at all nodal locations.

It is important to understand the term "design intent." This is the designed intention of the system or process, which can be interpreted in a few different ways. The most common interpretation is that the design intention is the normal operating condition of the process or system. The designed specifications can be specific maximums or minimums, but if the intention of the specification is a certain operating range, and the process parameter is outside that range, we may call this a deviation. In contrast, the design intent may be the specifications themselves. For example, the allowable reaction time in this example could be set to between two minutes and five minutes, and anything outside this range can be considered a deviation. Thus, the definition of the deviation condition is very important and may decide the success or failure of the HAZOP study.

The HAZOP process deeply relies on the team that is performing the examination of the process, procedure, or system. The team members performing the HAZOP should have the appropriate skills and understanding of the process, procedure, and system under review. Identification of the deviations can appear easy, but brainstorming and listing potential deviations, along with the cause and consequences, should be done by a team of people who understand the system, its constraints, and its drivers.

In the example above, in order to understand the cause of deviation, one will have to conduct a 5 Whys analysis, as follows:

1. Why is the molar mass of the output chemical different?

   Because it is a different chemical

2. Why is it a different chemical?

   Because the reactor was allowed to run too long

3. Why was the reactor running too long?

   Because the automatic timer shutdown did not work

4. Why did the automatic control not work?

   Because it was not programmed properly

5. Why was it not programmed properly?

   Because the line operators are not properly trained to modify programs for automatic operation

Hence, we can see that expertise is needed to ensure that a correct cause analysis is carried out. Similarly, the consequence analysis also depends on understanding the outputs of the various elements of the system and how they impact the whole.

IEC 61882:2016 divides the HAZOP process into four phases, as shown in Figure 43.3.

Definition: In the definition phase, the scope and the objectives of the study are identified. We must clearly define the boundaries, interface, and assumptions used in the study. The team responsible for performing the study should be identified and the membership confirmed. The team includes cross-functional members as needed. After team members are identified, we define their roles and responsibilities. We identify the study leader, recorder, designer, user, and specialists (SMEs).

FIGURE 43.3 The HAZOP process.

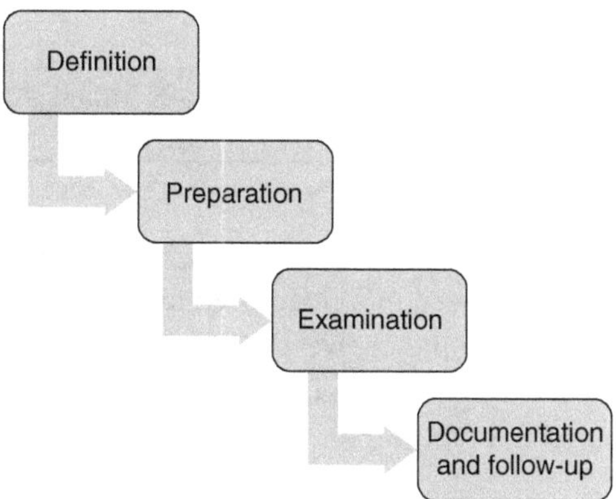

Preparation: The study leader prepares for the study by planning the study, collecting the data pertaining to the study, and scheduling the meetings. The study leader also identifies the format for recording the HAZOP study and the guide words used for the analysis.

Choosing the guide words is an important step as these words are used for identifying the deviations from the design intent. If the guide words are too specific, they can cause limitation of ideas and discussion; if they are too general, one can lose focus on the HAZOP study.

IEC 61882:2016 defines a guide word as:

> *Word or phrase which expresses and defines a specific type of deviation from an element's design intent.*[1]

A guide word is a modifier of the parameter or characteristic that can negate the design intent or modify, substitute, or change the time sequence of the parameter qualitatively or quantitatively. It can be any word, on application of which the parameter or characteristic of the element can be modified. In the example above, "more" and "less" could be suitable guide words—more reaction time and less reaction time. This is clarified in Table 43.1.

An example of deviations and their associated guide words from IEC 61882:2016 is reproduced in Table 43.2.

Examination: The examination phase starts by dividing the system into subprocesses or parts. We begin by identifying the relevant nodes and define the design intent. The characteristics of the nodes can be the parameters that control the output. It is important to identify the characteristics relevant to the selected node. Using the guide words defined in the planning phase, we identify the deviations for each part or

1. *Hazard and Operability Studies (HAZOP Studies) - Application Guide*, IEC 61882:2016 (Geneva, Switzerland: International Electrochemical Commission, 2016), p. 8, https://webstore.iec.ch/publication/24321. Copyright © 2006 IEC Geneva, Switzerland. www.iec.ch.

TABLE 43.1 "More" and "less" guide words.

Guide word	Node/element	Parameter/ characteristic	Deviation
More	Reactor 1	Time	Unexpected chemical/precipitate
Less	Reactor 1	Time	No reactions

subprocess. Based on the deviation(s) identified for the design intent, we identify the causes and consequences. From there we identify the protection, detection, and indication mechanisms for the deviation. Finally, we identify and record the possible mitigations for the deviations and repeat the process as needed.

Common Process Parameters

1. Time
2. Fill level
3. Length
4. Concentration
5. Wattage (power)
6. Flow
7. Viscosity
8. Pressure
9. Procedure
10. Communication
11. Position
12. Sequence/order
13. Speed
14. pH

This process is represented by the workflow shown in Figure 43.4.

IEC 61882:2016 provides a slightly more detailed diagram for iterative HAZOP processes, as reproduced in Figure 43.5. The standard does not mention nodes but instead talks about the part and its elements. The elements are assigned characteristics that may vary or may need to be specified or controlled. The guide words are applied to the characteristics and deviating conditions are uncovered.

Documentation: All the details of the study are documented in a template identified in the planning stage. The study leader makes sure that the output of the study contains the identified hazards and operability problems, consequences and causes, protection, detection, indication mechanisms for the deviation, and mitigations. In this stage, it is also required to follow up on any implemented mitigations and check whether any new elements have been added as part of the mitigations or were missed in the initial study. The final report for the HAZOP study should call out any process deviations or exclusions.

TABLE 43.2 Examples of deviations and their associated guide words.

Deviation type	Guide word	Example interpretation for process industry	Example interpretation for a Programmable Electronic System, PES
Negative	NO	No part of the intention is achieved, e.g. no flow	No data or control signal passed
Quantitative modification	MORE	A quantitative increase, e.g. higher temperature	Data is passed at a higher rate than intended
	LESS	A quantitative decrease e.g. lower temperature	Data is passed at a lower rate than intended
Qualitative modification	AS WELL AS	Impurities present Simultaneous execution of another operation/ step	Some additional or spurious signal is present
	PART OF	Only some of the intention is achieved, i.e. only part of an intended fluid transfer takes place	The data or control signals are incomplete
Substitution	REVERSE	Covers reverse flow in pipes and reverse chemical reactions	Normally not relevant
	OTHER THAN	A result other than the original intention is achieved, i.e. transfer of wrong material	The data or control signals are incorrect
Time	EARLY	Something happens early relative to clock time, e g. cooling or filtration	The signals arrive too early with reference to clock time
	LATE	Something happens late relative to clock time, e.g. cooling or filtration	The signals arrive too late with reference to clock time
Order or sequence	BEFORE	Something happens too early in a sequence, e.g. mixing or heating	The signals arrive earlier than intended within a sequence
	AFTER	Something happens too late in a sequence, e.g. mixing or heating	The signals arrive later than intended within a sequence

Source: Reproduced by permission from International Electrotechnical Commission, *Hazard and Operability Studies (HAZOP Studies) - Application Guide*, IEC 61882:2016 ed. 2.0 (Geneva, Switzerland: IEC, 2016). Copyright © 2016 IEC Geneva, Switzerland. www.iec.ch.

FIGURE 43.4 HAZOP examination process.

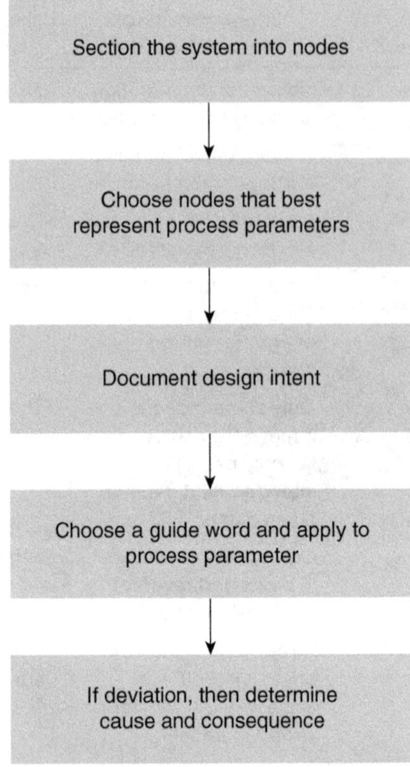

A simple HAZOP worksheet can contain the following headings:

1. Node/element/part/process (the location under study)
2. Guide word
3. Deviation
4. Consequence
5. Cause
6. Mitigations/safeguards

HAZOP Example

System Purpose

The system under study is an automatic braking system in a motor vehicle. The function of the automatic braking system is to automatically stop the vehicle when a sudden, unavoidable obstruction is detected in the vehicle's path.

System Description

The automatic braking system consists of multiple obstruction sensors. A signal amplifier increases the signal and reduces noise. An automatic braking system CPU detects a signal and, according to the sensor signal, sends a signal to the brakes, which send a

FIGURE 43.5 Detailed HAZOP process workflow.

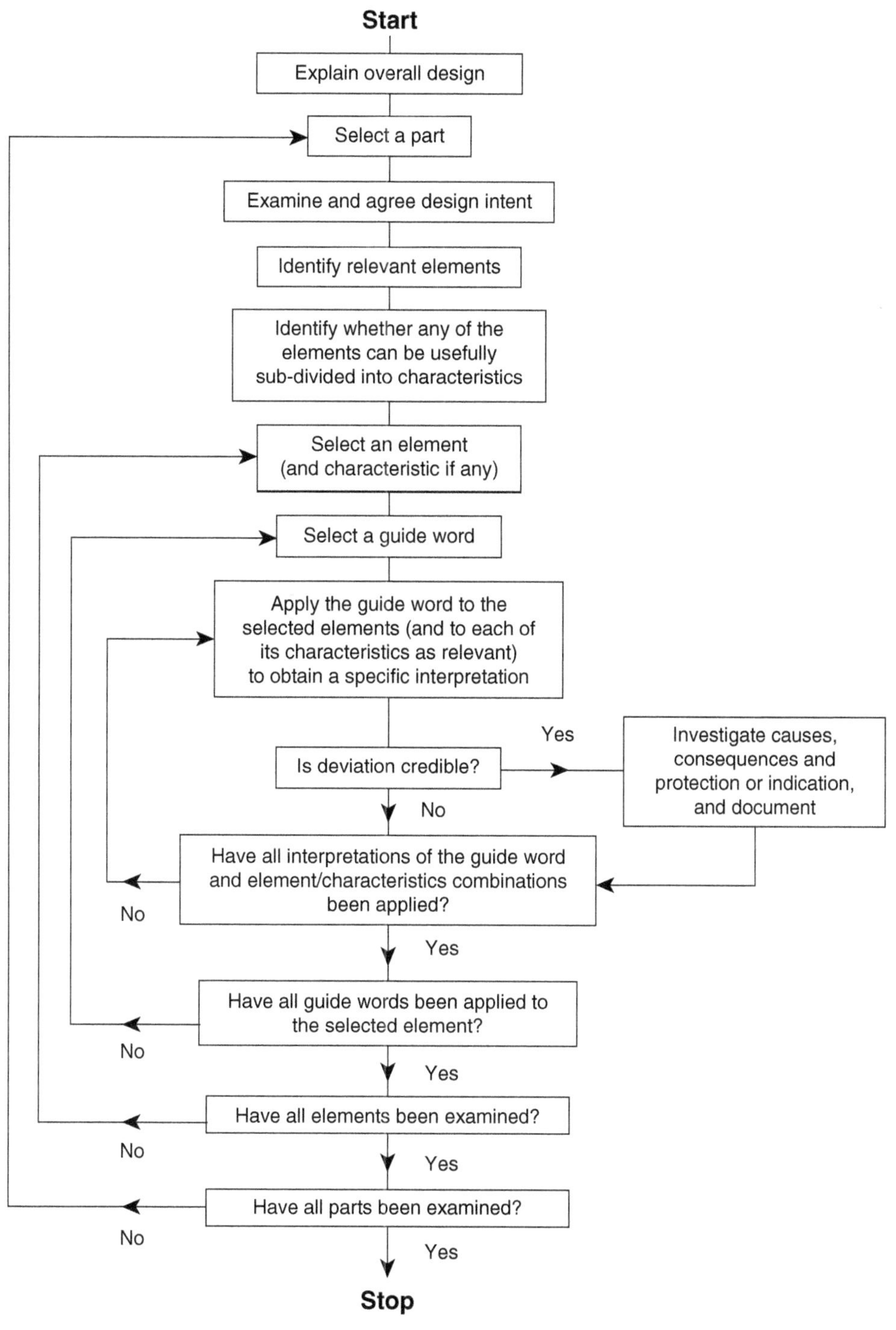

Source: Reproduced by permission from International Electrotechnical Commission, *Hazard and Operability Studies (HAZOP Studies) - Application Guide*, IEC 61882:2016 ed. 2.0 (Geneva, Switzerland: IEC, 2016).

TABLE 43.3 HAZOP table.

No.	Element/ part/ process	Guide word	Deviation	Causes	Consequences	Safeguards	Comments	Actions required	Action owner
1	Sensor	No	No signal from the sensor	Sensor failure Sensor obstructed	The automobile hits the obstruction	Sensor check Manual brake	Likely	Sensor check is displayed on the automobile screen	John
2	Sensor	Other than	Sensor sends signal without obstruction	Sensor error	The automobile stops without obstruction	Sensor check	Unlikely	Sensor check is displayed on the automobile screen	John
3	Sensor	More	Sensor detects obstruction with incorrect distance	Sensor failure	The automobile hits the obstruction	Manual brake	Unlikely	None	John
4	Amplifier	No	No signal from the amplifier	Amplifier failure	The automobile hits the obstruction	No signal detection	Likely	"No signal" indication on the automobile screen	Terrence
5	Braking system	Less	Less brake applied	Error in braking system	The automobile hits the obstruction	Braking system check	Unlikely	"Braking system error" indication on the automobile screen	Mary

FIGURE 43.6 Architecture of system under study.

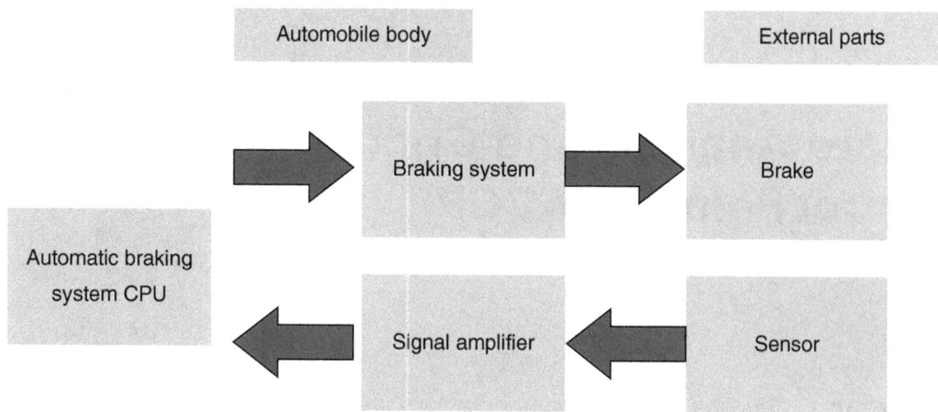

signal back when the automobile applies the brakes. This architecture of the system is shown in Figure 43.6. The out of the HAZOP exercise is shown in Table 43.3.

Advantages of HAZOP

- The systematic process of using a worksheet and guide words helps in documenting the hazards and operability problems in a structured manner
- It allows for and encourages cross-functional participation
- It covers operational and human errors and is process centric
- Risk mitigations and actions are identified in the process

Disadvantages of HAZOP

- Multiple deviations cannot be easily analyzed
- It does not focus on the combination of events
- An experienced and knowledgeable study leader is required to conduct HAZOP, and the output is highly dependent on the study leader

CHAPTER 44

Advanced Risk Tools: Hazard Analysis and Critical Control Points (HACCP)

HAZARD ANALYSIS AND CRITICAL CONTROL POINTS **(HACCP)** is a systematic process to identify the safety hazards and mitigate them by introducing controls at pre-identified and analyzed critical points of a process, procedure, or system. HACCP was initially developed by NASA for food safety in the space program, but the use of this method is now widespread in many industries and sectors. Many regulatory bodies in the food industry mandate process analysis using HACCP. This tool aims to assess and address the hazards (biological, chemical, and physical) in the initial identification process by specifically focusing on critical control points.

Shown in Figure 44.1 are the five preliminary steps that need to be completed before implementing the HACCP process.

Assemble team: A cross-functional team with expertise in the process or product should be identified from relevant functions, which may include design, manufacturing, quality, microbiology, sterilization, packaging, cleaning, and so on. A team leader experienced in the HACCP process needs to be identified who will drive the process. The leader with cross-functional consultation identifies the scope of the process under review and general hazards related to system.

Product description: It is necessary to document the description of the product and its value chain, which includes the raw materials, process activities, cleaning, storage conditions, packaging, sterilization, and distribution techniques.

Intended use and users: Identify the intended use of the product and potential users of the product.

Flow diagram of the process/product: Prepare a flow diagram covering all the steps involved in creation and distribution of the product.

Verification of the flow diagram: Verify the process flow diagram by onsite review.

Once the preliminary tasks are completed, the team applies the seven principles of HACCP (see Figure 44.2).

FIGURE 44.1 HACCP process.

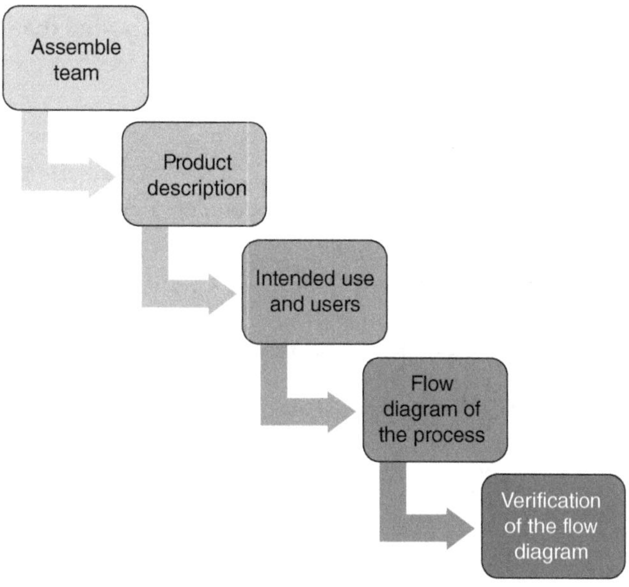

FIGURE 44.2 Seven principles of HACCP.

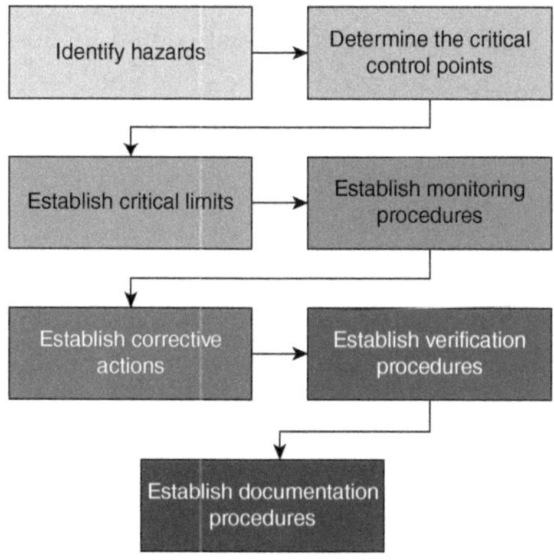

SEVEN PRINCIPLES OF HACCP

Identify the Hazards (Principle 1)

There are two stages in this principle: identification of the hazards and evaluation of the hazards. Identification of hazards starts by the team conducting a brainstorming session. The team reviews the production processes, product usage, storage, preparation, and raw materials of the product to determine the potential physical, biological, and chemical hazards. This may mean describing the product composition and/or structure, any process steps including treatments, packaging steps, storage, and further downstream steps of distribution. A flowchart should be constructed that details all operational steps specific to a product. In addition to drawing the diagram on paper based on recall, the team members must walk through the steps to validate the diagram. This often results in addition or deletion of certain steps.

Then, for each step, the associated hazards should be identified with a reasonable level of practicality. Once the hazard identification is complete, the possible consequences of these hazards are identified and documented. Based on these consequences, the severity and the occurrence of potential issues are estimated. Finally, the control measures are identified and implemented.

Determine the Critical Control Points (Principle 2)

Critical control points (CCPs) are defined as:

> *A step at which control can be applied and is essential to prevent or eliminate a safety hazard or reduce it to an acceptable level.*

If controls are not applied at these critical points, it can result in realization of adverse consequences of the hazards. A control point becomes "critical" when it is *essential* to apply a control at the location to prevent adverse events. For example, in food safety, refrigeration in restaurants is a CCP, and if the temperature is not monitored and is allowed to move out of bounds, microbial contamination of the food may occur. Hence, an alarm or a flag at this point can be said to be essential to ensure food safety.

The decision tree in Figure 44.3 can be used to determine the CCPs per a logical sequence.

Establish Critical Limits (Principle 3)

Each CCP will have a control measure, which will have working limits and critical limits of its own. A *critical limit* is defined as:

> *A maximum and/or minimum value to which a biological, chemical, or physical parameter must be controlled at a CCP to prevent, eliminate, or reduce to an acceptable level the occurrence of a safety hazard.*

ISO 22000:2018 defines critical limit as:

> *A measurable value which separates acceptability from unacceptability.*[1]

For one control measure, there could be one or more critical limits. The critical limits must be scientific and can be based on the regulatory standards and guidelines, previous HACCP, testing, and experts. For example, the upper and lower temperature limits

---

1. ©ISO. This material is reproduced from ISO 22000:2018, with permission of the American National Standards Institute (ANSI) on behalf of the International Organization for Standardization.

FIGURE 44.3 Decision tree to determine CCP.

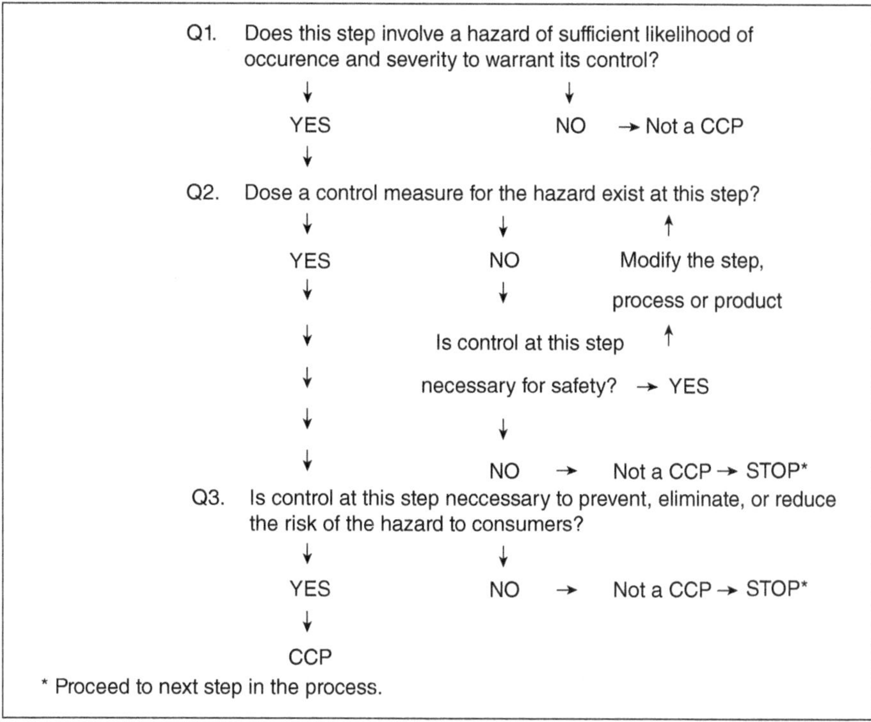
Q1. Does this step involve a hazard of sufficient likelihood of occurence and severity to warrant its control?
YES
NO → Not a CCP
Q2. Dose a control measure for the hazard exist at this step?
YES
NO
Modify the step, process or product
Is control at this step necessary for safety? → YES
NO → Not a CCP → STOP*
Q3. Is control at this step neccessary to prevent, eliminate, or reduce the risk of the hazard to consumers?
YES
NO → Not a CCP → STOP*
CCP
* Proceed to next step in the process.

Source: Reproduced from Center for Food Safety and Applied Nutrition, "HACCP Principles & Application Guidelines," U.S. Food and Drug Administration, August 14, 1997, https://www.fda.gov/food/hazard-analysis-critical-control-point-haccp/haccp-principles-application-guidelines.

of a fridge used to store sensitive foods can be said to be the critical limits, while the temperature itself is the control measure.

Establish Monitoring Procedures (Principle 4)

A monitoring procedure should be defined for each control measure to keep an eye on the critical limits. The Food and Drug Administration (FDA) defines *monitoring* as:

> *To conduct a planned sequence of observations or measurements to assess whether a CCP is under control and to produce an accurate record for future use in verification.*[2]

2. Center for Food Safety and Applied Nutrition, "HACCP Principles & Application Guidelines," U.S. Food and Drug Administration, August 14, 1997, https://www.fda.gov/food/hazard-analysis-critical-control-point-haccp/haccp-principles-application-guidelines.

The monitoring system must do the following:

1. Keep track of the processes or operations in terms of scientifically defined metrics
2. Be able to detect an abnormal variation in the control measures and an out-of-specification condition of the critical limits.

ISO 22000:2018 mentions that the following information must be documented for the monitoring system:

> *a) measurements or observations that provide results within an adequate time frame;*
> *b) monitoring methods or devices used;*
> *c) applicable calibration methods;*
> *d) monitoring frequency;*
> *e) monitoring results;*
> *f) responsibility and authority related to monitoring*[3]

Establish Corrective Actions (Principle 5)

The deviations from the control limits are identified through the monitoring process. Corrective actions should be taken whenever there is deviation from the control limits. The corrective action determination should be based on the root cause. Procedures must be defined to contain the nonconforming product, verify the actions to correct the root cause, and prevent recurrence. Where possible, corrective action plans must be defined that specify who, how, what, where, and when.

Establish Verification Procedures (Principle 6)

Here, we identify methods that help us verify whether the HACCP system is working effectively. The verification activities should confirm that the levels of safety hazards identified in the hazard analysis stage are within an acceptable level, no new hazards have emerged, and the control plan is effective. This can be done through a systematic review of the HACCP system, review of records, and review of the monitoring and corrective action record and audits.

Establish Documentation Procedures (Principle 7)

This begins with documentation of the HACCP process—the hazard analysis, CCPs, measures and limits, determination of the control limits, monitoring procedures, corrective action procedures, and verification procedures. It also includes creation of forms for relevant logs for control measures and checklists and creation of flowcharts,

3.

where necessary for ease of use. Diligence must be carried out regarding any specific documentation requirements of the statutory and regulatory authorities.

Table 44.1 shows a hazard identification worksheet.

Table 44.2 shows the determination of a CCP.

Table 44.3 shows an HACCP plan.

The following is an example of an HACCP.

HACCP team:

- HACCP lead
- Development
- Quality assurance
- Process engineer
- Plant engineer
- Maintenance engineer

TABLE 44.1 Hazard identification worksheet.

Product/process					
Process step	Hazard	Consequence	Severity	Occurrence	Control measure

TABLE 44.2 Determination of a critical control point.

Process step	Hazard	Q1. Does the step involve a hazard of sufficient likelihood of occurrence and severity to warrant it control? If no = not a CCP If yes = move to Q2	Q2. Does a control measure for the hazard exist at this step? If no = move to Q3. If yes = move to Q4	Q3. Is control at this step necessary for safety? If no = not a CCP If yes = modify the step, process, or product	Q4. Is control at this step necessary to prevent, eliminate, or reduce the risk of the hazard to consumers? If no = not a CCP If yes = CCP	CCP

TABLE 44.3 Headers for an HACCP plan.

Process step	Hazard	Critical limit	Monitoring	Corrective actions	Verification	Records

FIGURE 44.4 Process flow diagram of system under study.

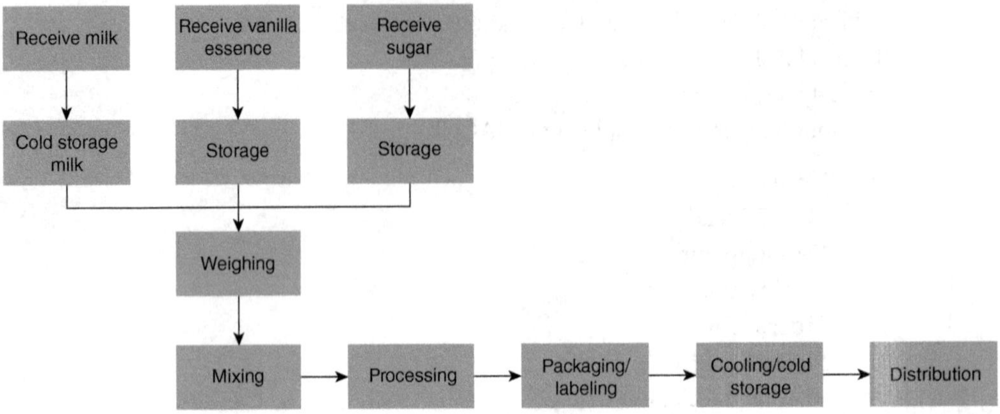

TABLE 44.4 Hazard analysis for creation of vanilla ice cream from milk.

Product/process					
Process step	**Hazard**	**Consequence**	**Severity**	**Occurrence**	**Control measure**
Receiving milk	Salmonella	Vomiting, diarrhea, and abdominal pain	Catastrophic	Likely	Pasteurization of milk
	E. coli	Life threatening			Filtering of the milk
	Foreign material				Maintain temperature while transporting
	Microbial growth				
Receiving vanilla essence	Foreign material	Vomiting, diarrhea, and abdominal pain	Severe	Unlikely	Filtering
Receiving sugar	Foreign material	Vomiting, diarrhea, and abdominal pain	Severe	Unlikely	Filtering and visual inspection
Cold storage for milk	Microbial growth	Vomiting, diarrhea, and abdominal pain	Catastrophic	Unlikely	Maintain temperature in the milk chamber
		Life threatening			
Storage for vanilla essence	Foreign material	Vomiting, diarrhea, and abdominal pain	Severe	Unlikely	Store in the clean designated area

TABLE 44.4 (continued)

Product/process					
Process step	**Hazard**	**Consequence**	**Severity**	**Occurrence**	**Control measure**
Storage for sugar	Foreign material	Vomiting, diarrhea, and abdominal pain	Severe	Unlikely	Store in the clean designated area
Weighing	Foreign material	Vomiting, diarrhea, and abdominal pain	Severe	Unlikely	Weighing performed in a clean environment
Mixing the ingredients	Foreign material	Vomiting, diarrhea, and abdominal pain	Severe	Unlikely	Weighing performed in a clean environment
Processing	Foreign material	Vomiting, diarrhea, and abdominal pain	Severe	Unlikely	Processing performed in a clean environment
Packaging/ labeling	Foreign material	Vomiting, diarrhea, and abdominal pain	Catastrophic	Likely	Packaging material to be controlled Inspect packaging materials and labeling before packaging and labeling
Cooling / cold storage	Microbial growth	Vomiting, diarrhea, and abdominal pain Life threatening	Catastrophic	Likely	Maintain temperature in the storage chamber
Distribution	Microbial growth	Vomiting, diarrhea, and abdominal pain Life threatening	Catastrophic	Likely	Maintain temperature Distribution vehicle

TABLE 44.5 CCP determination for creation of vanilla ice cream from milk.

Process step	Hazard	Q1. Does the step involve a hazard of sufficient likelihood of occurrence and severity to warrant it control? If no = not a CCP If yes = move to Q2	Q2. Does a control measure for the hazard exist at this step? If no = move to Q3 If yes = move to Q4	Q3. Is control at this step necessary for safety? If no = not a CCP If yes = modify the step, process, or product	Q4. Is control at this step necessary to prevent, eliminate, or reduce the risk of the hazard to consumers? If no = not a CCP If yes = CCP	CCP
Receiving milk	Salmonella	Yes	Yes		Yes	Pasteurization temperature
Receiving milk	E. coli	Yes	Yes		Yes	Pasteurization temperature
Receiving milk	Foreign material	No				
Receiving milk	Microbial growth	Yes	Yes		Yes	Temperature controlled in the vehicle container
Receiving vanilla essence	Foreign material	No				
Receiving sugar	Foreign material	No				
Cold storage for milk	Microbial growth	Yes	Yes		Yes	Milk chamber temperature
Storage for vanilla essence	Foreign material	No				
Storage for sugar	Foreign material	No				
Weighing	Foreign material	No				
Mixing the ingredients	Foreign material	No				
Processing	Foreign material	No				
Packaging/Labeling	Foreign material	No				
Cooling / cold storage	Microbial growth	Yes	Yes		Yes	Storage chamber temperature
Distribution	Microbial growth	Yes	Yes		Yes	Distribution vehicle temperature

TABLE 44.6 HACCP plan for creation of vanilla ice cream from milk.

Process step	Hazard	Critical limit	Monitoring	Corrective actions	Verification	Records
Receiving milk	Salmonella	Pasteurization temperature	Temperature for pasteurization monitored	If the temperature is out of spec, remove the ice cream made with the milk. Take corrective action to avoid recurrence	Receiving inspection audit	Verify all the monitoring data and the corrective actions
Receiving milk	E. coli					
						Maintenance log for the pasteurization unit
Receiving milk	Foreign material	N/A				
Receiving milk	Microbial growth	Temperature controlled in the vehicle container	Temperature in the vehicle container monitored	If the temperature is out of spec, remove the ice cream made with the milk. Take corrective action to avoid the recurrence	Receiving inspection audit	Verify all the monitoring data and the corrective actions
						Maintenance log for temperature container
Receiving vanilla essence	Foreign material					
Receiving sugar	Foreign material					
Cold storage for milk	Microbial growth	Temperature controlled in the milk chamber	Temperature in the milk chamber monitored	If the temperature is out of spec, remove the ice cream made with the milk. Take corrective action to avoid the recurrence	Storage process audit	Verify all the monitoring data and the corrective actions
						Maintenance log for milk chamber
Storage for vanilla essence	Foreign material					
Storage for sugar	Foreign material					

(continued)

Weighing	Foreign material					
Mixing the ingredients	Foreign material					
Processing	Foreign material					
Packaging/labeling	Foreign material					
Cooling / cold storage	Microbial growth	Temperature controlled in the storage chamber	Temperature in the storage chamber is monitored	If the temperature is out of spec, remove the ice cream made with the milk. Take corrective action to avoid the recurrence	Storage process audit	Verify all the monitoring data and the corrective actions
						Maintenance log for storage chamber
Distribution	Microbial growth	Temperature controlled in the vehicle container	Temperature in the vehicle container is monitored	If the temperature is out of spec, remove the ice cream made with the milk. Take corrective action to avoid the recurrence	Distribution process audit	Verify all the monitoring data and the corrective actions
						Maintenance log for vehicle container

Product description: vanilla ice cream from milk
Ice cream consumed by people aged 1–100
Ingredients / raw materials:

- Vanilla essence: 10 grams
- Milk: 5 gallons
- Sugar: 1 pound

Figure 44.4 is a diagram of the process flow.
Table 44.4 shows a hazard analysis.
Table 44.5 shows a determination of CCP.
Table 44.6 shows an HACCP plan.

CHAPTER 45

Advanced Risk Tools: Fault Tree Analysis (FTA)

FAULT TREE ANALYSIS **(FTA)** is a systematic approach to identify the failures/faults that can lead to a top-level failure event. It is a deductive top-to-bottom approach that utilizes logic gates (Boolean logic) to track the consequence hierarchy from initial precipitating events leading to the top-level event (see Figure 45.1).

FTA can be qualitative or quantitative based on the scope of analyses. In the quantitative approach, the probability of the likelihood of failures and events is estimated using the arithmetic of the logic gates. For example, the AND gate is multiplicative, the OR gate is additive, and NOT stands for complementation. The Boolean logic at each hierarchical level of analysis is used to calculate the overall probability of the top event.

After assembling the team and identifying the scope, we identify the top event that must undergo analysis. IEC 61025:2006 defines the *top event* as:

Outcome of combinations of all input events.[1]

The top event is the culmination of all preceding faults and is often known as the final event. This failure event is the reason the analysis is being carried out.

Once the top event to be analyzed is identified and defined, we identify the inputs to the top event. These will be the immediate causes of the top event, which could be subsystem failure events or faults. The events that are neither the top events nor the lowest-level basic events are known as intermediate events. These are the results of the basic level events and are drivers of the top events.

This downward branching of failures is continued until the primary events or events that cannot be developed any further are identified. These are known as basic events.

A list of symbols used for FTA is shown in Table 45.1.

The use of these symbols can be understood from the fault tree shown in Figure 45.2.

The final outcome of the FTA is the pictorial representation of all input failures and fault events that lead to the top-level failure. The example in Figure 45.3 shows an FTA for the top event of alarm system failure.

1. *Fault Tree Analysis (FTA)*, IEC 61025:2006 (Geneva, Switzerland: International Electrochemical Commission, 2006), p. 8, https://webstore.iec.ch/publication/24321. Copyright © 2006 IEC Geneva, Switzerland. www.iec.ch.

FIGURE 45.1 Top view of the FTA process.

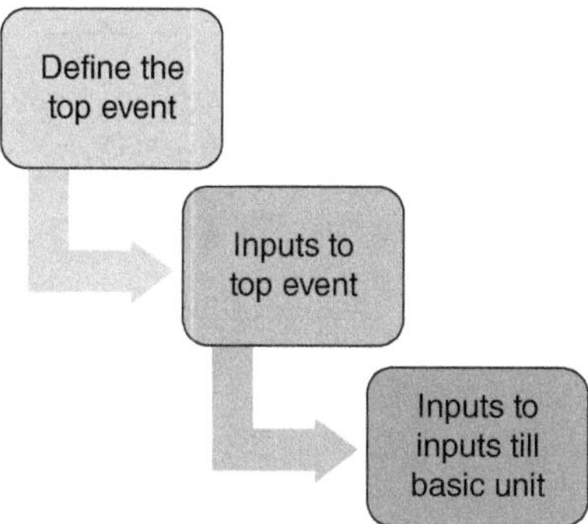

TABLE 45.1 Fault tree symbols, names, and corresponding descriptions.

Symbol	Name	Description
	Basic event	The lowest level of event.
	Faults or failures	Describes the intermediate faults or failure modes.
	Undeveloped event	An event that cannot be further broken down, and no analysis is possible. This acts as a contributor to the top event.
	OR gate	If any of the input events happen, the output event will occur.
	AND gate	All input events have to occur in order for the output event to occur.
	Transfer	Transfer to another tree.

TABLE 45.1 (continued)

Symbol	Name	Description
	NOT gate	The output event occurs when the input event DOES NOT occur.
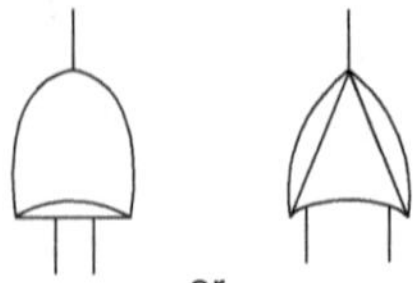 or	XOR gate	The output event occurs if ONLY one but not the other event occurs. (This should have exactly two inputs.)
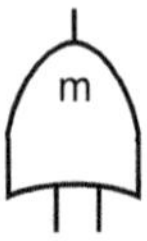 m	Majority vote gate	The output occurs if m or MORE input out of total n input occurs
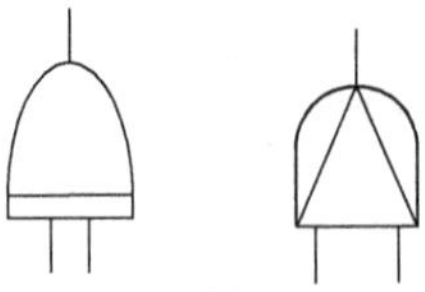 or	Priority AND (PAND) gate	Output occurs ONLY IF ALL input events occur in a sequence from left to right
	Inhibit gate	Output occurs when both input events occur and one of them is CONDITIONAL
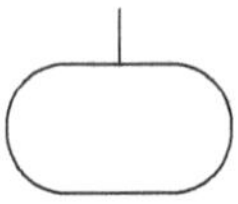	Conditional event	This gate describes an event that is used as a condition of occurrence for another event. It can be used with PAND and Inhibit gates.

RISK ANALYSIS USING FTA

The main advantage of FTA is that it is a combined tool for root cause analysis and risk analysis. The various basic and intermediate events present varying levels of risk to the system that culminate in the top event. This risk can be classified using the concepts of severity and occurrence as detailed in earlier chapters. The probability can be assigned to the basic events, and logical operations can be performed based on the Boolean logic of the gates to give us the probability of the next level event and so on. FTA lends itself to very easy probability calculations.

For the top event, a set of downstream events can be identified that, when they occur in sequence or parallel, lead to the top event; this is known as a *cut set*. The encircled

FIGURE 45.2 FTA symbols and their definitions.

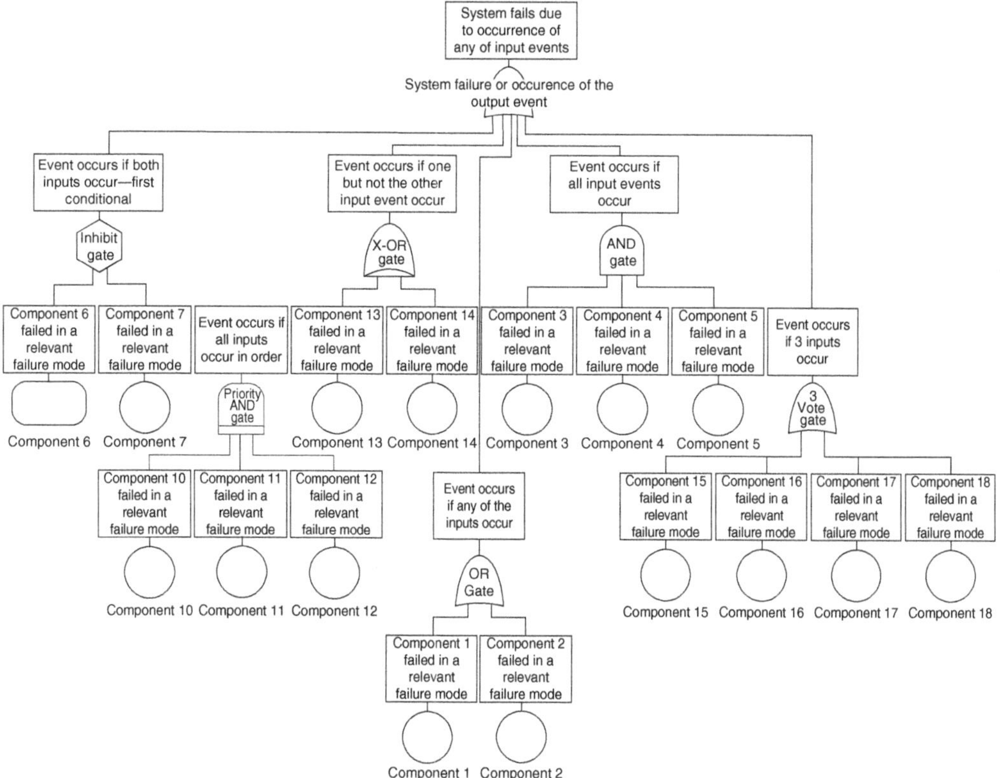

Source: Reproduced by permission from International Electrochemical Commission. Originally published as *Fault Tree Analysis (FTA)*, IEC 61025:2006 (Geneva, Switzerland: International Electrochemical Commission, 2006), p. 10. https://webstore.iec.ch/publication/24321. Copyright © 2006 IEC Geneva, Switzerland. www.iec.ch.

areas in Figure 45.4 make up the cut sets in Figure 45.3 since any one of the three can lead to the top event.

Identifying cut sets helps us isolate the paths to the top event and at the same time helps us isolate the risk associated with each path. Since the drivers of risk are also readily displayed, it is easy to assess the risk causes and mitigate them at suitable critical points.

Advantages of FTA

- FTA is good at analyzing failures from different components and their interactions
- The use of logic gates makes it naturally suitable for reliability studies by facilitating calculation of probability of occurrence of the top event by including probabilities of all downstream faults and events
- Process output is an organized pictorial representation of the system, which can help in understanding all interfaces and interactions

FIGURE 45.3 FTA for top event of alarm system failure.

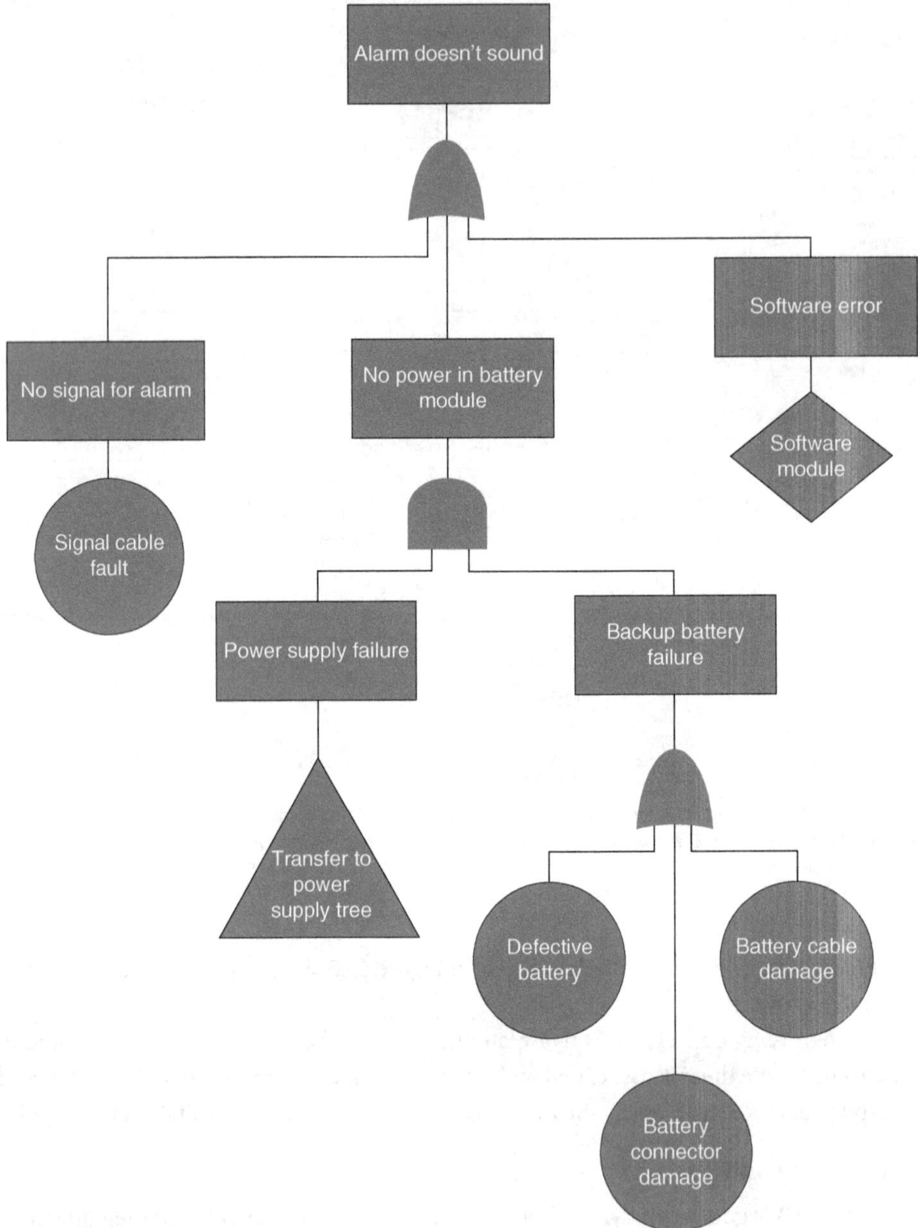

FIGURE 45.4 Making cut sets for FTA.

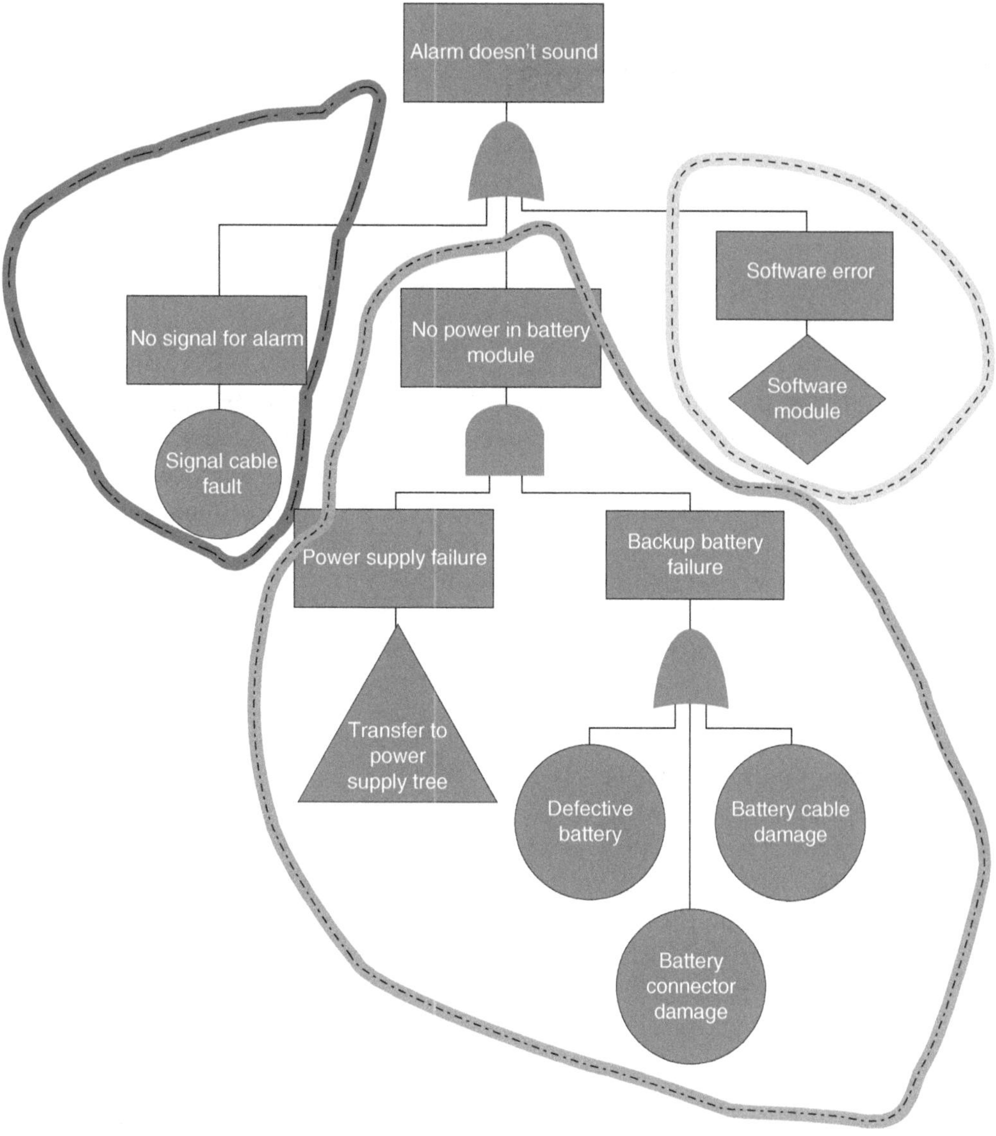

Disadvantages of FTA

- FTA analyzes only the failure of events that contribute to the occurrence of one top event
- As FTA is a top-down approach, it should be used as a complement to a bottom-up approach (e.g., FMEA)
- As the process is a pictorial representation of the top event and the corresponding failures with logic gates, the FTA can be very large and detailed for a complex system

CHAPTER 46

Advanced Risk Tools: Monte Carlo Analysis

THE GENESIS OF MONTE CARLO ANALYSIS goes back to a game of chance. When mathematician Stanislaw Ulam failed to estimate the probability of winning Canfield Solitaire using traditional combinatorial calculations, it struck him that large random calculations enhanced by a repeated sampling using a powerful computer processor may allow for prediction of probabilities.

So, what is Monte Carlo Analysis?

It is an inferential method that uses random sampling to estimate values of desired unknown quantity.

Random sampling is a critical concept on which the success of Monte Carlo simulation depends. The sample must be drawn from the population that includes all possibilities at random. Only when the sample is chosen at random can the sample be truly representative of the population. This is where the need for computational power arises.

In this book, we will not go into theoretical mathematical details of the model making and deterministic rationales behind it. Instead, we will look at the practical aspects from which actionable information can be gleaned for risk analysis and risk-based decision making.

Basically, the Monte Carlo technique can be used to estimate the likely values of an output parameter that is a function of various input parameters whose values are uncertain. For example, volatility in the stock market will lead to fluctuation of value of a 401(k) retirement account. If one can assign a range to volatility (of stock market fluctuation) based on different portfolios, then a range of values for the 401(k) after a certain amount of time can be obtained based on the upper and lower limits of volatility. Thus, Monte Carlo can be a method of quantifying the risk in both positive and negative terms (dollar profit or loss on the market in this case).

The steps as shown in Figure 46.1 can be carried out to conduct a basic Monte Carlo analysis.

Let us talk about probability distributions, as it is important to understand the nature of the data we are working with to ensure a successful output of Monte Carlo

FIGURE 46.1 Monte Carlo analysis steps.

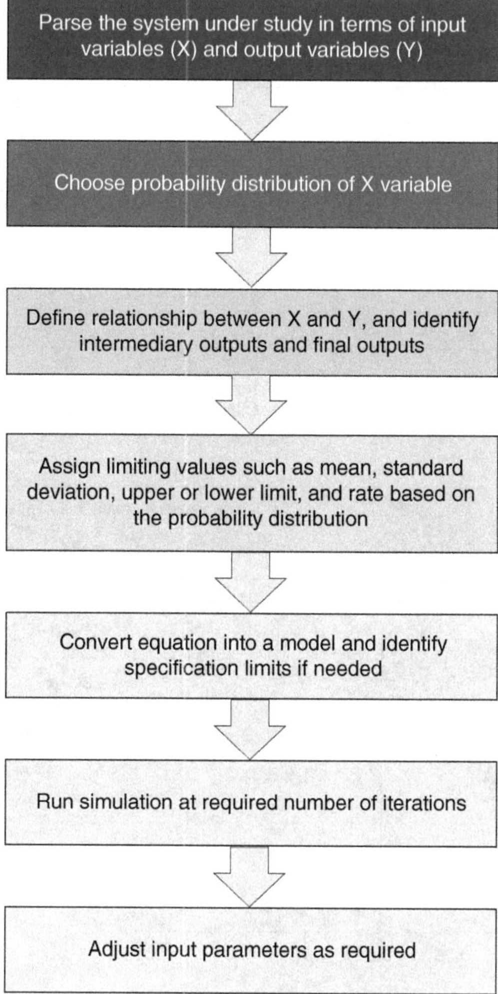

analysis. *Probability distribution* is the charting of data as a mathematical function that provides the probability of occurrence of possible outcomes of an event.

For example, for a coin tossed twice, we commonly understand that the probability of heads or tails for *each toss* is 0.5 since there is a 50% chance that heads will show up per toss. But can this be experimentally verified? Let us try it.

We get a coin and flip it two times. The probability distribution based on two flips of the coin (two iterations) is shown in Figure 46.2.

Here, for both tosses, we get tails. For two iterations of our experiment, we get the probability of heads as 0. Does this mean the probability is really zero? Of course not. It means we need more iterations.

Now let us toss the coin 10 times. We get the results shown in Figure 46.3.

FIGURE 46.2 Simulation results of a fair coin flip experiment with two flips.

Simulation results

Probability of heads

Summary statistics	
N	2
Mean	0
Standard deviation	0

FIGURE 46.3 Simulation results of a fair coin flip experiment with 10 flips.

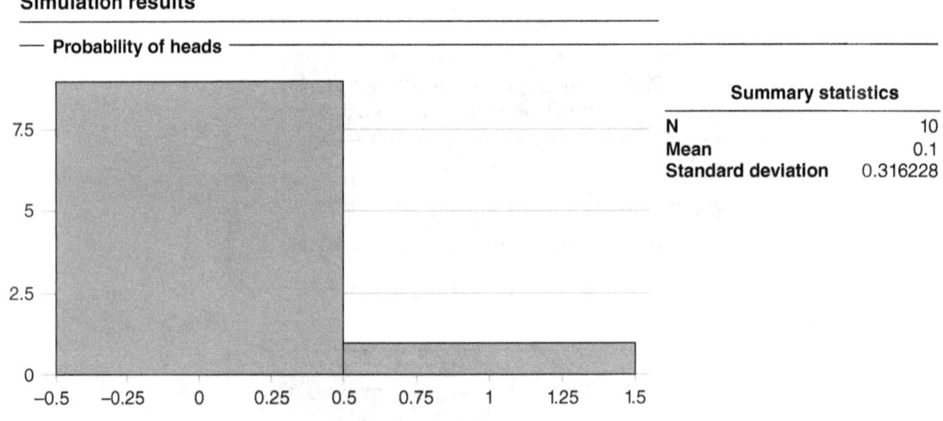

Here, we get 1 heads and 9 tails. So the probability of success, which is the probability of getting heads on 10 coin flips, is 0.1. Looks like we still need more iterations.

We keep tossing the same coin, and after 20 flips we get the probabilities shown in Figure 46.4.

Our experiment now at 20 flips shows a probability of success (of getting heads) of 0.55, which is much closer to the value of 0.5, which we know to be true.

Did you see how much variation we had in these three experiments? This can be attributed to nonrandom sampling and a low number of samples. The Monte Carlo technique aims to remove this variation by computerized random sampling at a very high rate. For example, Monte Carlo technique, in this case, will be to flip a few coins, let's say 50,000 times, which will give us a probability of success.

At 50,000 iterations, our probability distribution is shown in Figure 46.5.

FIGURE 46.4 Simulation results of a fair coin flip experiment with 20 flips.

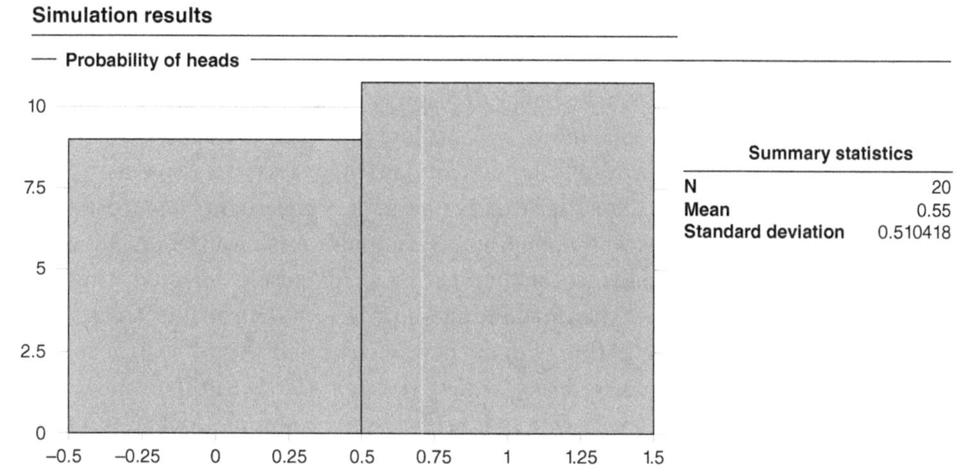

Simulation results

— **Probability of heads**

Summary statistics	
N	20
Mean	0.55
Standard deviation	0.510418

FIGURE 46.5 Simulation results of a fair coin flip experiment with 50,000 flips.

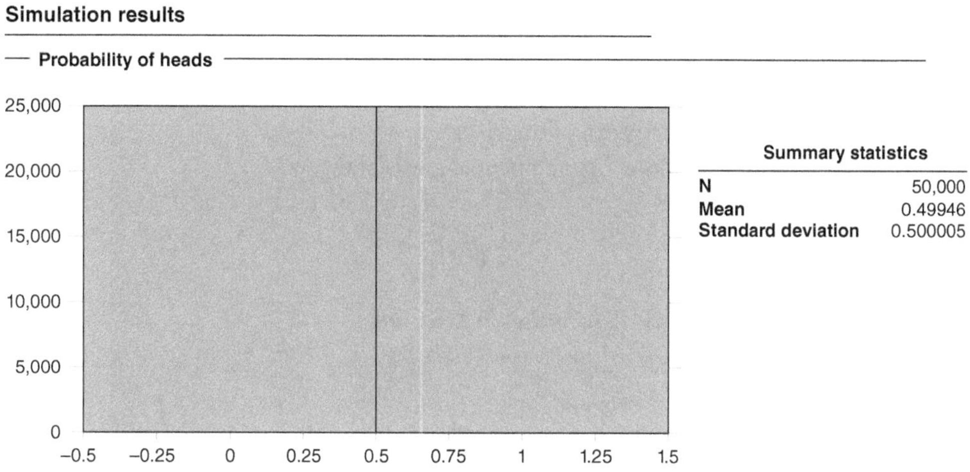

Simulation results

— **Probability of heads**

Summary statistics	
N	50,000
Mean	0.49946
Standard deviation	0.500005

Voila! The probability of getting heads is 0.49946, which is very close to 0.5. After 50,000 flips, almost half the flips were heads. The more iterations we run, the closer we get to the actual value.

Thus, Monte Carlo technique can predict outcomes with much certainty by producing a distribution of likely outcomes using the probability distribution.

Example

COVID-19 is an airborne respiratory illness caused by a coronavirus (SARS-CoV-2). The disease was first identified in December 2019 and rapidly swept across the globe throughout 2020. In early 2020 (and even today), there was a lot of debate about the severity of the disease and its fatality rate. There are some data available for countries that were hit hard early (South Korea and China), but due to reporting differences and other confounding factors, a lot of uncertainty surrounded these data.

We have also seen that many models have been used, especially by various governments around the world, to make policy decisions such as ordering supplies and building field hospitals. In this chapter, we will explore how such a model is created using Monte Carlo analysis—a proven technique for quantitative risk assessments.

Monte Carlo analysis allows us to assign a range to uncertainty and, based on the created model, provides us with the most likely outputs of risk realization. Let us apply the simple stepwise approach to come up with a simple model for predicting deaths and the number of people in the United Kingdom (UK) who can be infected by a hypothetical virus like COVID-19 (but with much less transmissibility).

The aim of this analysis is not to predict the actual risk but to show how a model is made and what parameters go into it; it highlights the power of Monte Carlo analysis in probabilistic risk modeling. A practical model should consider parameters like change in transmissibility due to lockdowns, social distancing, adaptation of personal protective equipment (PPE), virus mutations, and so on.

Step 1. ***Parse the system under study in terms of input variables and output variables.***

Input variables:

a) Population of UK
b) Infectiousness or spread of the virus
c) Mortality rate of the infected people (case fatality)

Final output:

d) Number of deaths

Step 2. ***Choose probability distribution of X variable***

a) Population of UK—*fixed*
b) Infectiousness—*triangular*
c) Mortality rate of infected (case fatality)—*triangular*

Triangular distributions are a good choice when we do not know the mean and standard deviation. They allow us to assign an upper and lower limit value and also set an expected mode. In detailed models, this may not be the case, and the case fatality equation and spread would be a complex model in itself.

Step 3. ***Define relationship between X and Y, and identify intermediary outputs and final outputs***

$$\text{Total number of deaths} = [(\text{Population of UK}) \times (\text{Infectiousness})] \times [\text{Mortality rate of infected people}] \tag{46.1}$$

Intermediate Output variable:

a) Number of people infected

Final Output:

b) Number of deaths

Step 4. ***Assign limiting values based on the probability distribution***

a) Population (fixed)—66.65 million
b) Infectiousness (triangular)—lower = 0.001, mode = 0.003, upper = 0.004
c) Mortality rate of infected (uniform)—lower = 0.0039, mode = 0.012, upper = 0.15

These parameters and limiting values are shown in Figure 46.6.

Infectiousness here is based on the percentage of the population expected to be affected. For this hypothetical virus, we are not expecting a lot of transmission and expect between 0.01% and 0.04% of the population to be affected. Another more specific parameter here is transmissibility, which is discussed in Chapter 47 along with another model. The mortality rate of the infected population is set between 0.39% and 15%.

Step 5. ***Define model***

$$\text{Total number of deaths} = [(\text{Population of UK}) \times (\text{Infectiousness})] \times [\text{Mortality rate of infected people}] \quad (46.1)$$

This is shown graphically in Figure 46.7.

Step 6. ***Run simulation***

The following output is shown at 50,000 iterations or cycles, which means that the simulation software (here Minitab) built the model in Figure 46.8

FIGURE 46.6 Parameters of the model and limiting values.

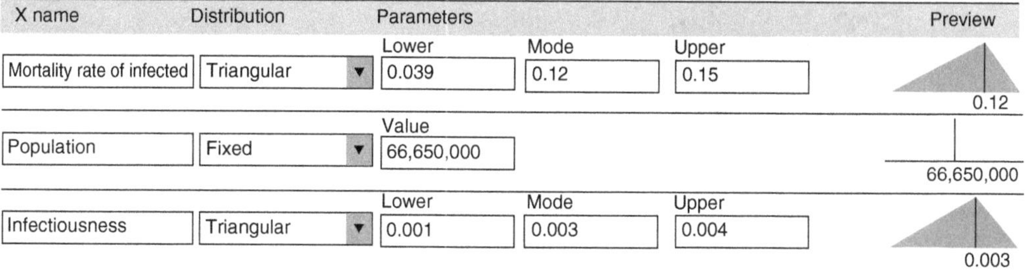

X name	Distribution	Parameters			Preview
		Lower	Mode	Upper	
Mortality rate of infected	Triangular	0.039	0.12	0.15	0.12
		Value			
Population	Fixed	66,650,000			66,650,000
		Lower	Mode	Upper	
Infectiousness	Triangular	0.001	0.003	0.004	0.003

FIGURE 46.7 The model for total deaths and infected population.

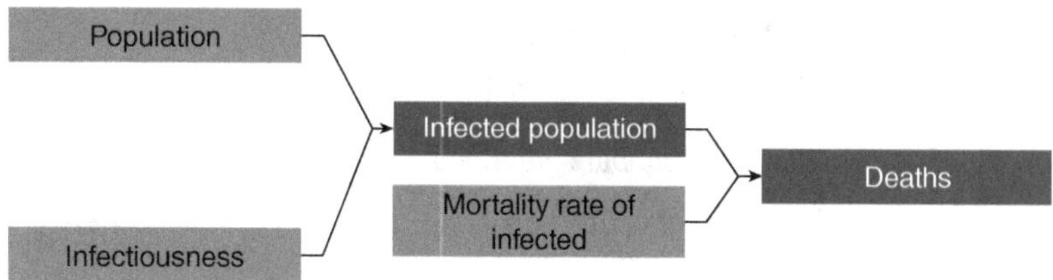

using a set of values at random from the specified probability distribution in Step 4 again and again.

Step 7. ***Adjust parameters as needed***

The simple model shown in Figure 46.8 estimates the total deaths in the UK from a highly transmissible virus to be 18,307 with a standard deviation of 6077, while in Figure 46.9 it shows the number of people infected to be 177,687 with a standard deviation of 41,655.

This model uses input parameters like case fatality rate and infectiousness, which are based on data from regions that experienced the virus earlier than the UK and that had slightly different responses to infections. Thus, as more data become available, parameters like infectiousness will have to be varied based on the effectiveness of measures to mitigate the virus, such as social distancing and wearing of masks and gloves.

A sensitivity analysis (see Figure 46.10) shows that if the standard deviation of the mortality rate of the infected or the case fatality rate can be decreased by 50% by better treatments and other measures, more lives

FIGURE 46.8 Monte Carlo simulation output for number of deaths.

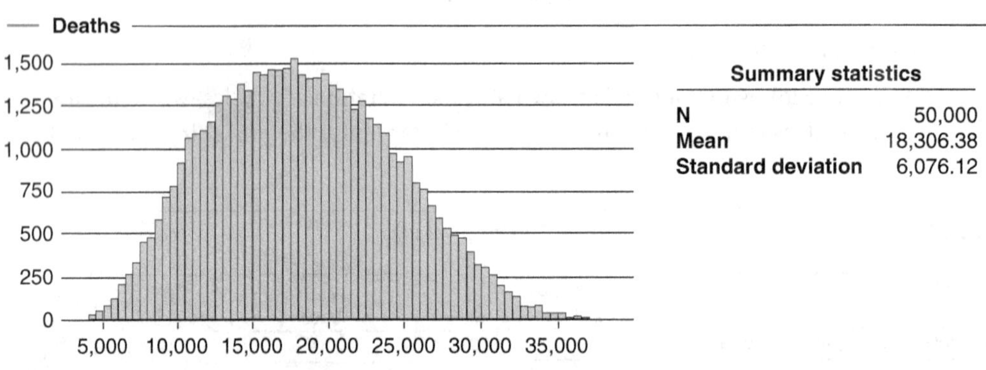

FIGURE 46.9 Monte Carlo simulation output for number of infected people.

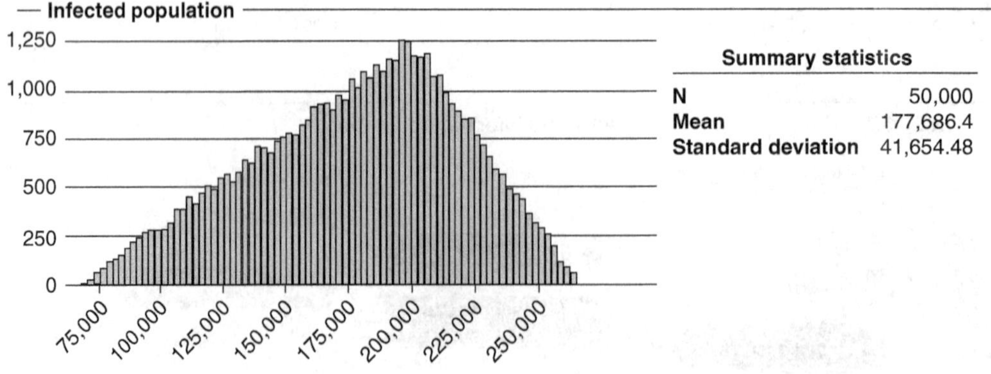

can be saved (16,745 with standard deviation of 7563). The new optimized model shows that in the best-case scenario, approximately 10,000 lives can be saved just by varying one parameter (updated model of death count shown in Figure 46.11).

Similarly, using factors such as regional herd immunity, vaccines, and new or experimental treatments, the parameter of case fatality rate along with infectiousness can be modulated based on available evidence based assumptions and the model can be updated as the issue progresses.

As can be seen above, Monte Carlo simulations, by quantitative risk analysis, provide us with a range of outcomes, which allows for better risk-based decision making. This is a very versatile tool that is used in a range of

FIGURE 46.10 Sensitivity analysis.

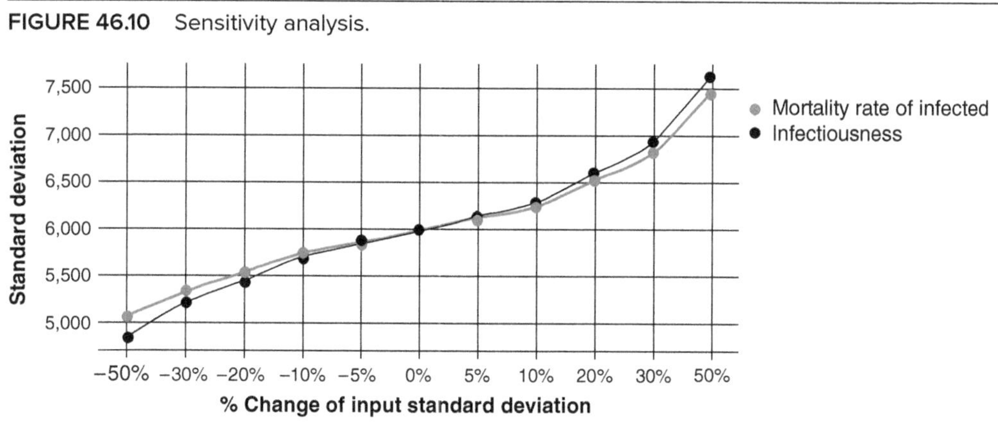

FIGURE 46.11 Monte Carlo simulation output of reduced deaths based on parameter adjustment as a result of sensitivity analysis.

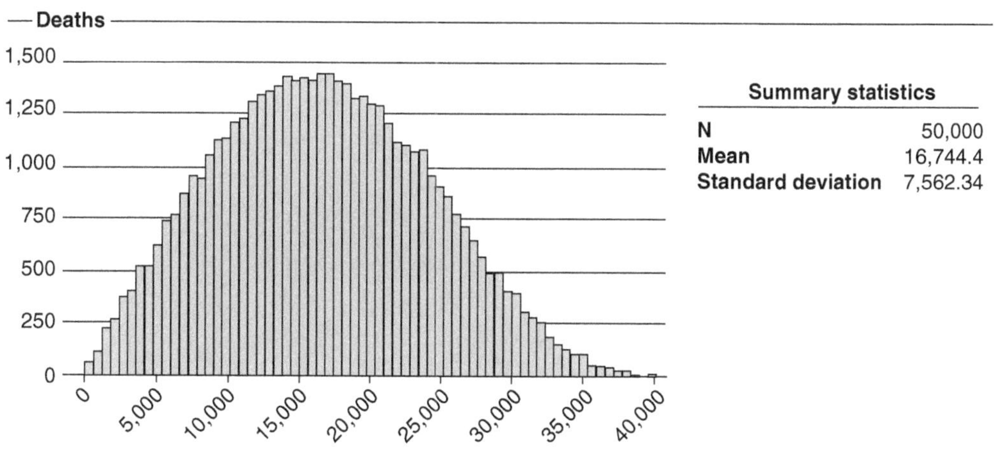

industries to account for aggregate risk and quantify probabilistic outcomes of risk realization.

Advantages of Monte Carlo Simulations

1. Easily lends itself to usage for empirical distributions
2. Ability to factor in a range of values to account for uncertainty
3. Outputs easily understood by nonmathematicians
4. The uncertainty related to a risk can be quantified to planning purposes
5. Probabilistic results show not only the quantified value of risk but also the probability of each level of uncertainty
6. Allows for sensitivity and parametric analysis as model and equations can be modulated
7. Allows for great flexibility, which helps to update/extend models as more information becomes available
8. Sets realistic expectations
9. Allows for stakeholder alignment in the face of risks
10. Allows for optimization to view best- and worst-case scenarios for risks

Disadvantages of Monte Carlo Simulations

1. Since a range of values are factored in, these are based on assumptions and the strength of underlying assumptions determines the accuracy of the model
2. Accuracy depends on the number of iterations or cycles
3. Solutions are inexact and over a large range
4. If historical data are not built into the assumptions, the simulation is unable to incorporate past trends

CHAPTER 47

Pandemic and Epidemic Risk Management

THE COVID-19 PANDEMIC AND ITS CASCADING EFFECTS have left a lasting mark on all industries and sectors. While the root causes, sources, and drivers of the pandemic will be discussed in great detail in countless forums in the coming time, our aim in this chapter is to discuss the management of its consequences, with a focus on business continuity, in the context of risk management.

There has been much conversation about black swan events, which have such low probability that they cannot be predicted and are, effectively, unforeseeable. Nassim Nicholas Taleb[1] popularized the theory of the black swan, which assigns the "black swan" label to events that come as a surprise and are hugely impactful.

In the case of COVID-19, one may well argue that this was foreseeable and not a black swan event. Taleb has called COVID-19 a "white swan"—that is, an event that is an eventuality with estimable impact.

Indeed, a related coronavirus had earlier reared its head with Middle East respiratory syndrome (MERS-CoV) in 2012, 2015, and 2018 and severe acute respiratory syndrome (SARS-CoV) from 2002 to 2004. The modus operandi of virus genesis was the same in these two cases as it was for the SARS-CoV-2, which is by zoonotic spillover (i.e., transmission of a pathogen from a vertebrate animal to a human).

Zoonotic spillover is an arduous process in which the virus mutates, selectively adapting to intermediate and final hosts. Despite multiple barriers and low probabilities of spillover events, two-thirds of human viruses have spilled over, including HIV (chimpanzee, green monkey, and sooty mangabey), Ebola (bat), Marburg filovirus (bat), and H1N1 (swine). H1N1, which first appeared in 1918 causing the disease then known as the Spanish influenza, has had at least 18 outbreaks since then with one as recent as 2020 in India.

Despite such repeated occurrences and a large body of knowledge on infectious diseases, why has the effect of SARS-CoV-2 been so disastrous? Was this risk truly an

1. Nassim Nicholas Taleb is the author of the 2007 book *The Black Swan*, which has been described by *The Sunday Times* as one of the twelve most influential books since World War II.

FIGURE 47.1 Contexts based on the spread of a disease.

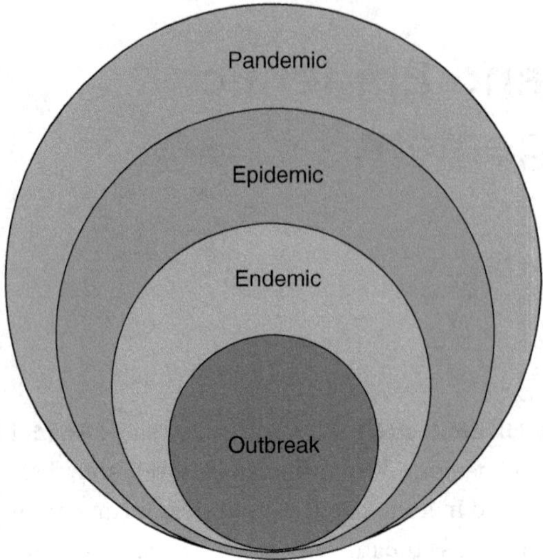

unforeseeable black swan? The answer lies in risk management—or rather the lack of it, which transformed this local outbreak of SARS-CoV-2 into a crippling pandemic.

Let us start by setting the context of risk management. In epidemiological risk management, there are four contexts (see Figure 47.1):

1. A disease that spreads more than expected (i.e., with a greater than anticipated occurrence rate within a local range or population) is known as an *outbreak.*
2. When the disease starts occurring at a predictable occurrence rate within a certain area or within a certain population, it is known as an *endemic.*
3. When the disease spreads with a much higher than normal occurrence rate and affects a greater than anticipated population set, it is called an *epidemic.*
4. An epidemic that has spread to multiple countries and populations is known as a *pandemic.* The World Health Organization (WHO) defines a pandemic as "an outbreak of a new pathogen that spreads easily from person to person across the globe."[2]

Each of these disease classes demands a separate and specialized risk management approach. As the spread of the disease starts increasing, the level of maturity of systemic risk management proportionally increases. The challenge here is to dynamically adapt the risk management approach to contain the risk as the disease progresses upward from an outbreak toward a pandemic. Failure to manage risk and contain the spread using risk-driven mitigative measures at each step allows the severity of the harm from

2. C. Sibthorpe, "Coronavirus Pandemic: What Does This Mean - and What Happens Next?," *Sky News,* March 12, 2020, https://news.sky.com/story/coronavirus-pandemic-what-does-this-mean-and-what-happens-next-11955553.

FIGURE 47.2 The risk assessment process with special stress on communication and information dissemination.

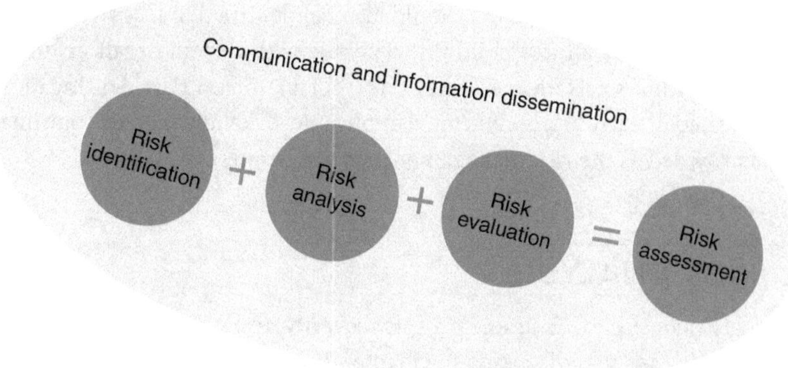

the disease to increase proportionally as it progresses toward the epidemic/pandemic stage.

We will apply the principles learned in earlier chapters—specifically, the phases of risk management per ISO 31000:2018 as detailed in Chapter 22—to tackle pandemic risk management in this chapter.

It is important to understand that from a policy standpoint, a pandemic is a systemic risk, which means that it poses a threat to the entire system as opposed to individual components or entities. A system is characterized by interdependent components. As a pandemic rages, if the risk is not properly managed, the whole system can strain toward collapse due to cascading component-level failures (e.g., healthcare delivery strain). Systemic risks require an interdisciplinary approach for accurate classification, and the process begins with epidemiological characterization, which is the first step of risk identification. Figure 47.2 reiterates the three steps of risk assessment, staying true to ISO 31000:2018, which we will follow in this chapter. As can be seen, communication and information dissemination is of utmost importance in every step of infectious disease risk management. If critical information about the spread of the pathogen or its novelty is not disseminated on a timely basis, then other regions may not have enough time to set policy and define appropriate mitigative measures, which could lead to loss of life.

STEP 1: RISK IDENTIFICATION

The first step starts in the initial outbreak phase. Once an outbreak has been identified, it should be clearly recognized and described. In epidemiological terms, the strain of the pathogen must be identified to check for novelty of genetic matter and mode of transmission. The pathogenicity of the disease, which is its ability to harm the host, must be classified, and the host-pathogen interaction must be mapped out. Pathogenesis, which refers to the manner of development of the disease when the pathogen interacts with the host, must also be clarified in this stage. The disease and its end points must be clearly described. On a higher level, the level of susceptibility of certain populations in terms of demographic parameters should also be identified in this stage—for example, the pathogen severely attacks children or people with certain organ insufficiencies or older adults within a certain age range. The information on risk identification must be communicated as early as possible to all applicable stakeholders and continual updates must be provided as the risk management process progresses.

STEP 2: RISK ANALYSIS

Risk analysis consists of assessment of the severity and occurrence of the disease. All concepts of risk analysis discussed in Chapter 25 also apply here.

First, when gauging severity, the pathogenicity (i.e., the ability of the pathogen to harm the host) is studied in terms of *virulence*, which is defined as the degree of pathology caused by the organism.

The following parameters can provide an indication of the severity of the disease:

1. Case fatality rate: the proportion of symptomatic cases that lead to death
2. Available treatment sensitivity
3. Outcome classification according to the four clinical severities of asymptomatic, symptomatic but mild, severe/grave disease presentation, and death

Occurrence of the disease is the second dimension, which can be gauged using the following parameters:

1. Transmission rate, which is the number of cases an individual will cause during his or her infectious period. This can also be called basic reproduction number, effective reproduction number or rate, infectiousness, or infectivity.
2. Number of deaths or excess mortality (i.e., increase in mortality attributed to the organism under study).
3. Number of serious adverse outcomes.
4. Hospital admission rate and intensive care admission rate.
5. Generation time: the mean delay between the time of infection of an index case and the times of infection of secondary cases caused by the index case.
6. Serial interval: the average length of time between symptom onset of individual cases and the persons they infect.
7. Clinical attack rate (CAR): the proportion of the population that is symptomatically infected in a given time period. CARs can be calculated for different demographics, localities, and risk groups.
8. Incidence proportion: the proportion of people who develop a new disease during a specified time period. This may take the form of a Proportional Reporting Ratio (PRR), where appropriate.
9. Prevalence: the proportion of people who have a disease at a specific time.

10. Weekly influenza-like illness (ILI) or medically attended acute respiratory illness (MAARI) cases as a proportion of total clinic/hospital visits, or incidence rates.

Many other risk parameters are identified in Table 47.2. It is also helpful to incorporate, at times, a detection dimension in the risk assessment, which can include factors such as testing capacity and capability. This is important for novel viruses where testing approaches may not be universal and well deployed.

From the list of the above severity and occurrence parameters (sometimes detection or exposure can be included as well), the most relevant must be chosen for the next step of risk evaluation. When selecting the parameters, special attention should be paid to data accuracy, reliability, and integrity.

STEP 3: RISK EVALUATION

Many methods, depending on the required outcome, can be employed to evaluate the risk of disease. The visual risk tracker introduced in Chapter 33 can be used to perform a comparative evaluation and to benchmark the disease in order to get an idea about risk and response strategies.

For the COVID-19 pandemic, we can choose the following two parameters (out of the list mentioned in the earlier step) and chart them over similar parameters from other epidemics and outbreaks to assess comparative risk:

1. Severity parameter: case fatality ratio
2. Occurrence parameter: basic reproduction number (R_0)

A simple multiplication of severity and occurrence parameters is not sufficient in this case. Here lies the challenge of assessing risk for infectious diseases: the spread is complex and outcomes do not follow a common linear relationship.

The spread of the virus is a major contributor to the excess mortality and can be given a higher weight than the case fatality rate. Using this logic, let us form a risk equation for disease risk as:

$$\text{Risk} = (R_0)^3 \times \textit{Case fatality ratio} \tag{47.1}$$

Based on the parameters we have chosen and our chosen risk equation, it can be seen (in Table 47.1) that by placing stress on transmissibility, the worst-case risk of COVID-19 is the highest among the six infections.

Of note is the range between the best case and the worst case. While this highlights the importance of mitigative measures to contain the disease (better mitigations, lower risk), it also indicates the need for a higher level of analysis that can better quantify the uncertainty in a probabilistic manner. We will look at this in detail in the coming sections. It is also important to note that as an outbreak progresses, the data must be actively sought, and the integrity of the data set must be maintained.

TABLE 47.1 Disease risk assessment example.

		Transmissibility (R_0)		Case fatality rate		Total risk	
Disease	Virus	R_{0w} (worst case)	R_{0b} (best case)	C_w (worst case)	C_b (best case)	Best case	Worst case
SARS	SARS-CoV	4	2	10	9.5	76	160
COVID-19	SARS-CoV-2	5.5	1.4	15	2	5.488	2495.625
Ebola	EBOV	2.5	1.5	82	45	151.875	1281.25
Bird flu	H7N9	0.4	0.03	59	56	0.001512	3.776
MERS	MERS-CoV	0.69	0.35	40	20	0.8575	13.14036
Seasonal flu (U.S)	Influenza A/B	2.1	0.9	0.21	0.1	0.0729	1.94481

The Risk Triangle

David Crichton introduced the risk triangle in 1999,[3] and since then it has been cited more than 400 times in research papers related to various hazard and risk assessments for a broad range of sectors and industries. Per this theory, the risk is a function of hazard, exposure, and vulnerability, as shown and defined in Equation 47.2 and Figure 47.3.

$$Risk = f\,(Hazard,\ Exposure,\ Vulnerability) \tag{47.2}$$

For pandemics and epidemics, the hazard can be the disease itself or its spread. Since hazard is defined as a potential source of harm, which here is the disease and its spread, it can also be resolved into the components of severity of potential harm and likelihood of occurrence of potential harm. This allows us to create a risk rhomboid for better quantification of risk, as shown in Figure 47.4, which gives us the risk equation as

$$Risk = f\,(Severity,\ Likelihood,\ Exposure,\ Vulnerability) \tag{47.3}$$

The two extra parameters of vulnerability and exposure in the risk equation allow us to consider the amount of population exposed to the disease and the subset of that population that is vulnerable to the disease. While it can be argued that elements of these two factors can be included in the "severity" and "likelihood" parameters, having these independently resolved helps with the epidemiological assessment of aggregate potential risk of the disease by assessment of the extent of human health damage and management of exposure accumulation.

Successful use of the risk triangle can be found in Pulchino and colleagues,[4] who have used this theory for quantitative risk assessments for COVID-19 in Italy.

---

3. D. Crichton, "The Risk Triangle," *Natural Disaster Management* 102, no. 3 (1999): 103.
4. A. Pluchino, G. Inturri, A. Rapisarda, A. E. Biondo, R. Le Moli, C. Zappala, N. Giuffrida, G. Russo, and V. Latora, "A Novel Methodology for Epidemic Risk Assessment: The Case of COVID-19 Outbreak in Italy," arXiv preprint arXiv:2004.02739 (2020).

FIGURE 47.3 Risk triangle with definitions showing original and reduced risk.

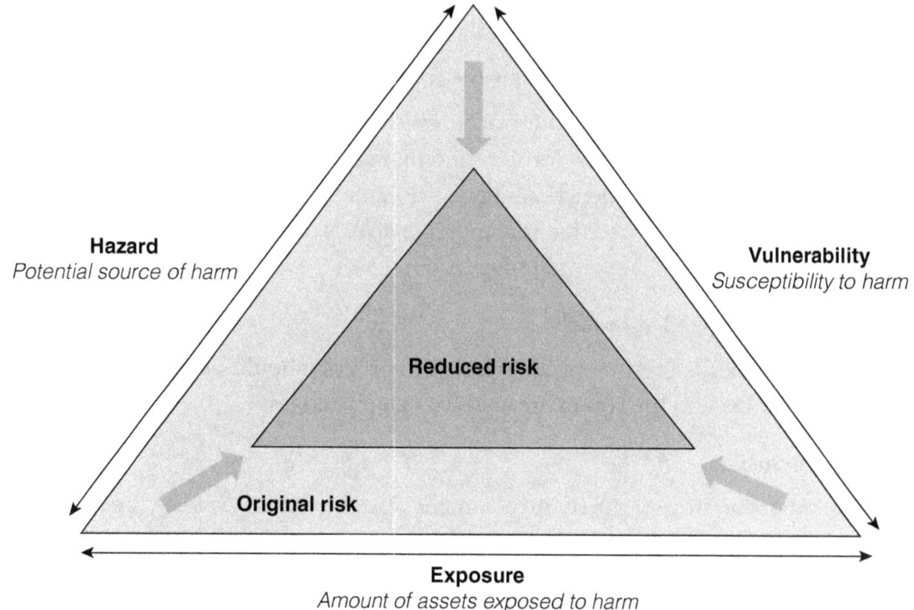

FIGURE 47.4 Risk rhomboid with definitions showing original and reduced risk.

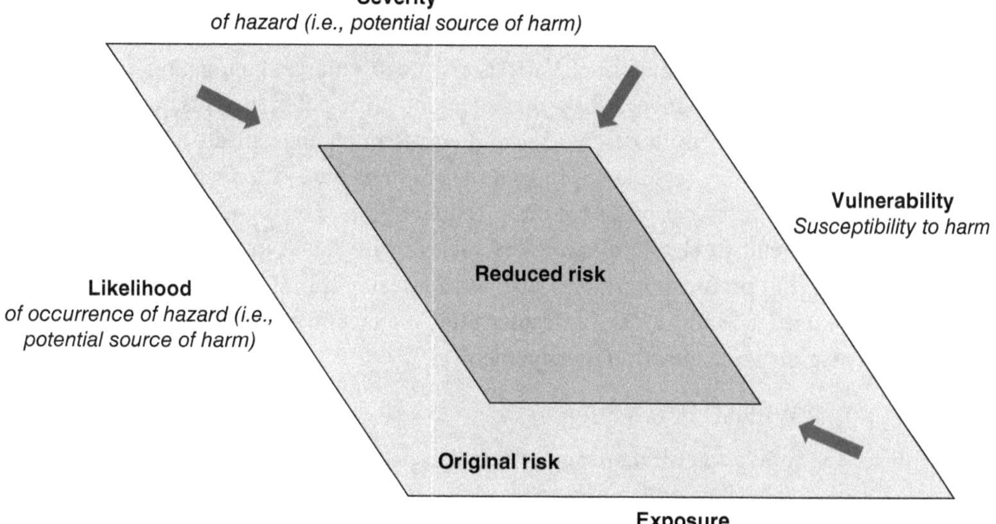

Regardless of the method or tool, the following tenets, based in ISO 31000:2018 theory, apply in totality to infectious disease risk management as the disease progresses through the four stages mentioned earlier:

1) **A structured and comprehensive approach**

   Any parameters selected for occurrence, severity, or detection must be scrutinized and the rationale for selection maintained. All assumptions must be challenged and use evidence-based decision making, and a risk model or equation should be developed that is comprehensive, is consistent, and gives comparable results across the required scope.

2) **A customized approach**

   The risk management framework and process should be customized and proportionate to the context related to final objectives.

3) **Inclusivity**

   Appropriate and timely involvement of stakeholders enables their knowledge, views, and perceptions to be considered. This results in improved awareness and informed risk management. The outbreak of a disease can encompass a small locality and can quickly encompass multiple countries. It is most important to involve all relevant stakeholders on every level to truly understand the nature and drivers of risk.

4) **Dynamic risk management**

   Risk of an outbreak is different from that of an epidemic, which is different from that of a pandemic. Various risks can emerge, change, or disappear as the context changes. Risk management anticipates, detects, acknowledges, and responds to those changes and events in an appropriate and timely manner. This may include appropriate changes in the risk equation or model and changes in risk parameters on a frequent basis. During an initial outbreak, it is difficult to classify parameters such as case fatality rate or transmissibility, and thus predictor variables such as the weekly ILI rate or the MAARI rate can be used as leading risk indicators. Risk management must be just as agile and responsive as infection management.

5) **Best available information**

   The inputs to risk management are based on historical and current information, as well as on future expectations. Risk management explicitly takes into account any limitations and uncertainties associated with such information and expectations. All assumptions must be explicit and continually challenged. If proven wrong, the risk process must be updated accordingly to preserve accuracy. Information should be timely, clear, and available to relevant stakeholders.

6) **Communication and transparency**

In the connected world of today, the movement of people and goods is happening at an unprecedented rate. This means that a pathogen can also move and spread at previously unprecedented rates. Targeted data mining based on risk and sharing of the risk data is critical to contain a pandemic risk. The spread of the pathogen is time dependent, and the rate of spread can be greatly contained by implementing mitigative measures based on risk early in the outbreak. As waves of disease strike, the importance of dissemination of information regarding the results of risk identification, assessment, and mitigation at the site of initial outbreak is critical since this information can be used to contain the spread and prevent overwhelming of healthcare provision systems.

QUANTITATIVE RISK MANAGEMENT

In the risk table for SARS, COVID-19, H1N1, MERS, and Ebola, we saw a large range of uncertainty in the risk level for diseases, based on our chosen parameters. Monte Carlo assessment, detailed in Chapter 46, gives us a tool to quantify this uncertainty in a probabilistic manner.

For example, in the wake of an epidemic a hospital may need to assess the number of beds available and plan capacity addition based on the projected levels of beds needed. Monte Carlo simulations can help in decision making in this regard. Let us use the parameters for transmissibility and the hospitalization rate to create a model using the stepwise formula shown in Chapter 46 to project the maximum bed capacity needed.

Let us consider, hypothetically, that an epidemic hits the UK and affects 108,692 people in a matter of a few months at the time of modeling. The transmissibility of the epidemic is debatable, and various small-sample studies show that it ranges from 2 to 5.5. The hospitalization rate varies by age and ranges from 1% of people less than 20 to 8% for people above 50 and 19% for people above 80. The case fatality rate varies from 1% to 13%. The number of beds required can be modeled per the equation:

$$\textit{Number of beds required} = (\textit{Current number of infection in the country} \times \textit{Transmissibility}) \times \textit{Hospitalization rate} \tag{47.4}$$

In addition, the same model can be used to predict the number of deaths from the epidemic by using the equation:

$$\textit{Number of deaths} = \textit{Total infected population} \times \textit{Case fatality rate} \tag{47.5}$$

This can be modeled as shown in Figure 47.5. The parameters and their limiting values can be seen in Figure 47.6.

Upon running the Monte Carlo simulation, the values shown in Figures 47.7, 47.8, and 47.9 are obtained.

It can be seen that the mean number of beds needed is 38.985 with a standard deviation of 17,315. The total number of deaths forecasted is 25,016 with a standard deviation of 11,805.

FIGURE 47.5 A model for predicting total number of beds and total deaths for an ongoing epidemic or pandemic.

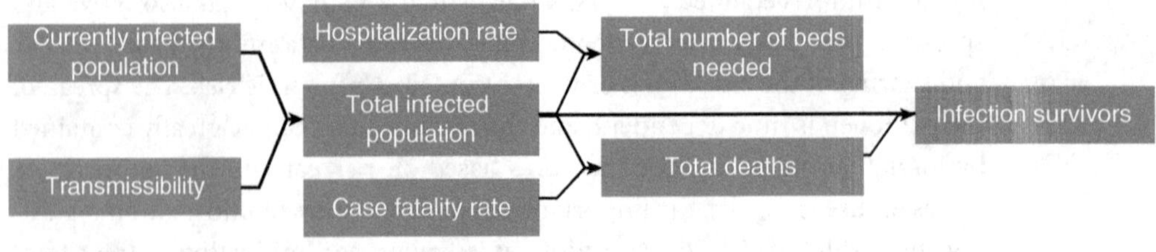

FIGURE 47.6 Parameters of the model and their limiting values.

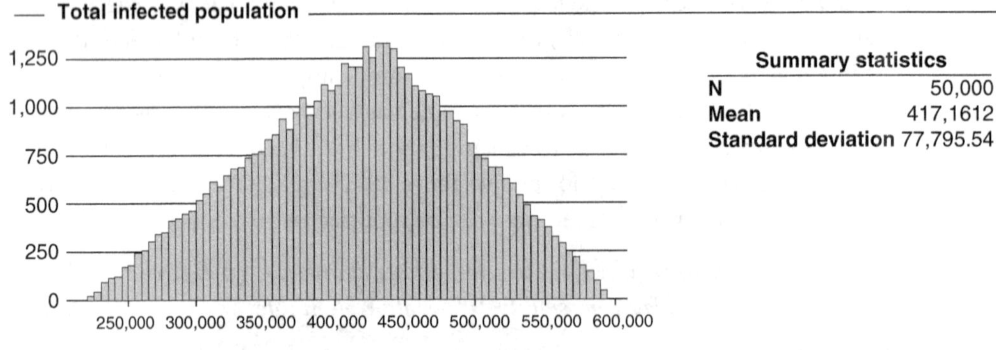

X name	Distribution	Parameters			Preview
Currently infected population	Fixed	Value: 108,692			108,692
Transmissibility	Triangular	Lower: 2	Mode: 4	Upper: 5.5	4
Hospitalization rate	Triangular	Lower: 0.01	Mode: 0.08	Upper: 0.19	0.08
Case fatality rate	Triangular	Lower: 0.01	Mode: 0.04	Upper: 0.13	0.04

FIGURE 47.7 Monte Carlo simulation output for total number of people infected.

FIGURE 47.8 Monte Carlo simulation output for total number of beds needed.

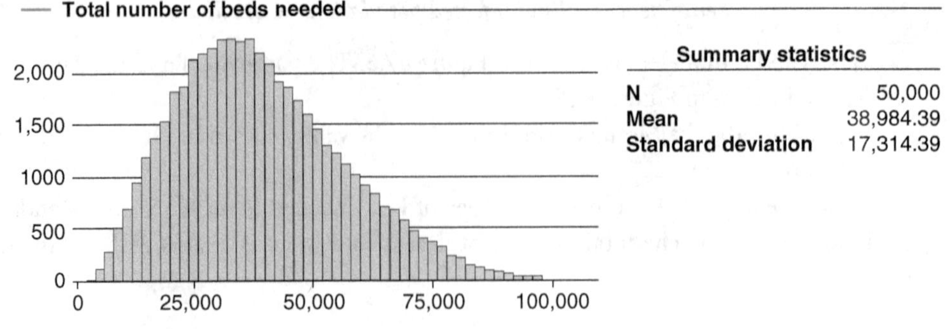

FIGURE 47.9 Monte Carlo simulation output for total number of deaths.

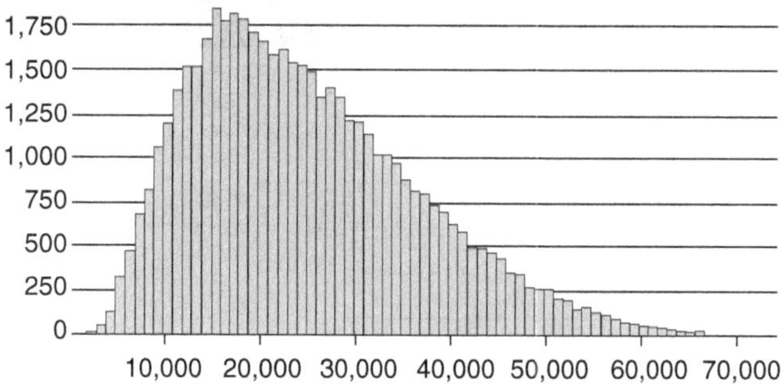

Summary statistics	
N	50,000
Mean	25,015.14
Standard deviation	11,804.35

Thus, from a risk planning standpoint, the estimates provided by Monte Carlo simulation are quite valuable in considering strategic resource allocation.

Other methods of risk evaluation include viral exposure evaluation, which can include models similar to those created using Monte Carlo modeling to evaluate the exposure to the virus from a dose response standpoint (i.e., a relationship between exposure dose and severity of the disease).

Detailed and mathematically advanced methods of risk assessment for epidemics and outbreaks can be found in the references summarized in Table 47.2.

RISK MITIGATION

All the analyses and assessments shown above should guide the level of mitigation efforts (see the full process in Figure 47.10), which may include the following:

1. Reduction of contact between the infected population and the uninfected population using applicable barriers to reduce transmission
2. Reduction of viral load in infected patients by medication
3. Pre-exposure and post-exposure prophylactic
4. Vaccination
5. Awareness
6. Population movement control

The measures should be proportional to the risk of the disease and must be ramped up per the dynamically updated risk assessments if the risk ramps up toward epidemic and pandemic levels.

RISK MONITORING

Once the risk has been evaluated, it must be continually monitored. All the parameters listed above, in the context of an infectious disease, are bound to change per population and per region as the outbreak progresses. It is very important to define the scope of risk monitoring and accordingly define relevant parameters to monitor.

TABLE 47.2 References for advanced epidemic risk assessment with their respective risk parameters and methods.

Sr. no.	Reference	Risk parameters	Method
1	Pluchino, A., G. Inturri, A. Rapisarda, A. E. Biondo, R. Le Moli, C. Zappala, N. Giuffrida, G. Russo, and V. Latora. "A Novel Methodology for Epidemic Risk Assessment: the case of COVID-19 outbreak in Italy." arXiv preprint. arXiv:2004.02739 (2020).	Air pollution	Correlation / linear and nonlinear least square fit with linear and multiplicative risk equations
		Human mobility	
		Winter temperature	
		Housing concentration	
		Healthcare density	
		Population size	
		Age group	
2	Liao, Y., B. Xu, J. Wang, and X. Liu. "A New Method for Assessing the Risk of Infectious Disease Outbreak." *Scientific Reports* 7 (2017): 40084.	Frequency/severity of occurrence	Baysian Belief Network (BBN) / linear regression
		Mortality	
		Rate of detection	
		Density	
		Average air pressure	
		Urbanization level	
		Maximum wind speed	
		Average relative humidity	
		Average temperature	
		Average wind speed	
		Minimum relative humidity	
		Rainfall	
		Sunshine	
		Temperature difference	
3	Tsallis, C., and U. Tirnakli. "Predicting COVID-19 Peaks around the World." *Frontiers in Physics* 8 (2020): 217.	Active cases	One body distribution / Boltzmann factor / q-exponential factor
		Deaths per day	
		Days since appearance of first case	
		Epidemiological strategy	
		Pathogen characteristics	
4	Chen, X., A. A. Chughtai, and C. R. MacIntyre. "Application of a Risk Analysis Tool to Middle East Respiratory Syndrome Coronavirus (MERS-CoV) Outbreak in Saudi Arabia." *Risk Analysis* 40, no. 5 (2020): 915–925.	Biorisk	Multiattribute, additive model to generate a weighted summary risk score (Grunow-Finke assessment tool)
		Biothreat	
		Special aspects	
		Geographic distribution	
		Environmental concentration	
		Epidemic intensity	
		Transmission mode	
		Time	
		Unusually rapid spread	
		Population limitation	
		Clinical/special insight	

5	Burke, S. A., and S. C. Trock. "Use of Influenza Risk Assessment Tool for Prepandemic Preparedness." *Emerging Infectious Diseases* 24, no. 3 (2018): 471.	Human infections	Multiattribute, additive model to generate a weighted summary risk score
		Transmission in lab animals	
		Receptor binding	
		Population immunity	
		Infections in animals	
	"Influenza Risk Assessment Tool (IRAT)." Centers for Disease Control and Prevention. Centers for Disease Control and Prevention, October 9, 2019. https://www.cdc.gov/flu/pandemic-resources/national-strategy/risk-assessment.htm.	Genomic variation	
		Antigenic relatedness	
		Global distribution in animals	
		Disease severity and pathogenesis	
		Antiviral drug and treatment options	
6	World Health Organization. *Rapid Risk Assessment of Acute Public Health Events*. No. WHO/HSE/GAR/ARO/2012.1. World Health Organization, 2012.	Clinical features and natural history of the disease	Questionnaire and risk matrix approach
		Timing of the event and the speed of spread	
		Geographical area and settings affected	
		Persons and populations affected	
		Number of people exposed.	
		Number of exposed people who are likely to be susceptible	
		Modes of transmission	
		Dose response	
		Incubation period (known or suspected)	
		Case fatality rate (CFR)	
		Estimation of the potential for transmission	
		Vaccine status of the exposed population	

Example:

The Centers for Disease Control and Prevention (CDC), as a part of COVID-19 risk monitoring, decided to use ILI visits to clinics, a metric that it actively monitors, to track mild or moderate COVID-19 cases. In the absence of widespread testing, this metric becomes a key risk indicator (KRI) and acts as a bellwether for other metrics such as hospitalization rate and transmissibility. The CDC identified the first peak around Week 51 of 2019 as that of influenza B, the second peak around Week 6 of 2020 was influenza A, and finally, the third peak at Week 12 of 2020 was that of the coronavirus.

In Figure 47.11, positive decreasing trends on ILI visits in the United States can be seen toward the 12th to 15th weeks of 2020, suggesting decreasing SARS-CoV-2 activity.

Another method to monitor activity in terms of deaths or new cases is to use a chart with a logarithmic scale. In infectious disease reporting, the cases are sometimes

FIGURE 47.10 The risk management process.

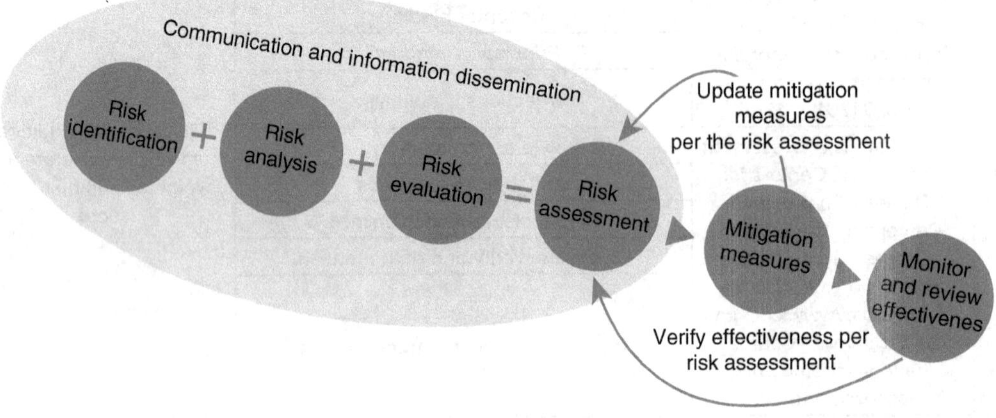

FIGURE 47.11 Percentage of visits for ILI in the United States from September 29, 2019, to April 11, 2020.

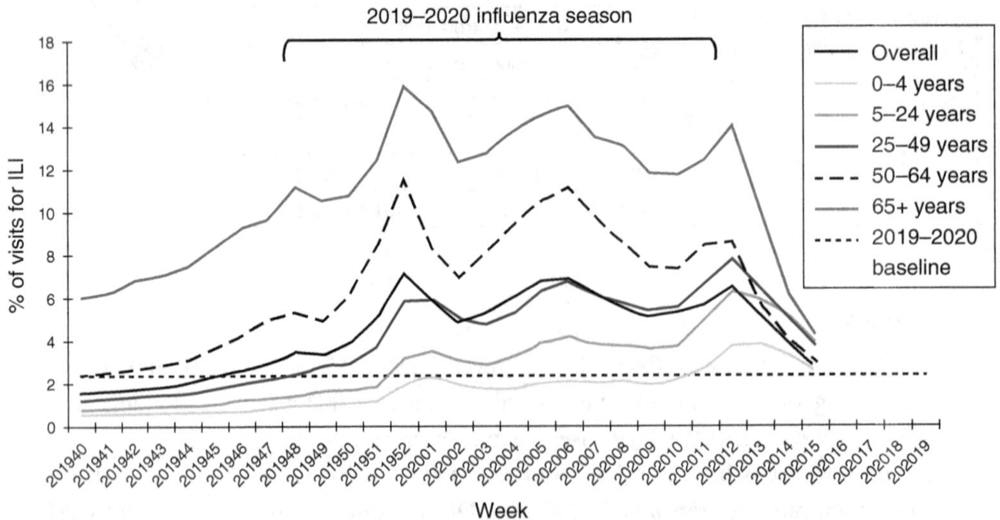

Source: "COVIDView: A Weekly Surveillance Summary of U.S. COVID-19 Activity," Centers for Disease Control and Prevention, June 12, 2020, https://www.cdc.gov/coronavirus/2019-ncov/covid-data/covidview/index.html.

in discrete bunches and tend to skew the data when charted linearly; thus, one can miss the forest for the trees. Using a logarithmic scale also provides a multiplicative factor by which percent change can be assessed. A logarithmic chart can give us a cumulative increase and a true relative rate of change.

FIGURE 47.12 J chart for trending infections and outcomes.

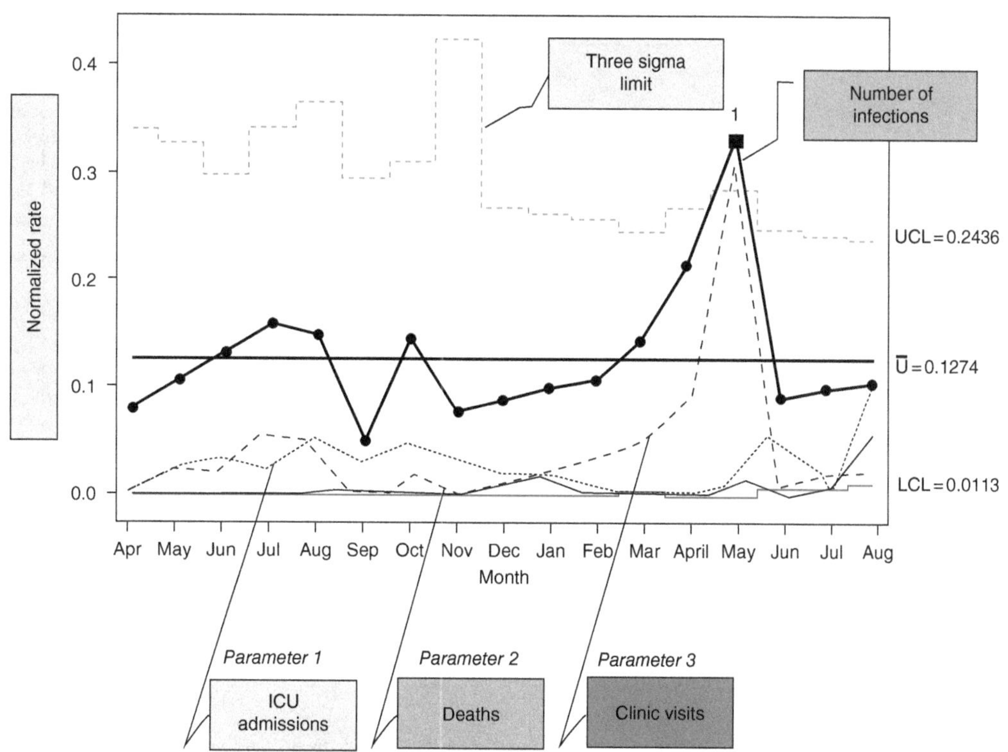

In addition, the J chart, introduced in Chapter 32, can also be used to track the trend of infections and their outcomes per month as they progress. Figure 47.12 shows an example where the main parameter trended is the number of infections per month, and secondary tracked parameters are clinic visits, ICU admissions, and deaths. The three-sigma limit gives a threshold of action that can be based on historical values or values computed based on parameters such as hospital capacity.

Establishing thresholds during charting and progress of the data points toward it is a useful proactive tool. The specificity and resolution of the data used to trend and establish the threshold are important. Figure 47.13 shows the data collected by the National Center for Health Statistics and the cyclical thresholds established for the number of deaths due to pneumonia, influenza, or COVID-19. The out-of-control data in 2020 seen on the right side of the chart were the result of the COVID-19 pandemic.

For infectious diseases, transmissibility or basic reproduction number (R_0) discussed earlier becomes an important parameter to monitor as a KRI. Many virologists may argue that R_0, which is the basic reproductive number, is a characteristic of the virus. Epidemiologists suggest using the term R_t, which is the effective reproductive number of the virus at a time *t*, which can vary widely based on local mitigation measures.

FIGURE 47.13 Pneumonia-, influenza-, or COVID-related mortality with epidemic threshold mortality.

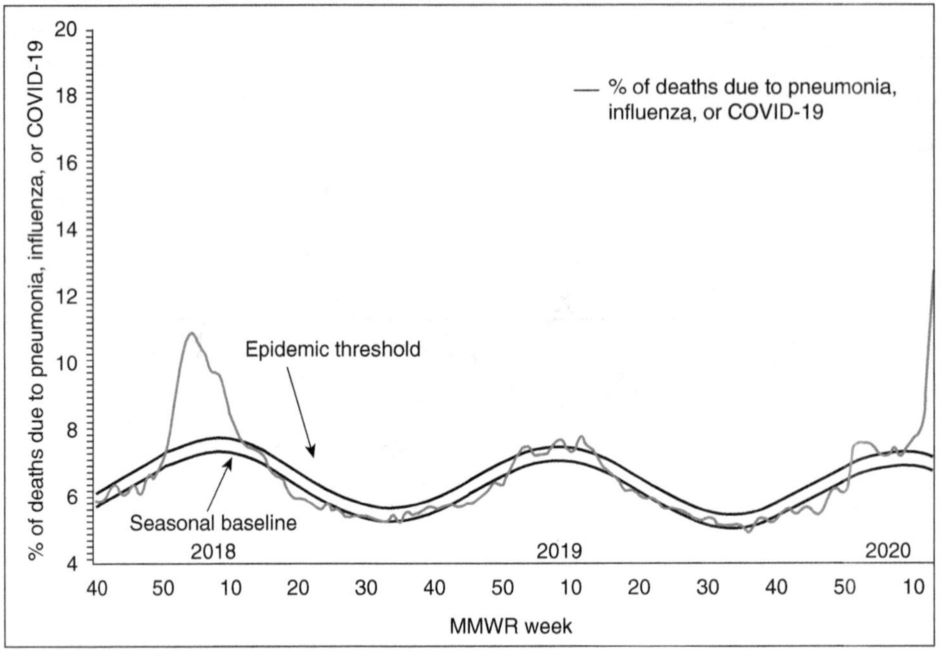

Data through the week ending April 11, 2020, as of April 16, 2020
Source: "COVIDView: A Weekly Surveillance Summary of U.S. COVID-19 Activity," Centers for Disease Control and Prevention, June 12, 2020, https://www.cdc.gov/coronavirus/2019-ncov/covid-data/covidview/index.html.

$R_t < 1$ translates to self-containment of the disease outbreak as one infected person affects less than one person (e.g., one new infection for every two already infected people with eventual end of outbreak). $R_t = 1$ or 1.2 translates to a manageable rate where every infected person infects about one other person. Allowing for time lags afforded by mitigations, this rate can usually be controlled and contained as it often does not overwhelm the hospital services. As R_t increases from 1.2 toward larger numbers and takes an exponential form of increase, it becomes harder and harder to manage and can inch toward becoming a highly transmissible pandemic. Figure 47.14 is the R_t chart compiled by the University of Hong Kong to track transmissibility of the coronavirus in Hong Kong.

R_t declined in February from highs since a travel pause was instituted from Hubei province in China on February 8, 2020. R_t dropped but slowly picked back up as students and professionals returned from overseas. Travel from other affected places was paused (parts of South Korea on February 25 and Iran on March 1) as well, but the internal increase of transmissions was probably due to asymptomatic individuals who arrived earlier from abroad. Due to this, R_t increased to the alert levels above 1 between March 23 and March 30. Social distancing measures were already in place in Hong Kong since January, but a ban on public gatherings of more than four people was instituted due to an increase in infections in March. This along with contact tracing,

FIGURE 47.14 Real-time reproduction number of SARS-CoV-2 in Hong Kong from February to April 2020.

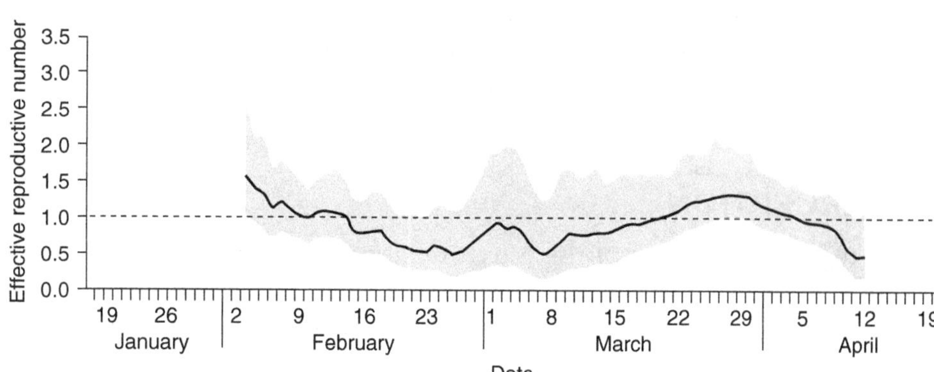

Source: Figure provided by Ben Cowling (Hong Kong University). Reproduced with permission from the University of Hong Kong.

quarantining, using PPE, and spreading awareness (and effecting behavior changes) led to low infections and a sustained decrease in R_t through the month of April 2020.

EPIDEMIC AND PANDEMIC PREPAREDNESS FOR BUSINESSES

For businesses, from an operational standpoint, the risk management planning process must include the following:

1. Identification of core/essential production and service workflows
2. Strategic risk management that includes risk identification, assessment, and mitigation measures in terms of business and financial impact
3. Identification of supply chain for core operations
4. Identification of human resources (and organizational hierarchies) and workplace resources
5. Identification of essential worker safety and stockpiling safety equipment
6. Identification of financial cash flow analysis in emergency situations
7. Creation of a worst-case and best-case risk scenario and planning for both by having a recovery plan for the worst-case risk. A plan for recovery and reopening is just as important as a plan for shutdown. Reopening planning must detail efforts to start up from zero activity and scaling to full operations.
8. Planning for proactive risk monitoring
9. Public and private partnerships for societal benefit

In case of highly transmissible diseases, businesses must place special attention on provision of PPE to the workers, reduction in gatherings in close quarters, leveraging online teleconferencing capability for as much work as possible, and special attention to the needs of mental health and the needs of the most vulnerable populations. In terms of the actual site of work, attention must be paid to disinfection techniques, hygiene, verification of PPE usage, vulnerable areas, safety practices (and training), limiting access, and targeted employee screening. Finally, communication should be consistent, categorical, and forward looking.

RISK PERCEPTION

The cognitive dimensions of risk perception discussed in Chapter 37 apply in their entirety to epidemic/pandemic risk management. To restate, the following two factors are major drivers of perception-driven risk decisions that are often incorrect:

1. Cognitive biases
2. Heuristics

When faced with an unknown, the human mind seeks to immediately transpose the available information into previously experienced situations. For example, most respiratory illnesses have similar symptoms, and so it is easy to compare the fatality rates and other parameters to those of a previously experienced/known illness (representativeness and familiarity heuristic). But in the face of a novel pandemic, such decision making is deeply flawed and can lead to disastrous consequences. Emotionally intelligent decision making can help overcome these heuristics and biases and guide us toward a rational, fact-based, and correct decision in the face of uncertainty. See Chapter 37 for more details on cognitive risk–based decision making.

Bibliography

American Society for Quality. "Quality Glossary of Terms, Acronyms, & Definitions: ASQ." ASQ. Accessed June 20, 2020. https://asq.org/quality-resources/quality-glossary/.

American Society of Safety Engineers. *Prevention through Design: Guidelines for Addressing Occupational Hazards and Risks in Design and Redesign Processes.* ANSI/ASSE Z590.3-2011. Des Plaines, IL: American Society of Safety Engineers, 2011.

ANSI/ASIS/RIMS. *Risk Assessment.* ANSI/ASIS/RIMS RA.1-2015. Alexandria, VA: American National Standards Institute, 2015. https://webstore.ansi.org/standards/asis/ansiasisrimsra2015.

Automotive Industry Action Group. *The FMEA Handbook: Failure Mode and Effects Analysis.* Southfield, MI: Automotive Industry Action Group, 2019.

Aven, T. "Safety Is the Antonym of Risk for Some Perspectives of Risk." *Safety Science* 47, no. 7 (2009): 925–930.

Aven, T. "SRA Glossary Draft." Society for Risk Analysis. Accessed June 20, 2020. https://www.sra.org/sra-glossary-draft.

Aven, T., and J. Kørte. "On the Use of Risk and Decision Analysis to Support Decision-Making." *Reliability Engineering & System Safety* 79, no. 3 (2003): 289–299.

Bank, K. F. K. *Mendelow's Matrix.* London: Kaplan Financial, 2012.

Benefit-Risk Balance for Marketed Drugs. Geneva, Switzerland: CIOMS, 2004.

Bennett, N., and J. Lemoine. "What VUCA Really Means for You." *Harvard Business Review* 92, nos. 1–2: 27.

Benneyan, J. C. "Statistical Quality Control Methods in Infection Control and Hospital Epidemiology, Part I Introduction and Basic Theory." *Infection Control & Hospital Epidemiology* 19, no. 3 (1998): 194–214.

Berger, S. "Vaginal Mesh Has Caused Health Problems in Many Women, Even as Some Surgeons Vouch for Its Safety and Efficacy." *Washington Post,* January 20, 2019. https://www.washingtonpost.com/national/health-science/vaginal-mesh-has-caused-health-problems-in-many-women-even-as-some-surgeons-vouch-for-its-safety-and-efficacy/2019/01/18/1c4a2332-ff0f-11e8-ad40-cdfd0e0dd65a_story.html.

Blackhurst, J. V., K. P. Scheibe, and D. J. Johnson. "Supplier Risk Assessment and Monitoring for the Automotive Industry." *International Journal of Physical Distribution & Logistics Management* 38, no. 2 (2008): 143–165.

Boada, J. N., C. Boada, M. García-Sáiz, M. García, E. Fernandez, and E. Gomez. "Net Efficacy Adjusted for Risk (NEAR): A Simple Procedure for Measuring Risk: Benefit Balance." *PloS One* 3, no. 10 (2008): e3580.

Bossert, J. L., ed. *The Supplier Management Handbook.* Milwaukee, WI: ASQ Quality Press, 2004.

Breban, R., J. Riou, and A. Fontanet. "Interhuman Transmissibility of Middle East Respiratory Syndrome Coronavirus: Estimation of Pandemic Risk." *Lancet* 382, no. 9893 (2013). https://doi.org/10.1016/S0140-6736(13)61492-0.

Campbell, A., J. Whitehead, and S. Finkelstein. "Why Good Leaders Make Bad Decisions." *Harvard Business Review* 87, no. 2 (2009): 60–66.

Center for Devices and Radiological Health. "Factors to Consider When Making Benefit-Risk Determinations in Medical Device Premarket Approval and De Novo Classifications." August 29, 2019. https://www.fda.gov/regulatory-information/search-fda-guidance-documents/factors-consider-when-making-benefit-risk-determinations-medical-device-premarket-approval-and-de.

Center for Food Safety and Applied Nutrition. "HACCP Principles & Application Guidelines." U.S. Food and Drug Administration, August 14, 1997. https://www.fda.gov/food/hazard-analysis-critical-control-point-haccp/haccp-principles-application-guidelines.

Chen, J. "Pathogenicity and Transmissibility of 2019-NCoV—A Quick Overview and Comparison with Other Emerging Viruses." *Microbes and Infection* 22, no. 2 (2020): 69–71.

Chen, K.-S., T.-C. Chang, K.-J. Wang, and C.-T. Huang. "Developing Control Charts in Monitoring Service Quality Based on the Number of Customer Complaints." *Total Quality Management & Business Excellence* 26, no. 5–6 (2015): 675–689.

Chuang-Stein, C. "A New Proposal for Benefit-Less-Risk Analysis in Clinical Trials." *Controlled Clinical Trials* 15, no. 1 (1994): 30–43.

Chuang-Stein, C., R. Entsuah, and Y. Pritchett. "Measures for Conducting Comparative Benefit: Risk Assessment." *Drug Information Journal* 42, no. 3 (2008): 223–233.

Chuang-Stein, C., N. R. Mohberg, and M. S. Sinkula. "Three Measures for Simultaneously Evaluating Benefits and Risks Using Categorical Data from Clinical Trials." *Statistics in Medicine* 10, no. 9 (1991): 1349–1359.

CIOMS Working Group IV. *Benefit–Risk Balance for Marketed Drugs: Evaluating Safety Signals.* Geneva, Switzerland: Council for International Organizations of Medical Sciences, 1998. https://cioms.ch/wp-content/uploads/2017/01/benefit-risk.pdf.

Clavien, P. A., J. Barkun, M. L. De Oliveira, J. N. Vauthey, D. Dindo, R. D. Schulick, E. De Santibañes, et al. "The Clavien-Dindo Classification of Surgical Complications: Five-Year Experience." *Annals of Surgery* 250, no. 2 (2009): 187–196.

Cortez, A. *The Complete Idiot's Guide to Risk Management: Get Dynamic Growth and Profitability through Successful Risk Strategies.* Indianapolis, IN: Penguin, 2010.

Crichton, D. "The Risk Triangle." *Natural Disaster Management* 102, no. 3 (1999): 103.

Crouch, E. A., and R. Wilson. *Risk-Benefit Analysis*, 2nd ed. Cambridge, MA: Harvard Center for Risk Analysis, 2001.

Department of Defense. *Department of Defense Risk, Issue, and Opportunity Management Guide for Defense Acquisition Programs.* Washington, DC: Office of the Deputy Assistant Secretary of Defense for Systems Engineering, 2017.

Dindo, D. "The Clavien–Dindo Classification of Surgical Complications." In *Treatment of Postoperative Complications after Digestive Surgery*, pp. 13–17. London: Springer.

Edwards, I. R., B. E. Wiholm, and C. Martinez. "Concepts in Risk-Benefit Assessment." *Drug Safety* 15, no. 1 (1996): 1–7.

Elahi, B. *Safety Risk Management for Medical Devices*. Academic Press, 2018.

Forna, A., P. Nouvellet, I. Dorigatti, and C. A. Donnelly. "Case Fatality Ratio Estimates for the 2013–2016 West African Ebola Epidemic: Application of Boosted Regression Trees for Imputation." *Clinical Infectious Diseases* 70, no. 12 (2020): 2476–2483. https://doi.org/10.1093/cid/ciz678.

Gaylor, D. W. "Risk/Benefit Assessments of Human Diseases: Optimum Dose for Intervention." *Risk Analysis: An International Journal* 25, no. 1 (2005): 161–168.

Goddard Space Flight Center. *Risk Management Reporting*. GFSC-STD-002. Greenbelt, MD: NASA, 2009.

Goleman, D. *Emotional Intelligence*. New York: Bantam, 2006.

Goleman, D. *Emotional Intelligence and Working with Emotional Intelligence*. London: Bloomsburg Publishing, 2004.

Goleman, D. "How Emotionally Intelligent Are You?" Daniel Goleman. April 22, 2015. http://www.danielgoleman.info/daniel-goleman-how-emotionally-intelligent-are-you/.

Goleman, D. "Leadership That Gets Results." *Harvard Business Review* 78, no. 2 (2000): 4–17.

Goleman, D. "What Makes a Leader." *Organizational Influence Processes* 82 (2003): 229–241.

Goleman, D., R. E. Boyatzis, and A. McKee. *Primal Leadership: Unleashing the Power of Emotional Intelligence*. Boston: Harvard Business Press.

Goleman, D., R. E. Boyatzis, A. McKee, and S. Finkelstein. *HBR's 10 Must Reads on Emotional Intelligence (with featured article "What Makes a Leader?" by Daniel Goleman)*. Boston: Harvard Business Review Press, 2015.

Hampton, J. *Fundamentals of Enterprise Risk Management: How Top Companies Assess Risk, Manage Exposure, and Seize Opportunity*. New York: Amacom, 2009.

Hare, L. B. "Statistics Roundtable: Follow the Rules." American Society for Quality. Accessed June 20, 2020. http://asq.org/quality-progress/2013/01/statistics-roundtable/follow-the-rules.html.

Her Majesty's Treasury. *The Orange Book*. Government Finance Function, 2020. https://www.gov.uk/government/publications/orange-book.

Hillson, D. *Risk Facilitation Made Easy*. Paper presented at PMI Global Congress 2015 EMEA, London, England. Newtown Square, PA: Project Management Institute, 2015.

Hillson, D., ed. *The Risk Management Handbook: A Practical Guide to Managing the Multiple Dimensions of Risk*. London: Kogan Page Publishers, 2016.

Hillson, D. "Towards a Risk Maturity Model." *International Journal of Project & Business Risk Management* 1, no. 1 (1997): 35–45.

Hillson, D. "Use a Risk Breakdown Structure (RBS) to Understand Your Risks." *Proceedings of the Project Management Institute Annual Seminars & Symposium* 10 (October 2002). https://www.pmi.org/learning/library/risk-breakdown-structure-understand-risks-1042.

Hillson, D. "Using a Risk Breakdown Structure in Project Management." *Journal of Facilities Management* 2, no. 1 (2003): 85–97.

Hillson, D., and R. Murray-Webster. "Understanding and Managing Risk Attitude." In *Proceedings of 7th Annual Risk Conference,* held in London, UK, on November 26, 2004.

Holden, W. L., J. Juhaeri, and W. Dai. "Benefit-Risk Analysis: A Proposal Using Quantitative Methods." *Pharmacoepidemiology and Drug Safety* 12, no. 7 (2003): 611–616.

Hopkin, P. *Fundamentals of Risk Management: Understanding, Evaluating and Implementing Effective Risk Management.* London: Kogan Page Publishers, 2018.

Hugonnet, S., and D. Pittet. "Transmission of Severe Acute Respiratory Syndrome in Critical Care: Do We Need a Change?" *American Journal of Respiratory and Critical Care Medicine* 169, no. 11. https://doi.org/10.1164/rccm.2403004.

Hunink, M. G., M. C. Weinstein, E. Wittenberg, M. F. Drummond, J. S. Pliskin, J. B. Wong, and P. P. Glasziou. *Decision Making in Health and Medicine: Integrating Evidence and Values.* 2nd ed. Cambridge: Cambridge University Press, 2014.

Hutchins, G. *ISO: Risk Based Thinking.* Portland, OR: Quality Plus Engineering, 2016.

Hutchins, G. *ISO 31000:2018 Enterprise Risk Management.* Portland, OR: Greg Hutchins, 2018.

International Electrochemical Commission. *Failure Modes and Effects Analysis (FMEA and FMECA).* IEC 60812:2018. Geneva, Switzerland: International Electrochemical Commission, 2018. https://webstore.iec.ch/publication/26359.

International Electrochemical Commission. *Fault Tree Analysis (FTA).* IEC 61025:2006. Geneva, Switzerland: International Electrochemical Commission, 2006. https://webstore.iec.ch/publication/26359.

International Electrochemical Commission. *Hazard and Operability Studies (HAZOP Studies)—Application Guide.* IEC 61882:2016. Geneva, Switzerland: International Electrochemical Commission, 2016. https://webstore.iec.ch/publication/24321.

International Electrotechnical Commission. *Risk Management: Part 3 Guide to Risk Analysis of Technological Systems.* IEC 60300-3-9:1995. Geneva, Switzerland: International Electrotechnical Commission, 1995.

International Organization for Standardization. *Application of Risk Management to Medical Devices.* ISO 14971:2019. Geneva, Switzerland: International Organization for Standardization, 2019. https://www.iso.org/standard/72704.html.

International Organization for Standardization. *Automation Systems and Integration—Key Performance Indicators (KPIs) for Manufacturing Operations Management—Part 2: Definitions and Descriptions of KPIs.* ISO 22400-2:2014. Geneva, Switzerland: International Organization for Standardization, 2014.

International Organization for Standardization. *Food Safety Management Systems—Requirements for Any Organization in the Food Chain.* ISO 22000:2018. Geneva, Switzerland: International Organization for Standardization, 2018. https://www.iso.org/standard/65464.html.

International Organization for Standardization. *Guidelines for Auditing Management Systems.* ISO 19011:2018. Geneva, Switzerland: International Organization for Standardization, 2018. https://www.iso.org/standard/70017.html.

International Organization for Standardization. *Quality Management Systems—Requirements.* ISO 9001:2015. Geneva, Switzerland: International Organization for Standardization, 2015. https://www.iso.org/standard/62085.html.

International Organization for Standardization. *Risk Management—Guidelines.* ISO 31000:2018. Geneva, Switzerland: International Organization for Standardization, 2018. https://www.iso.org/standard/65694.html.

International Organization for Standardization. *Risk Management—Risk Assessment Techniques.* ISO 31010:2019. Geneva, Switzerland: International Organization for Standardization, 2019. https://www.iso.org/standard/72140.html.

International Organization for Standardization. *Risk Management—Vocabulary.* ISO Guide 73:2009. Geneva, Switzerland: International Organization for Standardization, 2009. https://www.iso.org/standard/44651.html.

Johnson, F. R., S. Özdemir, C. Mansfield, S. Hass, C. A. Siegel, and B. E. Sands. "Are Adult Patients More Tolerant of Treatment Risks Than Parents of Juvenile Patients?" *Risk Analysis: An International Journal* 29, no. 1 (2009): 121–136.

Jones, B. "Breast Implant Scandal: What Went Wrong?" CNN, January 27, 2012. https://edition.cnn.com/2012/01/27/world/europe/pip-breast-implant-scandal-explained/index.html.

Karwowski, W., and A. Mital. "Potential Applications of Fuzzy Sets in Industrial Safety Engineering." *Fuzzy Sets and Systems* 19, no. 2 (1986): 105–120.

Katayama, H., Y. Kurokawa, K. Nakamura, H. Ito, Y. Kanemitsu, N. Masuda, Y. Tsubosa, et al. "Extended Clavien-Dindo Classification of Surgical Complications: Japan Clinical Oncology Group Postoperative Complications Criteria." *Surgery Today* 46, no. 6 (2016): 668–685.

King, M. *Statistics for Process Control Engineers: A Practical Approach.* Hoboken, NJ: Wiley, 2017.

Kraljic, P. "Purchasing Must Become Supply Management." *Harvard Business Review* 61, no. 5 (1983): 109–117.

Lam, J. *Enterprise Risk Management: From Incentives to Controls.* Hoboken, NJ: John Wiley & Sons, 2014.

Lee, J. H., D. J. Park, H. H. Kim, H. J. Lee, and H. K. Yang. "Comparison of Complications after Laparoscopy-Assisted Distal Gastrectomy and Open Distal Gastrectomy for Gastric Cancer Using the Clavien–Dindo Classification." *Surgical Endoscopy* 26, no. 5 (2012): 1287–1295.

Levitan, B. "A Concise Display of Multiple End Points for Benefit–Risk Assessment." *Clinical Pharmacology & Therapeutics* 89, no. 1 (2011): 56–59.

Levitan, B. S., E. B. Andrews, A. Gilsenan, J. Ferguson, R. A. Noel, P. M. Coplan, and F. Mussen. "Application of the BRAT Framework to Case Studies: Observations and Insights." *Clinical Pharmacology & Therapeutics* 89, no. 2 (2011): 217–224.

Macesker, B., J. J. Myers, V. H. Guthrie, D. A. Walker, and S. G. Schoolcraft. "Quick-Reference Guide to Risk-Based Decision Making (RBDM): A Step-by-Step Example of the RBDM Process in the Field." Air University. Accessed October 25, 2008. http://www.au.af.mil/au/awc/awcgate/uscg/risk-qrg.pdf.

Markowski, A. S., and M. S. Mannan. "Fuzzy Risk Matrix." *Journal of Hazardous Materials* 159, no. 1 (2008): 152–157.

Ministry of Defence. *Safety Management Requirements for Defence Systems.* Standard 00-56. Ministry of Defence, Directorate of Standardisation, Kentigern House, 2007.

Moon, J. "An Investigation into the Use of Laney U Chart as a Visual Schedule Tracker to Graphically Monitor the Schedule Performance Index." *Journal of Engineering, Project, and Production Management* 10, no. 1 (2020): 35–41.

Moon, J. "Effect of Emotional Intelligence and Leadership Styles on Risk Intelligent Decision Making and Risk Management." *Journal of Engineering, Project, and Production Management* 11, no. 1 (2021; in press).

Moon, J. "Theory and Application of J Charts for Holistic Risk Based Statistical Adverse Event Trending." *International Journal of Health and Economic Development* 4, no. 1 (2018): 9–31.

Mt-Isa, S., C. E. Hallgreen, N. Wang, T. Callréus, G. Genov, I. Hirsch, S. F. Hobbiger, et al. "Balancing Benefit and Risk of Medicines: A Systematic Review and Classification of Available Methodologies." *Pharmacoepidemiology and Drug Safety* 23, no. 7 (2014): 667–678.

Mussen, F., S. Salek, and S. R. Walker. *Benefit-Risk Appraisal of Medicines: A Systematic Approach to Decision-Making*. Chichester, UK: Wiley-Blackwell, 2009.

Myers, J. J. "Risk-Based Decision Making." *Journal of Safety and Security at Sea* 64, no. 1 (2007): 6–10.

Mylotte, J. M. "Analysis of Infection Surveillance Data in a Long-Term Care Facility: Use of Threshold Settings." *Infection Control and Hospital Epidemiology* 17, no. 2 (1996): 101–107.

NASA. *IV&V Management System, Guidelines for Risk Management*. S3001, rev. G. Fairmont, WV: NASA, 2017. https://www.nasa.gov/sites/default/files/atoms/files/s3001_guidelines_for_risk_management_-_ver_g_-_10-25-2017.pdf.

Ni, H., A. Chen, and N. Chen. "Some Extensions on Risk Matrix Approach." *Safety Science* 48, no. 10 (2010): 1269–1278.

Oka, T., H. Matsuda, and Y. Kadono. "Ecological Risk–Benefit Analysis of a Wetland Development Based on Risk Assessment Using 'Expected Loss of Biodiversity.'" *Risk Analysis* 21, no. 6 (2001): 1011–1024.

Ouellet, D. "Benefit–Risk Assessment: The Use of Clinical Utility Index." *Expert Opinion on Drug Safety* 9, no. 2 (2010): 289–300.

Pérez, J. R. *Handbook of Investigation and Effective CAPA Systems*. Milwaukee, WI: ASQ Quality Press.

Pérez, J. R. *Quality Risk Management in the FDA-Regulated Industry*. Milwaukee, WI: ASQ Quality Press, 2012.

Pluchino, A., G. Inturri, A. Rapisarda, A. E. Biondo, R. Le Moli, C. Zappala, N. Giuffrida, G. Russo, and V. Latora. "A Novel Methodology for Epidemic Risk Assessment: The Case of COVID-19 Outbreak in Italy." arXiv preprint arXiv:2004.02739 (2020).

Popov, G., B. K. Lyon, and B. Hollcroft. *Risk Assessment: A Practical Guide to Assessing Operational Risks*. Hoboken, NJ: John Wiley & Sons.

Porter, M. E. *Competitive Advantage: Creating and Sustaining Superior Performance*. New York: Free Press, 1998 [1985].

Preston, G., J. Moon, R. Simon, S. Allen, and E. Kossi. "The Relevance of Emotional Intelligence in Project Leadership." *Journal of Information Technology and Economic Development* 6, no. 1 (2015): 16.

Pritchard, C. L. *Risk Management: Concepts and Guidance*. Boca Raton, FL: Auerbach Publications.

Project Management Institute. *A Guide to the Project Management Body of Knowledge*. 5th ed. Newtown Square, PA: Project Management Institute, 2013.

Project Management Institute. *Practice Standard for Project Risk Management*. Newtown Square, PA: Project Management Institute, 2009.

Rausand, M. *Risk Assessment: Theory, Methods, and Applications*. Vol. 115. Hoboken, NJ: John Wiley & Sons.

Raz, T., and D. Hillson. "A Comparative Review of Risk Management Standards." *Risk Management* 7, no. 4 (2005): 53–66.

"Regulation (EU) 2017/745 of the European Parliament." EUR-Lex. April 5, 2017. https://eur-lex.europa.eu/eli/reg/2017/745/oj.

Rose, K. H. *A Guide to the Project Management Body of Knowledge (PMBOK Guide)*. Newtown Square, PA: Project Management Institute, 2013.

Sarac, S. B., C. H. Rasmussen, M. A. Rasmussen, C. E. Hallgreen, T. Søeborg, M. Colding-Jørgensen, P. K. Christensen, S. Thirstrup, and E. Mosekilde. "A Comprehensive Approach to Benefit–Risk Assessment in Drug Development." *Basic & Clinical Pharmacology & Toxicology* 111, no. 1 (2012): 65–72.

Shiroiwa, T., A. Igarashi, T. Fukuda, and S. Ikeda. "WTP for a QALY and Health States: More Money for Severer Health States?" *Cost Effectiveness and Resource Allocation* 11 (2013): https://doi.org/10.1186/1478-7547-11-22.

Sibthorpe, C. "Coronavirus Pandemic: What Does This Mean - and What Happens Next?" *Sky News*, March 12, 2020. https://news.sky.com/story/coronavirus-pandemic-what-does-this-mean-and-what-happens-next-11955553.

Simchi-Levi, D., W. Schmidt, and Y. Wei. "From Superstorms to Factory Fires: Managing Unpredictable Supply Chain Disruptions." *Harvard Business Review* 92, no. 1–2 (2014): 96–101.

Standards Australia. *Risk Management Guidelines - Companion to AS/NZS ISO 31000:2009*. SA/SNZ HB 436:2013. Sydney: Standards Australia, 2013. https://infostore.saiglobal.com/en-us/Standards/SA-SNZ-HB-436-2013-119721_SAIG_AS_AS_250882/.

Tuckman, B. W. "Developmental Sequence in Small Groups." *Psychological Bulletin* 63, no. 6 (1965): 384–399.

University College London. "Irrational Decisions Driven by Emotions." ScienceDaily, August 3, 2006. www.sciencedaily.com/releases/2006/08/060803171138.htm.

U.S. Department of Defense. *Department of Defense Standard Practice: System Safety*. MIL-STD-882E. Washington, DC: U.S. Department of Defense, 2012.

U.S. Department of Energy. *Risk Management Guide*. DOE G 413.3-7. Washington, DC: U.S. Department of Energy. https://www.directives.doe.gov/directives-documents/400-series/0413.3-EGuide-07a.

Van Vreeswijk, M., J. Broersen, and M. Nadort. *The Wiley-Blackwell Handbook of Schema Therapy: Theory, Research, and Practice*. John Wiley & Sons, 2012.

Weber, E. U., A. R. Blais, and N. E. Betz. "A Domain-Specific Risk-Attitude Scale: Measuring Risk Perceptions and Risk Behaviors." *Journal of Behavioral Decision Making* 15, no. 4 (2002): 263–290.

Wilkinson, L. "Revising the Pareto Chart." *American Statistician* 60, no. 4 (2006): 332–334.

Wood, H. O., and F. Neumann. *Modified Mercalli Intensity Scale of 1931*. Albany, CA: Seismological Society of America, 1931.

Woolhouse, M., F. Scott, Z. Hudson, R. Howey, and M. Chase-Topping. "Human Viruses: Discovery and Emergence." *Philosophical Transactions of the Royal Society B* 367 (2012): 2864–2871.

World Health Organization. *Pandemic Influenza Risk Management: A WHO Guide to Inform and Harmonize National and International Pandemic Preparedness and Response*. Geneva, Switzerland: World Health Organization, 2017.

Yoon, P. D., V. Chalasani, and H. H. Woo. "Use of Clavien-Dindo Classification in Reporting and Grading Complications after Urological Surgical Procedures: Analysis of 2010 to 2012." *Journal of Urology* 190, no. 4 (2013): 1271–1274.

Zadeh, L. A. "Fuzzy Sets." *Information and Control* 8, no. 3 (1965): 338–353.

Zimmer, B. "'Hazard': From Medieval Dice to the Risks Faced by Frontline Workers." *Wall Street Journal*, May 14, 2020. https://www.wsj.com/articles/hazard-from-medieval-dice-to-the-risks-faced-by-frontline-workers-11589481761.

Zsidisin, G. A., L. M. Ellram, J. R. Carter, and J. L. Cavinato. "An Analysis of Supply Risk Assessment Techniques." *International Journal of Physical Distribution & Logistics Management* 34, no. 5 (2004): 397–413.

Index

Note: Page numbers followed by *f* or *t* refer to figures or tables, respectively.

C

D

E

F

G

H

I

J

K

L

M

N

O

Q

R

About the Author

Jayet Moon is a Senior ASQ member and holds ASQ CQE, CSQP, and CQIA certifications. He has earned a master's degree in biomedical engineering from Drexel University in Philadelphia and is a Project Management Institute (PMI) Certified Risk Management Professional (PMI-RMP). He is also an Enterprise Risk Management Certified Professional (ERMCP) and a Risk Management Society (RIMS) certified Risk Management Professional (RIMS-CRMP), a certification that holds official accreditation from the American National Standards Institute (ANSI) under ISO/IEC 17024:2012. He is a doctoral candidate in Systems and Engineering Management at Texas Tech University.